METROPOLITAN TRANSPORTATION—1980

METROPOLITAN TRANSPORTATION — 1980

A framework for the long-range planning
of transportation facilities to serve the
New York-New Jersey Metropolitan Region

**COMPREHENSIVE PLANNING OFFICE
THE PORT OF NEW YORK AUTHORITY**

New York • 1963

FOREWORD

Planning is basic to the responsibilities of The Port of New York Authority. It is obviously the only intelligent approach to the formulation of a regional program for the continuing development of the Port District's public terminal and transportation facilities and other facilities of commerce. The need for continuous study, analysis and comprehensive planning was clearly recognized when the Port Authority was established by the Port Compact of 1921. Indeed, the adoption of that Compact by the States of New Jersey and New York had been preceded by the Comprehensive Planning Report of the New York, New Jersey Port and Harbor Development Commission.

The broad authorizations of port development outlined in the Compact of 1921 were expressly limited to a program that could be carried forward on a completely self-supporting basis. The Authority was told to establish its own credit and to develop the revenue sources that would enable the two States to proceed with a broad program of regional development without support from state or local appropriations or taxes. In its early years therefore, the Authority had largely limited its efforts to planning, developing and operating tunnels and bridges linking New York and New Jersey. However, beginning in 1946, it became possible to go forward, as a matter of financial practicability, with the active planning of the broader program of port facilities which had been outlined by the two States in their Port Compact. On the basis of these plans the Authority then developed the regional system of airports, inland terminals and marine terminals, piers and docks, and expanded the arterial connection between the two States.

As Port Authority planners became heavily involved in the details of facility planning, it became increasingly difficult to assign the responsibility for long-range, comprehensive planning to the same staff responsible for facility planning, with all the latter's day-to-day pressures. It was therefore decided in 1955 to establish comprehensive planning as a separate, but related, operation in order to free those responsible for the Port District's long-range planning from pressures and close deadlines.

The comprehensive planning program was set up to conduct long-range studies and to assemble data that would cast light on probable future trends in transportation in the New York-New Jersey metropolitan area. Topics were broadly defined to include demographic and economic aspects of the totality which comprises the vast backdrop of the region's transportation problems. Data reflecting present and probable future trends of such factors as population, business, finance, gross national product, home building, and suburban growth are essential to realistic planning.

Furthermore, adequate planning must reflect, in correct perspective, the proper interrelation of all forms of transportation. Specifically, in planning for future steamship pier development it is necessary not only to estimate the number of berths that will be needed for the entire harbor, but also to appraise the impact on our waterfront terminals of any probable changes in the forms of land transportation linking the port with the interior. Estimates of overseas travel by air must take into account the prospective levels of overseas travel by steamship. The future of mass transportation within the region is intimately related to the probable influence of the automobile and motor truck in facilitating the decentralization of population and employment.

The chapters which follow constitute a summary of the product of six years of research and effort by a dedicated group of economists and transportation analysts under the direction of Mr. Frank W. Herring, who had been the Port Authority's Director of Planning until he was made responsible for this project. Mr. Herring was ably assisted by a small professional staff composed of Messrs. Nathan Cherniack, David L. Glickman, Carl A. Franzmann, John Carroll, James B. Kenyon and John R. Dragonette. For special studies, other members of the Port Authority staff also participated, including Messrs. John S. Gallagher, Jr., Wesley V. Hurley, Thomas L. Collins, Warren S. Quimby, Edward G. Wetzel and Jack Storm.

The Port Authority staff was also advised and assisted by several distinguished consultants, including Dr. Alex Hart, Professor Harold Mayer of the University of Chicago; and Dr. Ralph J. Watkins and Mr. Wilfred Owen of the Brookings Institution.

It is not to be assumed that the interpretations and conclusions of these transportation specialists represent in all cases the considered policy positions of the Commissioners of The Port of New York Authority. This is a report prepared by a competent staff, for the consideration of the Commissioners, and the staff takes responsibility for it. The Commissioners believe that giving it publication is in the public interest.

The material in the report presents a framework for the planning for transportation facilities within the New York-New Jersey metropolitan area. It is the hope of the Port Authority that the findings, conclusions and opinions herein will be of help to all those responsible for providing the facilities of transportation and commerce in the Port District, to scholars and interested organizations of citizens, as well as to the Port Authority Commissioners and staff.

Planning is a continuous process. New data are produced continually, on the basis of which conclusions must be reshaped. For this reason, the present study will be kept under review by the Port Authority during the years ahead and its findings modified to reflect changes in conditions, in experience and judgment.

The task at hand was not one that could be carried out by merely studying the current problems of the region's transportation system and by proposing appropriate solutions. The situation is far too dynamic for such an approach. Some of today's problems will no longer be causing concern in 1980. Conversely, transportation problems of an entirely different sort will then have to be faced. History teaches us to expect such an eventuality; as witness the fact that the able Planning Report that preceded the adoption of the 1921 Port Compact was written before the explosive development of the truck and the automobile and is dated by that revolution in the technology of transportation.

The present study and report analyzes developments in recent years within each segment of the total transportation system within the region. During this time a tremendous number of changes have occurred, both in the region and in its transportation facilities. Mr. Herring and his associates then project the direction in which each segment of the transportation picture is apparently headed, not only on the basis of the history of that segment, but also in terms of various pertinent regional factors. Careful study is also given to the potential effect of foreseeable advances in the technology of transportation.

Such studies cannot be limited to transportation factors alone. The first section of the report discusses in some detail prospective levels of population and employment in the region and of the various components of the economic structure of the region — manufacturing, wholesaling, retailing and related service industries. Some of this material covers ground dealt with by the New York Metropolitan Region Study completed in 1961 under the sponsorship of the Regional Plan Association. The present study, however, differs from that project in that its research and analysis is focused on transportation requirements.

The report considers separately the problems related to the movement of goods and the movement of people. These two primary components of the over-all transportation picture are interrelated, for most forms of transportation involve the movement of both people and goods, particularly in terminal facilities, where the demands for the accommodation of passengers and freight together constitute the total terminal demands.

In general, the approach has been to examine trends in transport magnitudes over the past few decades — the volumes of commodities shipped and received, the number of persons traveling, the number of vehicles moving — and the role which each mode of transport has played; to search for and to identify the forces which have brought about those trends; to appraise those forces as to the likelihood of their continuance into the future and to search out new ones likely to come into play; and to judge whether the trends disclosed will continue or will be modified.

Much of the material contained in the report is, of necessity, of a technical nature. An attempt has been made, however, to make the material of value not only to experts in the particular field under discussion, but also to those interested in transportation as a whole.

The report does not presume to set forth a program outlining the transportation facilities which the region will require in the year 1980. The current overall picture of transportation within the region is at the moment undergoing tremendous change. Because of the dynamic quality of the subject and the interrelationships that exist among various forms of transportation, many of the factors which are described will produce growth in one aspect of the over-all picture and in turn may have a harmful effect upon another. The present study, therefore, is intended to describe the factors which will cause change and to set forth as clearly as possible the trends which are now evident, in order to establish a general outline of the transportation needs which will probably have to be met during the next 20 years. It must be remembered, however, that the assumptions and projections set forth in the current report are based on conditions as they existed in early 1963. Developments after that date may well have an almost immediate effect upon many of the projections made in the report, and undoubtedly between now and 1980 there will be unpredictable events which will strongly influence the region's future transportation tasks. Moreover, some of the developments which can be foreseen with reasonable confidence do not lend themselves to quantitative evaluation in terms of such factors as tons of freight, or number of passengers, or numbers of motor vehicles.

Future programs and policies developed at both the public and private level will change the basic pattern of transportation facilities throughout the region. It is hoped that in the years ahead, the present report will provide a reliable basis on which to judge specific proposals for such transportation facilities. Some of these facilities are anticipated in the current report. For example, The Port of New York Authority hopes over the next ten years, to continue its improvements to the region's airports, to continue its program of marine terminal development, and to construct the World Trade Center and other such essential facilities. Other agencies will be responsible for similar components of the regional transportation network.

It is hoped that the present report will be of value to all such agencies within the region so that in the years ahead such programs and facilities as are developed by all the agencies and organizations concerned with the over-all problem, can together assure the region's ability to play its proper role in the advancing economy of the nation and of the world.

AUSTIN J. TOBIN
Executive Director

CONTENTS

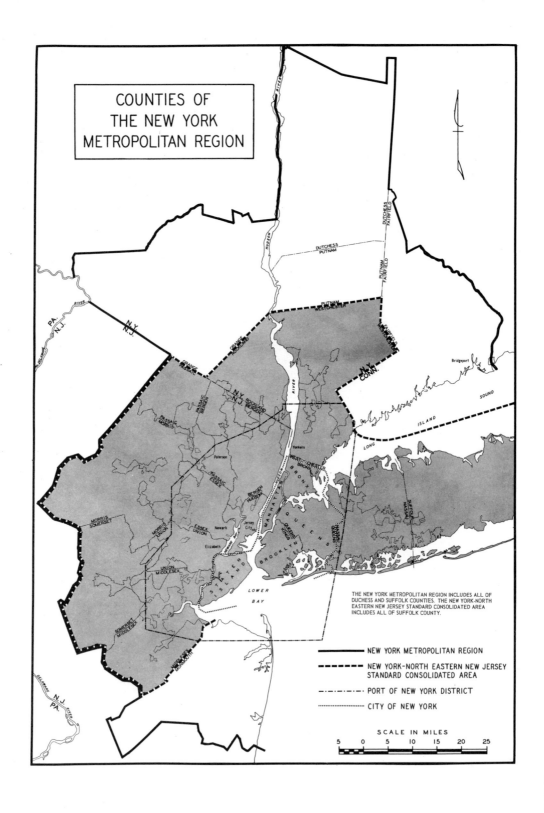

COUNTIES OF
THE NEW YORK
METROPOLITAN REGION

THE NEW YORK METROPOLITAN REGION INCLUDES ALL OF
DUCHESS AND SUFFOLK COUNTIES. THE NEW YORK-NORTH
EASTERN NEW JERSEY STANDARD CONSOLIDATED AREA
INCLUDES ALL OF SUFFOLK COUNTY.

———————— NEW YORK METROPOLITAN REGION

– – – – – – NEW YORK-NORTH EASTERN NEW JERSEY
STANDARD CONSOLIDATED AREA

–·–·–·–·– PORT OF NEW YORK DISTRICT

················ CITY OF NEW YORK

SCALE IN MILES

5   0   5   10   15   20   25

PREFATORY NOTE

In the chapters which follow, the reader will encounter several terms which are frequently used to refer to the New York-New Jersey urban complex or to its various parts — region, area, sector and district. When the word is used in a generic sense, without reference to any specific boundary lines, it is not capitalized. When the need is for a term to denote a particular statistical base, the word is capitalized.

Region, capitalized, is used to refer to two different statistical areas, but as the contexts of the two usages are quite different there is little likelihood of confusion.

First, Region is used to refer to the U. S. Census Bureau's Middle Atlantic Region, comprising the states of New York, New Jersey and Pennsylvania. Second, Region is used to refer to the twenty-two counties comprising the New York Metropolitan Region as defined by the Regional Plan Association. Those counties are: the five counties making up New York City, Nassau, Suffolk, Westchester, Putnam, Dutchess, Rockland and Orange Counties in New York, Hudson, Bergen, Passaic, Essex, Morris, Union, Somerset, Middlesex and Monmouth Counties in New Jersey, and Fairfield County in Connecticut.

Area, capitalized, is used when referring to U. S. Census Bureau's Statistical Areas. These include (1) the New York Standard Metropolitan Statistical Area, comprising the five New York City counties and Nassau, Suffolk, Westchester and Rockland Counties, (2) the Newark Standard Metropolitan Statistical Area, comprising Essex, Morris and Union Counties, (3) the Jersey City Standard Metropolitan Statistical Area, comprising Hudson County, (4) the Paterson-Clifton-Passaic Standard Metropolitan Statistical Area, comprising Bergen and Passaic Counties, and (5) the New York-Northeastern New Jersey Standard Consolidated Area, comprising the four foregoing Statistical Areas plus Middlesex and Somerset Counties.

Sector is used when the reference is to the New Jersey or the New York portion of the Standard Consolidated Area.

Port District refers to the area described in detail in the Interstate Compact which established The Port of New York Authority in 1921 and defined the area within which the new agency's authorizations applied.

PART I

The Metropolitan Background

CHAPTER 1

A FRAMEWORK FOR TRANSPORTATION PLANNING

Much of the history of civilization has been shaped by transportation. Transportation has permitted the values of natural resources to be realized and the products of labor to be interchanged. Natural site advantages have been exploited, workers and production have become specialized and over-all productivity has increased. Transport facilities have tied our nation together socially, economically and politically. Since Colonial days our commerce with other nations has been of basic importance to our well-being. World-wide transportation has assumed ever-greater significance as the world has grown in population and production and as technology has advanced.

The role of transport in the United States has changed markedly, from one of linking a few seaboard colonies with a European base to one of interconnecting a multitude of regional economies and linking them all to the economies of other lands. As our national population and economic activity increase in the future, the transport task will also increase, both in the need for shipment of goods and in the need for travel.

A nation does not grow in the manner of a photographic enlargement, but rather by rapid rates of growth in some areas and slow growth or even decline in others. Typically, growth is most rapid in areas of shorter history. The more mature portions of the country, although continuing to grow in absolute terms, tend to account for a declining proportion of the national totals of population and production.

Changing proportions are as evident in the metropolitan scene as in the nation as a whole. Metropolitan growth in population and employment is most prominent in areas which a few decades ago were not urban at all. It is least, or is not growth at all, in the long-established centers of urban population and industry. The broad dispersal of urban population and employment and the great expansion in urbanized area have changed the task of metropolitan transportation. Transportation facilities and services have had to change, as well as to grow, in order to accommodate it.

The impact of technological development has been as great on transportation as it has been on other aspects of our culture. In the long history of ocean shipping, the source of power for propulsion has been, one after the other, the oarsman, the sail, the steam engine driving a paddle wheel and then a screw propeller, the steam turbine, the diesel engine, and now atomic energy. Aviation has seen the reciprocating gasoline engine, the gas turbine, and the jet engine. Space travel has introduced us to rocket propulsion. Horses drew the first cars to ride on rails and were succeeded by locomotives powered by steam generated by wood fires. Coal- and oil-fired steam locomotives gave way to electric and then to diesel locomotives. Other aspects of transportation technology, such as communications, signaling and traffic control, also have taken advantage of advancing technology. Technological obsolescence has played an important part in transportation history, and there is little doubt that it will also make its demands in the future.

Although the achievement of an efficient and economic transportation system is a valid goal, maximum transportation efficiency in itself is not an adequate goal for national policy. The broader objective is the maximization of the efficiency of the entire national economy, of which transport is but one component. Assembly of materials, production, and distribution of products, all served by transportation, are primary and it may be that optimization of the total economy would be achieved with transport itself at less than maximum efficiency. For example, transport operations would be more economical if shipments were larger and if their flow were steadier, but this would probably involve higher investment in inventories, greater storage space requirements and other increases in the cost elements of production and distribution.

COMMON FACTORS

When the different modes of transportation are viewed more closely and their trends during recent decades are compared, a number of phenomena can be observed which are common to them all.

First, the values derived from transportation are not limited to those enjoyed by its users. Site accessibility, in its own right, is a value to the property owner, to the community and to the nation as a whole. The owner of a farm, a city residence, an industrial site or a mineral deposit has a tremendous stake in the adequacy of the available transportation service, whether he makes use of the transportation himself or not. The economic health of an entire community may rest upon its accessibility. Consequently, transportation cannot be viewed merely as an item in the market place, with the extent and quality of service controlled solely by the decisions of the sellers and buyers of transportation service.

From this consideration stems the pervasive influence of government in the transportation field. Throughout our history government has promoted and aided transportation through a wide range of activities. Today those activities range from complete proprietary roles, such as the ownership and operation of the subway system of the city of New York, through the provision of travelways, such as highways, airways and waterways, to subsidies to operators of common-carrier services considered essential, such as the feeder airlines and ocean shipping lines on specified trade routes. Government is also concerned with the safety of the traveling public, and with the economic consequences of service levels and rates and charges, and expresses its concern through its regulatory activities.

Second, there is a profoundly important dichotomy in transportation: private transport and public, or common-carrier, transport. It manifests itself in all transport modes. There are the private automobile and the railroads and bus lines; the privately-owned airplane and the commercial airlines; the privately-owned motor truck and the common carriers of domestic freight; and the private carriers in water transportation — the ore carriers of the steel companies and the tankers of the oil companies — and the ocean steamship lines.

Private transportation is not a recent intruder in the field. It antedates common carriage by many centuries. Indeed, in historical perspective the transport of freight and passengers as a business in itself is a relatively modern development. It may be that in land transportation, at least, we are witnessing a resurgence of private transport, made possible by the internal combustion engine.

The availability of private transport today presents more than price competition to the common carriers. It makes possible a choice between private and common-carrier transportation, shipment by shipment or trip by trip, by the shipper who owns a truck or the traveler who owns an automobile or the corporation which owns an airplane. The choice may be to use the private vehicle when the task is convenient in time or simple in performance and to relegate to common carriage the task of accommodating the peak overflow or the shipment that is costly to handle. Common-carrier rates, stemming from a time when common carriage was dominant, can be adjusted to this situation only with difficulty.

Third, all forms of transportation must cope with a strong rhythm of demand. There are times of the day when we go to work and when we go home. There are preferred times for the shipment and the receipt of freight. Intercity travelers do not want to arrive at their destinations in the middle of the night. Recreational travel is heavier in times of mild weather than in the cold and dreary seasons. Farm products are shipped when the growing season has done its work. Transportation of products for the Christmas trade is concentrated within a few months.

A load curve with prominent peaks and valleys is the consequence. It is apparent in commuter railroad travel, in the volume of automobile traffic crossing the George Washington Bridge, in the number of planes arriving at International Airport, in the number of buses needing berthing space at the Bus Terminal, in the number of cargo ships in the harbor. Transportation capacity must be geared to the periods of maximum demand and much of the time a transportation facility or service has a light load or may be entirely idle.

Although this rhythmic phenomenon, the periodic peaking of demand, is not unique to transportation it has special sig-

nificance here because of two important factors: (1) Transport facilities involve high investment charges and idle time is exceptionally costly. (2) During the periods of low demand, private transportation is especially attractive to the traveler or shipper. The common carrier is called on mostly during the high demand periods.

Fourth, all modes of transportation show a wide disparity between high speeds and relatively low costs in inter-terminal operations, and time consumed and high costs experienced in the terminal areas. In common parlance, a railroad makes a profit on its road haul and loses it in its terminal operations. The value of the high speed of air travel can be negated by time spent in travel to and from an airport. One of the important objectives of steamship line management is to minimize ship time in port, loading and discharging cargo; again it is said that terminal costs can eat up a large share of the ocean shipping rate. The motorist traveling from one city to another may spend a large proportion of his total travel time on relatively few miles of city streets at his origin and destination.

TRENDS IN THE NEW YORK METROPOLITAN REGION

Many of the recent changes and trends in the distribution of population and economic activity in the New York Metropolitan Region parallel those observed in other metropolitan areas. Outstanding among these trends are growth of population in the outlying areas, in residential districts developed at low land-use density, and decline in the older, more densely developed neighborhoods. Regional population growth between 1960 and 1980, estimated to be some six million, is expected to be accounted for almost entirely by increases in the suburban counties ringed about New York City and about the older, more densely populated portions of New Jersey. The New Jersey counties will absorb about half the population growth, and their share of the Region's population will rise correspondingly. Connecticut will also increase its share of the population. The New York sector will decline relative to the other sectors.

Similarly, the Region's jobs have shown a comparable decentralizing trend, particularly in manufacturing. Most of the employment increase during the next two decades will probably take place in the suburban counties. The New Jersey sector is expected to account for some 44 per cent of the new employment. But as this proportion will be less than its share of the Region's population growth, metropolitan New Jersey's residents will continue to lean heavily on jobs in other portions of the Region. Conversely, the prospective growth in employment in the New York counties will be at a rate somewhat higher than their rate of population growth.

A strong note of decentralization is observed in goods-handling activities as well as in manufacturing. The wholesaling phases of distribution are tending toward the separation of warehousing from sales transactions; there is growth in warehousing and shipping operations in the outlying locations while buying and selling tend to remain centralized. Retailing has also been following the population to the suburbs and the recent growth of suburban shopping centers has been spectacular.

On the other hand, there are some trends in the Region which deviate from those shown in other metropolitan areas. For example, there has been striking growth in employment in executive office, professional, and business service estab-

lishments. As employment of this type is located primarily within the Central Business District, Manhattan's loss in manufacturing employment has been offset by rises in white collar jobs. Central Business District employment, as a whole, therefore, has been virtually stabilized and will probably continue so for some while.

There have been migrations of the large department store retailing establishments to suburban locations. But there has been a healthy growth in specialty retailing in the central core, in the retailing of high-quality or high-fashion items and of those items of such a special nature that a large metropolitan, or even national, market is required for their support. The net result has been a rise in total Central Business District retailing in Manhattan, a trend at variance with that shown in most other metropolitan areas.

In manufacturing there is a clear trend in the New York Region toward the lighter, final-stage processes and a relative decline in the heavy-industry activities and in those involving the initial processing of raw materials. Nondurable goods, of which apparel is the most important, have dominated the industrial output and the prospect is that they will continue to do so in the decades ahead.

TRENDS IN TRANSPORTATION

Ocean shipping of general cargo through the Port of New York is expected to increase by about 37 per cent in tonnage during the next two decades. More than half of the increase will be due to cargoes handled over specialized or industrially owned facilities. The increase in general cargo handled over conventional facilities will probably be some 23 per cent. Nevertheless, the port's share of the nation's total tonnage of exports and imports is likely to continue to decline, as a result of higher growth rates in population and economic activity in the South, Southwest and Far West, and of changing patterns of natural resource use. The improvement of marine terminal facilities, the proposed World Trade Center, and other improvements, however, should strengthen New York's position relative to competing ports.

Improvements in steamship berth utilization and in cargo handling methods may be expected. However, in common with industrial practices generally, there may be a moderate reduction in the number of working days on the water front. The number of steamship berths required to accommodate future conventional general cargo tonnage is estimated to be about 170, a number little different from the number currently in use. Many of the existing marine terminals in the harbor are old and will need replacement during the period for which we are planning. If an age of 50 years were to be adopted as a presumptive test of the need for replacement, 59 new berths would need to be built between 1962 and 1980, in addition to those now being built and those firmly committed for construction.

The growth of containership operations in domestic trade has been rapid in recent years, and it is likely that this form of transportation will come to dominate coastal, offshore and intercoastal shipping. Consequently, there will be a need for additional containership berths. The number needed will depend largely on how many containership operators there are, rather than on handling capacities of containership berths. In foreign trade the prospect for containership traffic is less bright, owing to administrative impediments such as customs regulations in foreign countries, the nature of foreign trade shipments, the need to concentrate movements in a limited number of ports, and the different land transportation practices in foreign countries.

Consistent with the national pattern of domestic transportation, the volume of the Region's freight handled by the railroads has been declining. The declining trend is particularly pronounced in export and import freight. In view of the importance of the Region's shipments of merchandise freight, which is highly susceptible to competition by over-the-road trucking, the decline is likely to continue, although its pace should slow down. The development of piggyback operations, however, gives the railroads the potentiality for reclaiming some of the tonnage they have lost to the motor carriers, and it is possible that the downtrend may be halted.

The rising volume of motor freight has come to be served by several important clusters of truck terminals. There has been a strong orientation toward the New Jersey counties, and perhaps the cluster of greatest importance is that along the edge of the Hackensack Meadows. The network of major highways has been a dominant force influencing truck terminal location. The likelihood is that the volume of motor freight into and out of the Region will continue to rise, much of it by private carrier.

Air freight has been growing rapidly in recent years, but it still represents an extremely small proportion of the Region's total freight volume. Its brief history does not permit a firm projection of future tonnage but there is no doubt that there is a great potentiality for further growth. Future air cargo volumes certainly will be many times present volumes. No need is foreseen, however, for all-cargo airports.

Intercity travel should increase in the years ahead at least in proportion to the increase in population and national income. Railroad passenger travel, however, has been falling steadily since the end of World War II, and most long-distance travel is now accounted for by air transport. For trips of from 250 to 500 miles air travel is expected to continue its past patterns of growth. For trips of less than 100 miles the automobile has become the traveler's principal reliance. In the mileage bracket of, say, 100 to 300 miles, problems are likely to develop as a consequence of the continuing decline in railroad passenger service. These trips are too short to permit the full advantage of airplane speed, in view of the ground-access time to and from the airports, and not long enough to be profitable to the airlines. For this travel component the buses have not yet provided the full spectrum of service needed for growth and development. Nevertheless, travel by bus has been rising, and the average length of bus trips has been slowly increasing.

Overseas travel is also expected to increase during the decades that lie ahead. Travel on all overseas routes is now dominated by air transportation, and the prospect is that growth will be accounted for almost entirely by the airlines. Steamship travel is still strong on the transatlantic routes but traffic volumes appear to have reached a stable level. It is also likely that there will be growth in cruise travel as national income and leisure time increase.

The modest increase anticipated for total steamship passenger travel should be accommodated with no increase in the number of passenger ship berths, but will require some modernization and possibly some replacement of existing facilities.

Within the time span considered in this report the capacity of the Region's present airports to accommodate plane movements will be exceeded by the demand. The rapid rate at which the Region's open land is being developed or committed to other uses warns that provision of additional airport capacity will become progressively more difficult.

Metropolitan travel behavior has been changing in response to the dispersal of residences and economic activities. There has been a declining trend in regional rail travel, particularly between New Jersey and New York, and rising trends in bus and automobile travel. It is plain that mass transportation, by both rail and bus, has its principal role in serving work trips generated by the Central Business District, Manhattan south of Central Park. As a relatively stable level of employment in that district may be expected, there is little promise of market expansion for mass transportation except possibly for reverse travel, between a worker's centrally located home and a job in the suburbs. It is not unlikely, however, that Central Business District workers will live farther out and consequently have longer journeys to work. On the other hand, since much of the Region's projected population growth and employment increase will occur in the outlying areas, suburban and intersuburban travel volumes will increase and will have to rely heavily upon the private automobile; route densities sufficient to warrant new high-capacity mass transportation will be uncommon.

The number of persons forming a household in the Region has been declining over many decades and, consequently, the rate of increase in households has outpaced the rate of population rise. Moreover, the number of automobiles owned has been rising more rapidly than the number of households. The combined result has been growth in the number of automobiles far greater than growth in population. Assuming the continuation of these trends, average automobile ownership in the Region should rise to approximately one automobile per household in 1980. Automobile traffic should increase commensurately with the rise in the number of automobiles in the Region.

CHAPTER 2

POPULATION AND EMPLOYMENT IN THE FUTURE

Basic to the transport problems that will be faced by the New York Metropolitan Region in 1980 are the growth prospects for population and for business and industry.

In 1958, population projections for the Region and for each of its 22 counties were prepared for the New York Metropolitan Region Study by the Graduate School of Public Administration of Harvard University. This study was completed and published before the results of the 1960 census of population became available. The census returns diverged sharply from the 1958 projections that had been made on the basis of firm population data up to only 1950, and there was obviously a need for modification. Accordingly, the projections were revised in 1961 by the same analysts who had prepared them originally. The revised figures have been utilized as basic data throughout this study of transportation.

Estimates of employment in future years made in 1958 under the same auspices were also in need of revision, and this was done. Further modifications of the revised projections have been made in the present study where they appeared to be necessary. Also, the distribution of the future regional employment, county by county, has been estimated.

POPULATION

Between 1830 and 1930, the Region's share of the nation's population grew from 4.90 per cent to 9.48 per cent. In 1940 New York's position crested at 9.51 per cent. The trend since 1940 has been a gradual

decline, for in 1950 the Region's population share of the nation dropped to 9.26 per cent, and in the most recent census, 1960, it declined to 9.04 per cent.

The Outlook

Several forecasts of future population of the New York Metropolitan Region[1] have been made in recent years. There have been the Regional Plan Association's 20-year forecast made in 1955, the forecast made by the Corps of Engineers in its *Economic Base Survey of the Delaware River Service Area*, carried through 2010, and the revision of the New York Metropolitan Region Study's projections, referred to above. This latest estimate, though higher than the others when related to the Census Bureau's forecast of future national population, shows for the Region a declining share of national growth (Table 1). The rate of this relative decline is gradual, however, and in 1980 the New York Metropolitan Region is expected to enjoy almost the same proportion of the nation's population that it held in 1920 (8.64 per cent).

Nevertheless, the absolute growth envisioned for the Region is of formidable proportions: an increment of over 6 million people during the next 25 years. This is equal roughly to the Region's net growth during the 35 years preceding 1960. While the Region is expected to fall short of the *rate* of expansion foreseen for

[1]The "New York Metropolitan Region" in this context comprises 22 counties in three states: In Connecticut, Fairfield; in New Jersey, Bergen, Essex, Hudson, Middlesex, Monmouth, Morris, Passaic, Somerset, Union; in New York, Dutchess, Nassau, Orange, Putnam, Rockland, Suffolk, Westchester, Bronx, Kings, New York, Queens, Richmond.

TABLE 1. PROJECTED POPULATION IN
THOUSANDS: THE REGION AND THE
NATION COMPARED

	Nation[a]	Region[b]	Per Cent of Nation
1965	193,643	17,180	8.87
1970	208,199	18,395	8.84
1975	225,552	19,700	8.73
1980	245,409	20,898	8.52
1985	—	22,170	—

[a]Series III in Illustrative Projections of the Population of the United States . . . 1960–1980. U. S. Bureau of the Census. November, 1960 (Series P-25, No. 187).

[b]Revision of April, 1961, of New York Metropolitan Region Study projection Appendix 1.

the nation as a whole, it will maintain a strong momentum in absolute growth.

The nation as a whole, however, is not the most meaningful point of reference for measuring metropolitan growth. New York's current position and its prospects for the future may be seen more clearly in the comparison with other large metropolitan areas.

The Trend Toward Metropolitanization

A high birth rate and a shift of population out of rural areas have been the key factors during the past 15 years in intensifying the urban cast of the nation. Economic opportunity has varied appreciably from region to region and as a consequence has motivated intranational migration unprecedented in magnitude.

The metropolitan areas of the nation have been the major recipients of population increase and mobility. During 1950-1960 the metropolitan areas accounted for 85 per cent of the nation's gain in population. Between 1940 and 1950, they absorbed 80 per cent of the population increase. Thus not only is the nation becoming more and more a folk of city dwellers; it has sought out the larger form of urbanization, the metropolitan area, as the favored locale for settlement.

As may be seen in Table 2, the growth rate of metropolitan areas has varied widely from region to region, with the sharpest gains, understandably, occurring in areas undergoing rapid economic expansion.

TABLE 2. GROWTH OF METROPOLITAN AREAS
IN THE REGIONS OF THE NATION

	Per Cent of Nation's Metropolitan Area Population in 1950	Per Cent of Metropolitan Area Growth 1950–1960
Northeast	34.8	16.7
North Central	28.2	25.3
South	21.8	29.9
West	15.2	28.1

The growth rate of the metropolitan areas in the South and in the western states has been highly disproportionate to the shares of the nation's metropolitan area population enjoyed by these regions in 1950. Typical of the metropolitan areas in the South is the Atlanta area which during 1950–1960 jumped from a population of 727,000 into the million-plus category. The Houston area climbed from 870,000 in 1950 to 1.2 million in 1960. In the West, the San Diego area, an extreme among extremes, grew by 80 per cent from a population of 557,000 in 1950 into the million-plus group in the short span of ten years.

By contrast, the gains in the northeastern states have been much more modest. The Boston and Providence metropolitan areas each grew by less than 8 per cent. Metropolitan Philadelphia and metropolitan Baltimore, with growth rates of 17.2 and 21.5 per cent, respectively, represent the high-gain centers in the Northeast. The New York Metropolitan Area's population increase of 13.5 per cent during 1950–1960 was neither the highest nor the lowest among the metropolitan areas in the northeastern states. Its rate of expansion has been slightly greater than that of the metropolitan areas in the Northeast, taken as an aggregate, but markedly lower than those of the metropolitan areas in other regions of the nation. As may be seen in Table 3, the Northeast is unique in that it has exhibited a higher growth rate outside metropolitan areas. By contrast, growth outside metropolitan areas in the north central states and in the South was slight in comparison with large gains in their metropolitan areas.

TABLE 3. POPULATION GROWTH RATES WITHIN AND OUTSIDE METROPOLITAN AREAS PER CENT GAIN DURING 1950–1960

	Within Metropolitan Areas	Outside Metropolitan Areas	Total
Nation	25.3	6.5	17.5
Northeast	12.1	13.3	12.4
North Central	22.7	6.0	15.4
South	34.6	2.0	15.4
West	46.7	18.4	37.4

Regional Pattern of Population Development: 1920–1960

In 1920, 70.8 per cent of the Region's population was found in the New York portion (61.5 per cent in New York City alone), 25.7 per cent in New Jersey and 3.5 per cent in Connecticut.

(See Appendix Tables 1 and 2)

During 1920–1930 the Region added 2.5 million people to its population — an absolute increase and a rate of growth not matched in any of the succeeding decades. The census of 1930 disclosed that Manhattan had lost almost 420,000 in population and that there was a vast settlement in the still vacant lands in other boroughs of New York City, which as a whole accounted for 45 per cent of the Region's total growth during the decade. Queens more than doubled its population. The Bronx fell just short of doubling while Brooklyn added over a half-million. On the New York side of the Region this wave of expansion spilled over the boundaries of the city; Nassau and Westchester counties each doubled population and together accounted for 12.2 per cent of the total regional gain. Although New Jersey expanded, its rate of expansion did not match its apportionment of population in 1920. Essex, Bergen and Union counties, in that order, collectively accounted for most of the population expansion in New Jersey.

The 1930–1940 decade of depression witnessed a decided change in the scope and pattern of population expansion. The absolute growth fell far below that of the previous decade, scarcely more than a third of the earlier gain. The New Jersey sector was at a virtual standstill, accounting for only 10 per cent of the regional gain. New York City accounted for more than half (58 per cent) of the Region's population gain. Manhattan gained slightly, while the Bronx, Brooklyn and Queens followed the previous growth pattern, Queens showing the strongest rate of growth. Among the New York counties outside of the city, Westchester and Nassau forged ahead.

The developments in the 1940–1950 decade are, to a great measure, obscured by the war years. New York City added substantially to its population, and as in the previous decade, all boroughs participated in the city's growth. There was one dramatic development: the sharp rise in the suburban counties. On the New York side, most of suburban growth took place in Nassau. The New Jersey portion of the Region spurted and accounted for almost 33 per cent of the Region's population

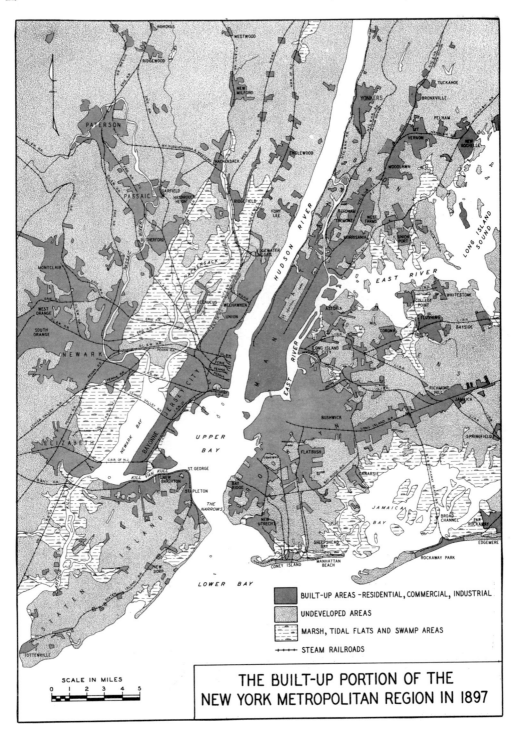

THE BUILT-UP PORTION OF THE
NEW YORK METROPOLITAN REGION IN 1897

FIG. 1

gain (Bergen County alone accounted for 9 per cent of total regional growth).

In the most recent decade, the pattern of population development broadly resembles that of 1920–1930. Nassau County stepped into the role of Queens and absorbed roughly the same number of new inhabitants, 626,000. Suffolk assumed the part played earlier by Nassau, and Westchester added to its population by about the same amount as in the earlier period. In the New Jersey portion of the Region, Bergen County again was the largest contributor to the population growth, followed closely by Middlesex.

However, 1950–1960 saw a new element enter into the picture. This was a consistent pattern of population loss in the older, developed portions of the Region. In Hudson County, on the New Jersey side, where population decline had set in as early as 1930, there was a further loss. In the New York State portion, the Bronx, Brooklyn and Manhattan collectively declined by about 400,000, more than offsetting the gains in Queens and Richmond. As a result, New York City in 1960 for the first time not only lost population in toto, but also accounted for less than 50 per cent of the Region's total population. Here, too, the trend fits into the course of development shaping the metropolitan areas in the nation, the most distinctive feature of which is the decline — in some cases absolute, in others relative — of the older central areas.

The Retreat from Older Settlements of Population

From 1900 through 1950, the rate of population growth in the central cities of the nation's metropolitan areas declined from decade to decade shrinking from 37 per cent in 1900–1910 to 14 per cent in 1940–1950. The most recent decade, 1950–

1960, witnessed another decline in their growth rate (Table 4), this time to slightly over 9 per cent. Among the larger metropolitan areas — the values cited above refer to the aggregate of large and small areas — absolute declines in the population of central cities during 1950–1960 were the general rule.

TABLE 4. POPULATION CHANGES IN MAJOR METROPOLITAN AREAS AND THEIR CENTRAL CITIES: 1950–1960

	Metropolitan Area	Central City
Baltimore	+21.5%	− 2.9%
Boston	+ 6.5	−14.9
Chicago	+19.2	− 3.0
Cleveland	+21.9	− 4.9
New York	+13.5	− 2.3
Philadelphia	+17.2	− 4.8
St. Louis	+19.0	−12.8
San Francisco	+21.6	− 7.1
Washington, D. C.	+34.4	− 7.0

There are exceptions, to be sure. Among these, Houston actually increased its population at a greater rate than the surrounding metropolitan area. Los Angeles grew by 25 per cent — a rate, however, considerably below the rest of its area. The room for growth, on one hand, and change in the statistical area, on the other, must be taken into account here. In Los Angeles, extensive boundaries permitted growth of a high order, while in Houston a vigorous policy of annexation enveloped contiguous communities almost as fast as they developed.

Space for growth appears to have been the key factor in the showing of central cities. Those cities which grew spatially, by territorial annexations, during 1950–1960 grew as a group by almost 21 per cent, while those without annexations suffered a loss of about 4 per cent. The pattern of population loss among central cit-

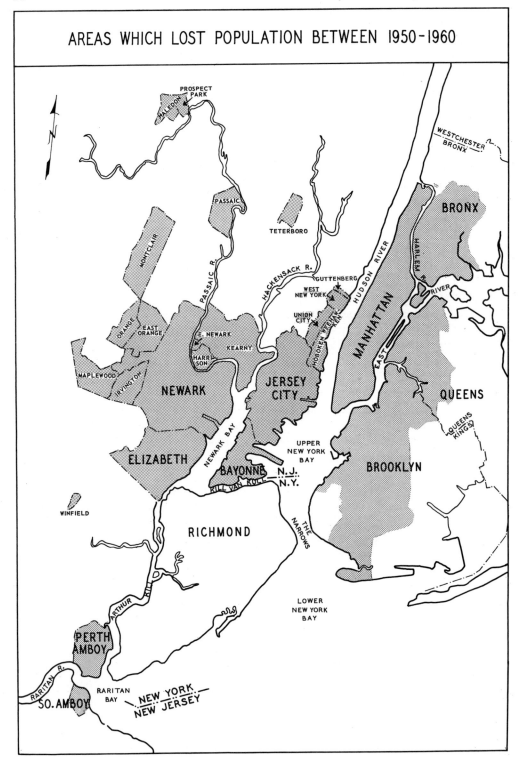

FIG. 2

ies without annexations is evident in all sections of the country.

Population decline during the past decade has been particularly striking in most of the older, established population centers in New York and New Jersey.

In New York State only Yonkers and Niagara Falls, among the cities of more than 100,000 population, showed a gain. All others, among them Buffalo, Albany, Rochester, Syracuse and New York City, lost substantially. With respect to Yonkers, the availability of space in the eastern portion of the city, insulated from the earlier development by topography, yielded a gain sufficient to compensate for losses in the older, settled portion of the city.

In New Jersey, the influence of earlier settlement, which used up available sites, is even more pronounced. Only Clifton and Paterson, among cities of 50,000 or more, gained during the last census period. The increase in Clifton amounted to 27 per cent, in Paterson only 2 per cent. Hudson County, completely hemmed in at an early stage by surrounding urban development, declined in population as early as 1940. There are other important urban pockets of population decline, exemplified by such older cities as Elizabeth (− 4.5 per cent) and Newark (− 7.6 per cent).

Population data that have been published for congressional districts in New York State and for municipalities in New Jersey permit a closer analysis of the relationship between the age of communities and population decline in the New York–New Jersey Metropolitan Region (compare Figs. 1 and 2). These data show that in addition to losses incurred in the older portions of the central cities, some of the older outlying areas also registered declines. Typical of the latter are the Amboys, Passaic, Montclair, East Orange and Maplewood.

At one extreme is Manhattan which lost 13.4 per cent of its population between 1950 and 1960. The proportion of its present population under 18 years of age is among the lowest in the nation, 22.7 per cent, and the proportion of persons 65 years of age and over is relatively high, 12.2 per cent. The fertility ratio, 298 — the number of children under 6 years of age per 1,000 women in the 15 to 45 age group — falls considerably below that of the Metropolitan Area as a whole as well as below the national average. While there was an 11 per cent increase in the number of households in Manhattan, the average number of persons per household was extremely low, 2.36.

At the opposite extreme is Suffolk County where the population increased by almost 142 per cent. There, the proportion of the population under 18 years of age is just under 38 per cent, the proportion of the population over 65 is low, 8.5 per cent, and the fertility ratio is high, 575. The number of persons per household is 3.59.

Manhattan represents the extreme, but the other boroughs of the city which lost population during 1950–1960 have the same basic characteristics of settled areas in decline. In Brooklyn, as well as in the Bronx, the percentage of the population which is below the age of 18 is significantly lower than in the Metropolitan Area as a whole, and the proportion of the population which is over 65 years of age is greater. These older areas, despite influx of new, young population, have experienced the departure of large numbers who are in the family-formation stage of life. There has been left behind a population which is older, which has fewer children, and which has fewer persons in each household.

The thinning out of population is by no means confined to those boroughs showing a net loss. A case in point is Queens,

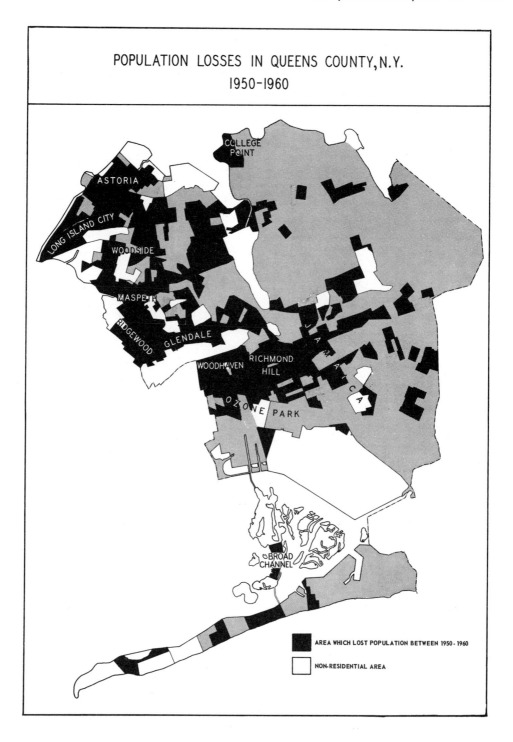

POPULATION LOSSES IN QUEENS COUNTY, N.Y.
1950–1960

AREA WHICH LOST POPULATION BETWEEN 1950-1960

NON-RESIDENTIAL AREA

FIG. 3

whose western portions and lands adjacent to rail transportation and transit lines were well settled before World War II. This borough merits closer inspection to contrast growth between its old and its newer sections and to see the process which with varying degrees will overtake other sections of the Metropolitan Area in the future.

Population Changes in Queens County: 1950–1960

By virtue of its 16.7 per cent increase in population during the past census period, Queens County has been hailed as the fastest-growing homeowner borough in the city of New York. The final census data show that the borough's total population increased from 1,550,849 in 1950 to 1,809,578 in 1960 — a gain of 258,729. As a result of this gain and a loss in Manhattan of approximately the same magnitude, Queens has now replaced Manhattan, or New York County, as the second most populous county in New York State.

To understand better the county's population growth pattern, it is necessary to examine data for the individual census tracts. The most conspicuous changes in the growth pattern that are disclosed by these data can be summarized as follows (see also Fig. 3):

1. The areas of population decline are extensive, even though there has been a large county-wide increase.

2. Most of the areas of decline are near Manhattan and Brooklyn, but there are declining areas that are farther out.

3. Losses have taken place in the older parts of the county, irrespective of their proximity to the central city. Included in this grouping are widely separated areas in College Point, Bayside, Jamaica, Springfield Gardens, Richmond Hill and Hammel.

4. In addition to the solid belt of declining older areas in the western sector, two other loss areas are distinguishable. Both of them parallel and virtually abut branches of the Long Island Rail Road.

5. Substantial gains have been registered in areas not served by rapid transit. Conversely, the areas of decline generally have good access to rapid transit facilities.

6. In the Astoria–Long Island City complex, the only census tracts showing a gain are those that have been redeveloped for residential use.

It may be concluded that the areas that have lost population are generally the older and more densely developed but not necessarily closer to the central city. We may anticipate that the little remaining vacant land in Queens will be built upon in the not-too-distant future and that the borough will have approached population saturation at that time. Population changes in the future will be largely the result of changes in the residential density of land already developed.

The Population Forecast

The population gain foreseen for the New York Metropolitan Region over the next 25 years amounts to about 6 million (Table 5). In absolute terms this increment will exceed the gain during the 25 years preceding 1960, and the rate of gain in percentage terms is somewhat higher.

TABLE 5. HISTORICAL AND PROJECTED POPULATION GAIN IN THE REGION

Period	Gain in Thousands	Per Cent Gain	Average Annual Rate (Per Cent)
1935–1960	4,061 (Est.)	33.6	1.2
1960–1985	6,029	37.4	1.3

There have been wide fluctuations in the Region's rate of gain from decade to decade (Table 6), however, and the average annual gain over the earlier period is heavily weighted by the huge increases which took place during 1920–1930.

TABLE 6. REGIONAL POPULATION GROWTH
BY DECADES: 1920–1980

1920–1930	27.4%
1930–1940	7.5
1940–1950	11.4
1950–1960	15.7
1960–1970	14.0
1970–1980	13.6

*Regional Distribution of
the Future Population*

We may consider the Region as composed of three major sectors: the New York sector, subdivided in turn among New York City and the other counties; the New Jersey sector; and the Connecticut sector. Table 7 shows the percentage gains by sector and by county of the Region's population by decade, past and projected.

The population growth or decline in the New York sector is expected to be as follows: Bronx, Kings (Brooklyn) and New York (Manhattan) counties will decline absolutely, while Queens will be virtually stable and only Richmond will add substantially to its population. As a result the New York City share of the regional population will decline from 48.2 per cent in 1960 to 34.4 per cent in 1985.

Of the other New York counties, Dutchess, Orange and Putnam will maintain rising rates of growth throughout the forecast period. Nassau County will add to its population but its pattern of growth will resemble that of Queens during the past decade. The limited supply of undeveloped land is expected to slow down the

rate of increase in Westchester County. A massive gain of almost a million will take place in Suffolk County, resembling the rapid filling up of Nassau County which took place during the post-World War II period. Orange and Rockland counties, taken together, are expected to add close to 600,000 to their population with Orange County accounting for roughly three-fifths of it.

An intensive rate of population development is foreseen for the New Jersey counties in the Region, which are expected to account for 50 per cent of the Region's growth during the forecast period. Their absolute gain is estimated at slightly over 3 million. The actual shift in proportion of total population, despite this gain, will be only from 27.3 per cent of the Region's population in 1960 to slightly over 33 per cent in 1985. Bergen, Morris and Somerset counties will add about 400,000 each; but the sharpest increase is expected for Middlesex and Monmouth counties, the former to add 710,000 and the latter 821,000. These two counties, in fact, are expected to account for over 50 per cent of the entire net gain in population foreseen for northern New Jersey. Hudson County is expected to decline in population, but the losses will be at a somewhat lower rate than those during the past three decades.

Fairfield County in Connecticut will increase its share of the Region's population from 4.1 per cent in 1960 to 6.4 per cent in 1985, adding roughly 770,000 people to its current 654,000.

The Region's population in 1960 and population projections for 1965, 1970, 1975, 1980 and 1985, county by county, are presented in Appendix Tables 1 and 2. They are based on the projections made for the New York Metropolitan Region Study, as revised in 1961 to take into account 1960 census data.

TABLE 7. Per Cent Changes in the Population of the
Metropolitan Region, 1920 to 1980

	1920–1930	1930–1940	1940–1950	1950–1960	1960–1970 Projected	1970–1980 Projected
Metropolitan Region	27.4	7.5	11.4	15.7	14.0	13.6
New York sector	27.1	9.2	9.8	12.4	8.2	7.5
New York City	23.3	7.6	5.9	− 1.4	−1.1	−0.8
Bronx	72.8	10.3	4.0	− 1.8	−3.5	−1.8
Kings	26.9	5.4	1.5	− 4.1	−2.9	−2.9
New York	−18.3	1.2	3.7	−13.4	−7.2	−4.8
Queens	130.1	20.3	19.5	16.7	5.0	1.3
Richmond	35.0	10.1	10.3	15.6	31.5	30.1
Other New York	52.4	18.2	29.0	67.5	29.6	22.8
Dutchess	14.1	15.2	13.2	28.5	43.2	46.4
Nassau	40.5	34.3	65.4	93.2	11.5	5.2
Orange	8.3	7.7	8.6	21.1	45.7	62.7
Putnam	27.3	21.4	17.6	60.0	37.5	56.8
Rockland	30.4	23.3	20.3	53.9	70.1	43.3
Suffolk	46.4	22.4	40.1	141.7	62.1	35.5
Westchester	51.5	10.2	9.1	29.2	16.7	11.0
New Jersey sector	29.1	2.7	15.0	22.9	24.5	23.3
Bergen	73.0	12.3	31.5	44.7	28.6	14.6
Essex	27.9	0.4	8.2	2.0	2.8	0.5
Hudson	9.9	−5.6	−0.8	− 5.6	−5.9	−4.3
Middlesex	30.9	2.4	22.1	63.8	55.5	46.1
Monmouth	40.0	9.5	39.8	48.4	64.1	69.3
Morris	32.5	14.5	30.2	59.8	57.6	50.6
Passaic	16.6	2.3	9.1	20.8	9.8	5.6
Somerset	35.4	13.8	33.8	45.5	59.7	81.3
Union	52.5	7.5	21.3	26.6	18.7	8.7
Conn. (Fairfield) sector	20.6	8.0	20.6	29.8	36.2	38.6

The changes in population distribution are summarized in Table 8.

TABLE 8. Distribution of Regional
Population in 1960 and 1985

	1960	1985	1960–1985 Gain
Population (thousands)	16,141	22,170	6,029
New York sector	68.6%	60.2%	37.3%
New York City	48.2	34.4	—
New Jersey sector	27.3	33.4	50.0
Connecticut sector	4.1	6.4	12.7

Changes in Demographic Characteristics

There are no formal estimates of the expected changes in the composition of the population. The make-up of the Region's population will probably tend more and more to resemble that of the nation as a whole. Trends in the recent past support this assumption. Thus, while the Region as measured in the census of 1960 differs from the nation in certain respects, the trend is toward convergence rather than divergence. Taking only one characteristic, the successive censuses of 1940,

1950 and 1960 reveal a progressive change in the proportioning of the Region's population among the age groups toward the national norm.

A striking feature of the projection is the declining role of migration. The population inflow, historically, has been attracted by job opportunity and has been predominantly in the family-formation stage of the life cycle. The outflow has been primarily of older people. With a declining "surplus" of jobs, resulting in part from the greater participation in the labor force of the Region's population in conformance to a trend toward the higher national rate of participation, the net migration is expected to decline from 1.1 million in 1955–1965 to 396,000 in 1965–1975, and finally yield a deficit in the terminal decade of the forecast. In this terminal decade the outflow of older people will exceed the immigration of the young.[2]

EMPLOYMENT

The number of employed persons in the New York Metropolitan Region is expected to increase by 2,443,400 between 1956 and 1985. The rise during the first

[2]Berman, Chinitz and Hoover, *Projection of a Metropolis*, (Technical Supplement to New York Metropolitan Region Study).

decade of the forecast will be modest, with the major increases taking place during the later decades (Table 9).

TABLE 9. PROJECTED GAIN IN REGIONAL EMPLOYMENT

1956–1965	7.1%
1965–1975	12.0
1975–1985	15.1

The elements which make up the economic structure of the Region are not expected to develop at the same rate, however, and therefore significant changes will take place in the composition of the employment (Table 10).

Manufacturing is expected to decline in *relative* importance, yet to remain the largest single source of employment in the Region. Among the major components of the manufacturing industries only one is expected to show an absolute decline. This is women's and children's apparel in which an absolute employment decrease of almost 40,000 is foreseen. Printing and publishing will keep pace with regional expansion in manufacturing, while electronics will grow at a more rapid pace.

Heavy industry, characterized by high consumption of fuel and power for processing raw or base materials brought into

TABLE 10. DISTRIBUTION OF JOBS IN THE REGION IN 1956 AND 1985

	Distribution of Jobs		Distribution of the Gain in Jobs
	1956	1985	1956–1985
Manufacturing	29.5%	28.0%	24.2%
Wholesale trade	6.9	6.4	5.0
Consumer trade, services	21.5	19.8	15.4
Finance, business services	20.2	24.1	34.2
Public utilities	7.7	6.0	1.5
Contract construction	3.6	3.6	3.7
Government	9.9	11.5	15.7
Miscellaneous	0.7	0.6	0.3
Total	100.0%	100.0%	100.0%

the Region by water transport, is expected to rise but at a slower rate than manufacturing as a whole. Also expected to gain at a slower-than-regional rate is employment by manufacturers geared to the national market and by those operating large-scale plants. Expected to grow at a greater-than-regional rate is employment in manufacturing of consumer goods geared to the regional market and in the smaller plants producing specialty items for a national market.

In general, it might be said that the Region will follow its historical trend and tend more and more toward light manufacturing. Where outside markets are concerned, production will be more heavily weighted by specialty, high-value goods.

A *relative* decline will also be seen in wholesale trade, consumer services and public utilities.

The major growth element will be the financial and business services group, a complex bundle of activities which includes banking, insurance, real estate, central office employment, services to business (including among other activities duplicating services, advertising, management, management consulting and commercial research), legal, medical and other professional services, and nonprofit organizations. This group alone is expected to account for 34 per cent of the total employment gain in all categories of industry within the Region. Generally speaking, the financial and business services will be marked by an unusually large number of middle-income jobs. The impact of gains for these services will have qualitative overtones and locational implications which will heighten their overall importance.

Government employment, growing more rapidly than the aggregate, will absorb almost 16 per cent of the employment gain. This rise is contingent upon the role of government expanding rather than contracting during the years that lie ahead. However, even if the role of government does not change materially, the effect of population growth alone will yield a net increase in government employment sufficient to account for 12.2 per cent of the total job increment in the Region during the forecast period.

Distribution of Jobs within the Region

Employment growth in the major geographic divisions of the Region is summarized in Table 11. As may be seen, the New York sector of the Region is not expected to maintain its share of regional employment; the major decline in job shares will take place in New York City. Conversely, the gains of the New Jersey sector will be disproportionate to present job shares (Table 12). Fairfield County, which will account for 7.1 per cent of the Region's gain, will increase materially its share of regional employment.

TABLE 11. EMPLOYMENT IN THE REGION BY MAJOR GEOGRAPHIC DIVISIONS

	1956	1985	Gain 1956–1985
Regional employment (thousands)	6,402.6	8,846.0	2,443.4
New York sector	72.3%	65.8%	48.8%
New York City	60.8	47.9	14.2
Other New York	11.5	17.9	34.6
New Jersey sector	23.9	29.5	44.1
Connecticut sector	3.8	4.7	7.1

TABLE 12. SHARE OF REGIONAL EMPLOYMENT
IN THE NEW JERSEY SECTOR, BY MAJOR
INDUSTRY GROUPS: 1956 AND 1985

	Regional Jobs 1956	1985	Regional Gain 1956-1985
Total	23.9%	29.5%	44.1%
Manufacturing	33.8	40.1	51.1
Wholesale trade	16.0	26.1	62.4
Consumer trade & services	22.1	25.7	35.3
Finance & business services	14.8	20.9	30.3
Utilities	22.7	32.2	65.0
Construction	26.0	24.0	18.9
Miscellaneous	36.9	30.4	11.0
Government	22.0	33.4	44.2

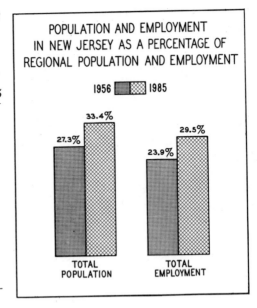

FIG. 4

Despite the fact that New Jersey will provide more than a million of the Region's new jobs, the increase will not match the expected rise in population (Table 13).

TABLE 13. THE NEW JERSEY SECTOR'S SHARE OF REGIONAL POPULATION AND EMPLOYMENT

	1960	1985
Population	27.3%	33.4%
Employment	23.9	29.5

If we assume that the various skill groups of the labor force will be distributed by residence in the future as they are at present, it can be reasoned that the New Jersey sector of the Region will need to attract labor for manufacturing jobs, but will export workers for employment in wholesale trade, in retailing, and in financial and business services. Although employment in New Jersey in these latter groups will rise during the forecast period, the number of New Jersey residents seeking employment in these fields outside of their area will probably be larger than at present.

Employment in New York City is expected to grow by about 9 per cent, or by 345,000 jobs. The bulk of its growth, 277,000, will take place in the boroughs outside of Manhattan. With the exception of the utilities group — in which a decline in railroad employment has been projected — all other categories of employment will either remain stable or show an increase. Manufacturing and the business services will absorb most of the growth in the rest of the city. While both of these will gain in relative importance, the basic economic structure of the outlying boroughs will not undergo the same degree of modification as will Manhattan.

Changing Manhattan

An estimate of future employment in Manhattan, discussed in detail in the Appendix, denotes a small increase in the 1980's over the present number of jobs.

The magnitude of the increase, considering the margin of error of the estimate, is not of a decisive order, some 68,000 above the current employment of approximately 2.4 million (Table 14). One might better characterize the employment prospect as one of approximate stability. However, this is stability in the total, for the estimate is the net sum of gains and losses in the constituent industries and indicates some far-reaching changes in the economic structure of the borough.

The financial, business and professional services group, now the dominant source of employment in Manhattan, will enhance its dominance. The number of new jobs in this field is estimated at 180,000.

TABLE 14. CURRENT AND PROJECTED
EMPLOYMENT IN MANHATTAN:
1956 AND 1985[a]

	1956 Employment (thousands)	1985 Employment (thousands)
All industries	2,405.8	2,473.7
Manufacturing	499.4	372.7
Wholesale trade	257.1	257.1
Consumer trade	436.8	458.0
Finance, business & professional services	770.7	949.7
Utilities	218.9	183.0
Construction	45.5	65.0
Government	175.8	186.2
Miscellaneous	1.7	2.0

[a]Developed from the employment base for New York City in the New York Metropolitan Region Study. See Appendix for rationale of Manhattan distributions.

Many of the elements that make up the financial and business services group are statistically elusive. Some we can measure, notably services oriented to the central office function. These are highly concentrated in Manhattan and reveal extreme reluctance to migrate out of the Region's business center. As for central office employment itself there are no comprehensive statistics. One major element, however, office employment in manufacturing, exhibits unusual growth. There are about 125,000 such employees in the New York Metropolitan Area, and most of these are concentrated in Manhattan. During 1954–1958 the absolute increase in the Metropolitan Area amounted to 18,094 employees.

The New York Metropolitan Region Study estimated total central office employment in New York City at 143,000 in 1956, and projected that it would grow to 184,000 by 1985, a rise of 41,000 over a 30-year period. Although differences in definition may blur the comparison, this seems to be on the low side in view of the rapid growth rate of the one known component of this complex during 1954–1958.

In view of recent trends, consumer trade and services are expected to show a slight increase in employment in Manhattan. With the expected growth of employment in finance and business services it can be reasoned that the larger number of relatively high-income workers in Manhattan's daytime population will add substantially to the borough's retailing potential.

Wholesale trade employment in Manhattan is expected to remain at a constant level, which means that it will decline in relative importance regionally. Although recent trends (1954–1958) reveal a significant upturn, it is likely that the progressive sloughing-off of goods handling in almost all branches of the trade which deal in standardized products will offset the borough's growth in specialty wholesaling and in wholesale transactions.

Government employment is expected to show a slight increase, not as the result of increases in Manhattan's requirements for government services, but as the consequence of the location in the borough of headquarters for municipal, state and federal services.

Manufacturing, currently the second-ranking source of employment in Manhattan, is expected to show a decline of at least 125,000 over the forecast period. This represents a gradual loss in all lines except specialty manufacturing, in which the cost of materials handling is a relatively minor factor in production cost. The largest single source of job loss is expected to be in the women's apparel field. The estimated decline may be understated, for the progressive attrition of loft space in Manhattan could well bring about even sharper drops in manufacturing employment, possibly as much as 200,000 during the forecast period.

Quite aside from the unadaptability of much of the existing loft structure in Manhattan to efficient production in all but a fairly narrow band of industries, and the economic impracticability of replacing it with new industrial plants, there is another factor that argues against growth or even the maintenance of the status quo in manufacturing and in the goods-handling phase of wholesale trade in Manhattan. Urban redevelopment programs in the past have replaced substantial amounts of industrial and warehouse space by residential space. While areas undergoing redevelopment may yield a net gain in housing units, the business activity in redeveloped areas is usually drastically reduced. For example, the Washington Square Southeast Project, containing 2,000 dwelling units, displaced more than 1,000 firms that had occupied old loft space on a ground area of 14.5 acres. Similarly, the Penn Station South Redevelopment Project now under construction has also uprooted a large number of industrial and commercial tenants. The future housing projects now envisaged for Manhattan below 60th Street will also displace industrial and commercial tenants.

Only a strong reorientation of urban redevelopment programs toward the provision of industrial and commercial accommodations can prevent further shrinkage in the city's stock of loft space.

CHAPTER 3

THE MANUFACTURING INDUSTRIES

The New York–New Jersey Metropolitan Area contains the nation's largest single concentration of manufacturing activity. When measured by either volume of employment or by value added by manufacture, the primacy of the New York Area is indisputable (Table 1). The New York sector of the Area by itself outranks the Chicago Area in manufacturing employment, and the New Jersey sector is exceeded only by the Chicago and the Los Angeles areas.

The New York Area does not excel in rate of growth of manufacturing plant. In 1958 the New York Area was outranked in capital expenditures for new plant and equipment by the Chicago Area (Table 1). Although the New Jersey sector had but a third of the Area's manufacturing employment in 1958, its factories in that year accounted for almost half of the Area's total capital expenditures.

These contrasts in capital expenditures between the New York Area and other industrial centers in the nation and between the two major sectors making up the New York Area suggest a uniquely structured manufacturing community and some basic differences in growth characteristics.

THE INDUSTRIAL STRUCTURE OF THE NEW YORK AREA

The basic pattern of industry in the New York Area may be readily grasped by comparing the distribution of its employment among the major industry groups with that of the nation. This comparison is portrayed graphically in Figure 1.

TABLE 1. STRENGTH OF MANUFACTURING IN RANKING METROPOLITAN AREAS: 1958

Metropolitan Area	Manufacturing Employment (in thousands)	Value Added (in millions)	Capital Expenditures for New Plant and Equipment		
			Total Expenditures (in millions)	Per Manufacturing Employee	Per Dollar of Value Added by Manufacture
New York	1,805	$15,293	$607	$336	$.04
New York sector	1,191	9,351	311	261	.03
New Jersey sector	614	5,942	296	482	.05
Chicago	995	9,470	717	721	.08
Los Angeles	728	6,987	318	437	.05
Philadelphia	539	4,845	290	538	.06
Detroit	468	4,278	210	449	.05
Pittsburgh	318	2,625	270	849	.10
Boston	298	2,378	100	336	.04
Cleveland	265	2,452	142	536	.06
St. Louis	256	2,328	152	594	.07
Baltimore	198	1,933	85	429	.04

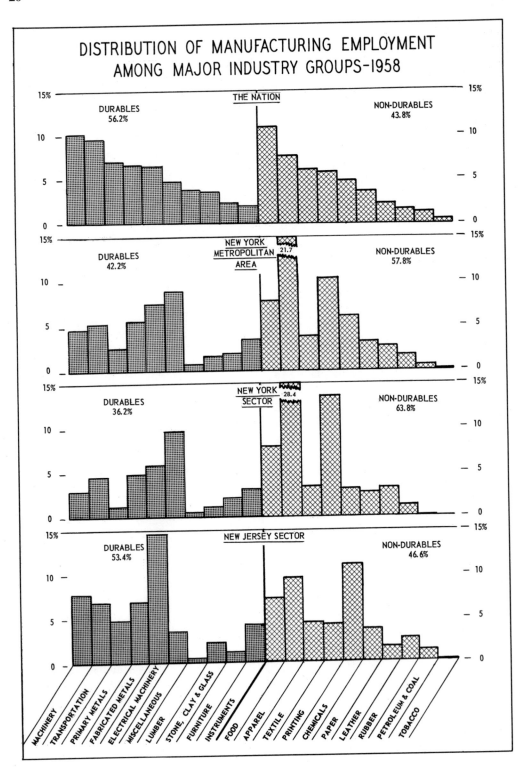

Fig. 1

In the nation, the manufacture of durables, accounting for 56 per cent of total manufacturing employment, predominates. In the New York Area, however, employment in nondurables is predominant. The difference stems chiefly from the overwhelming influence of the apparel trade and the printing and publishing industry in the New York Area.

In durables there is a wide deviation from the national pattern. Miscellaneous manufactures, electrical machinery and fabricated metals, in that order, come to the fore in the New York Area. For the most part, these industries engage in the finishing stages of manufacturing, rather than in the basic transformation of raw materials. The production of primary metal products and of stone, clay and glass products, which requires basic processing, is relatively unimportant in the Area's pattern of manufacturing employment.

A contrast also prevails between the New York Area and the national pattern in the nondurables field. For example, in chemicals manufacture the New York Area ranks high as a source of employment as a result of the preponderance of drugs and pharmaceuticals, not in consequence of the more basic chemical processing industry.

The distribution of manufacturing employment between the New York and the New Jersey sectors of the Metropolitan Area reveals contrasts as striking as those observed between the Area and the nation. In the New York sector, employment in nondurables production overshadows that in durables, with printing and apparel accounting for almost 42 per cent of the sector's total manufacturing employment. Among the durables, the light phase of production stands forth boldly.

The so-called miscellaneous manufactures group is vitally important in the Area's manufacturing activity. Products range from jewelry (including gem cutting), musical instruments, games, toys, athletic goods, office supplies, artists' materials, buttons and novelties to fireworks, barber shop equipment and matches. These goods appear equally prominent in the Area's foreign and domestic wholesaling trade.

The distribution of manufacturing employment in the New Jersey sector conforms more closely to the national pattern. The proportioning of employment between durables and nondurables approaches the division prevailing for the nation. Chemicals stands out among the nondurables and electrical machinery among the durables. Machinery, transportation equipment and primary metals are more prominent than in the New York sector, but New Jersey, too, gives the impression of leaning toward the lighter forms of industry.

HEAVY AND LIGHT INDUSTRY

In popular understanding, heavy industry is typified by plants processing iron ore into iron and steel products, and light industry by establishments making watches, or radios or women's dresses. No quantitative measure of the degree of heaviness or of lightness, however, has been proposed heretofore. In the course of the present study it became apparent that the expenditure for fuel and power as a proportion of the value added by the manufacturing process is a useful measure of heaviness and is used hereafter in this report to compare the character of manufacturing in different areas.

There are wide differences among manufacturing industries as to the amount of fuel and electric power they consume. In blast furnace operations the cost of fuel and power amounts to 29 cents for each dollar of value added by manufacture. In apparel production, at the other extreme, fuel and power costs amount to less than 1 cent per dollar of value added. These differences indicate the fundamental contrast between heavy and light industry. In any area, the total of fuel and power costs per dollar of total value added in all branches of manufacture provides a score or index of heaviness of industry in that area. For the nation as a whole, the level of such costs in 1954 was rather low, 4.2 cents per dollar of value added.

Using the national values as a reference point, the relative heaviness of industry varies considerably from region to region. New York and New Jersey share with New England a low index, reflecting a preponderance of light industry. Heavy industry is prominent in the East South Central and in the Mountain States. The heaviness index for the Middle Atlantic States is fairly high, primarily because of the heavy industry in Pennsylvania.

Among the 25 ranking sources of manufacturing employment in the New York Metropolitan Area, accounting for 68 per cent of the Area's manufacturing employment in 1954, there was only one industry whose fuel and power requirements exceeded that of the national norm: organic chemicals with fuel and power costs amounting to 5.4 cents per dollar of value added. This was the only industry among the leading 25, with the exception of men's and boys' furnishings (other factors enter into that industry's decline), which had an appreciable loss in employment between 1947 and 1954.

Among the next 25 ranking industries, accounting for another 22 per cent of the Area's manufacturing employment in 1954, miscellaneous chemical products, miscellaneous food products, and textile finishing, each with fuel and power costs in excess of 3 cents per dollar, declined as sources of employment. On

the other hand, manufacturing of dairy products, having a fairly high fuel and power requirement (4.6 cents) and of primary metals other than iron and steel (5.2 cents) showed substantial *increases* in employment. It is to be noted that the former is a consumer-oriented activity while the latter depends on imports of nonferrous metals for its base materials.

TABLE 2. FUEL AND POWER COSTS PER DOLLAR OF VALUE ADDED, IN 1954
(4.2 cents per dollar of value added = 100)

New England	69
Middle Atlantic	95
New York State	67
New Jersey	62
Pennsylvania	155
East North Central	107
West North Central	74
South Atlantic	114
East South Central	183
West South Central	114
Mountain	195
Pacific	71

It appears that where heavy industry occurs in the Area it is based either on regional consumption or on water-borne raw materials. Sugar refining reflects both factors. Fuel and power costs in sugar refining amount to almost 10 per cent of the value added; in fact, this industry ranks seventh in terms of heaviness among all industries in the nation. New York's share of the nation's sugar refining employment is large, 13 per cent, and is growing.

The degree to which the heaviness of an industry appears to affect its growth or decline in the New York Area may be seen by examining certain major industry groups. In the textiles group, the finishing phase requires a substantial amount of fuel and power, 6.9 cents, while in textile fabrication the fuel and power requirement drops to less than 1 cent per dollar of value added. Employment in the finishing phase (dyeing, bleaching, printing) dropped in the Area, while employment in the fabricating phase increased slightly. The same contrast may be seen in the chemicals group, within which organic chemicals represents the heavy phase, 5.4 cents, and drugs and medicines lighter phases, 1.4 cents. Here again, the heavy phase dropped in its share of national employment while the lighter phase grew.

Not all light phases of industry gained, nor did all heavy phases of industry decline during the period under observation (Table 3). At least one heavy industry, inorganic chemicals, gained substantially

in employment. The gain in the industry aggregate, however, stems from one item of production, sulfuric acid, with a highly localized market.

Effect of the Heaviness Factor on Industrial Location within the Area

Over the years there has been a decided tendency for heavy industry to grow more rapidly in the New Jersey sector. In 1947, 67 per cent of the Area's employment in chemicals was concentrated there; in the heavy phases New Jersey's share was over 90 per cent, and in the lighter phases about 60 per cent. During 1947–1958, the

TABLE 3. INFLUENCE OF EXPENDITURE FOR FUEL AND POWER UPON EMPLOYMENT IN SELECTED INDUSTRIES IN THE NEW YORK METROPOLITAN AREA: 1947–1954

	Fuel and Power Cost (cents per dollar value added)	Trend in Area Share of National Employment 1947–1954
Textiles		
Heavy phases		
Textile finishing	6.9	down
Woolen, worsted	4.5	down
Yarns and thread	4.6	down
Light phases		
Knitting mills	2.6	up
Miscellaneous textiles	2.9	up
Chemicals		
Heavy phases		
Inorganic chemicals	22.7	up
Organic chemicals	5.4	down
Vegetable oil processing	8.5	down
Light phases		
Drugs and medicines	1.4	up
Soap and related products	1.3	up
Paper and paper products		
Heavy phase		
Pulp and paper	11.9	down
Light phases		
Paper coating	2.2	up
Envelopes	1.2	up
Paper bags	1.1	up

New Jersey share of Area employment in the chemicals industries declined to 64 per cent as a result of some heavy phases moving out of the Area altogether.

New Jersey in 1947 also accounted for 64 per cent of the Area's employment in the production of paper and paper products, again with a concentration in the heavier phases. Between 1947 and 1958 this share declined, not so much as a result of losses in the heavy phase, as from the growth on the New York side of the manufacture of paper products, especially of packaging materials.

EXPENDITURE FOR NEW PLANT AND EQUIPMENT

The New York Metropolitan Area, like the Middle Atlantic Region as a whole, has accounted for a progressively smaller proportion of the nation's expenditure for new manufacturing plant and equipment. In part, this trend reflects the maturity of the industrial plant in the Area; renovation of plant and replacement of equipment take place as a continuous process. In contrast, large initial expenditures for new plant and equipment are characteristic of newly developing areas undergoing rapid industrial expansion.

Within the New Jersey sector of the Area there are marked differences from county to county in the proportioning of capital expenditures for old and for new plant. Figure 2, compiled from data made available by the New Jersey Department of Labor, shows the relationship between new plant construction and alterations, additions to and modifications of existing plant. Capital investment for new plant is comparatively larger in the rapidly expanding industrial counties — Bergen, Middlesex and Union — and there is greater emphasis on alterations in the older industrial areas.

The progressive shrinkage in over-all capital expenditure reflects the changing character of manufacturing in the New York Area, where light industry with its lower investment requirements has gained more rapidly than heavy industry.

Although the time lag between investment in production facilities and increased production must be allowed for, there is a correspondence between the level of capital expenditure devoted to an industrial category and its production strength. In most of the industries in the New York Area which from 1947 to 1958 gained relative to the nation in value added by manufacture, there was a rise in the Area's share of the nation's expenditure for capital equipment (Table 4). In all cases where the Area's capital expenditure share declined, there was also a pronounced drop in the Area's share in value added. The correspondence is evident in the case of textiles, wood products, leather goods, fabricated metal and transportation equipment. The converse has not always been true, however, for some of the industries which had had larger shares of the total national investment experienced relative declines during the period. Outstanding is the spurt in investment in the apparel trades, in furniture and in machinery, as well as in printing and publishing. With the exception of apparel, the absolute gains in these industries have been notable, even though they did not match the national rate of growth.

The influence of heaviness of industry on the amount of capital expenditure per employee may be seen in the case of chemicals. The shift toward the lighter phases in the Area is indicated by the low investment in new plant and equipment in comparison with the nation as a whole, $4,377 against $15,464. The value for the New York Area in the main reflects the preponderance in chemicals of drugs and

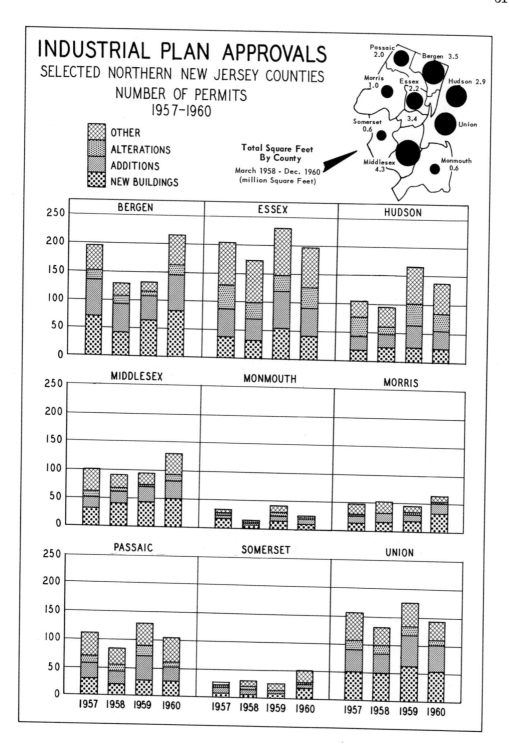

Fig. 2

pharmaceuticals, where capital investment requirements per employee are much less than those in the production of basic chemicals. A similar contrast may be seen in the pulp and paper products group, in which New York's participation is growing only in the manufacture of paper products and not in the production of paper stock. With few exceptions, and none of them important, capital expenditures per employee in the New York Metropolitan Area are lower, industry by industry, than in the nation.

SIZE OF ESTABLISHMENT

The prominence of the small establishment in the Area is almost entirely due to the unique character of the apparel industry. For other industries the size-of-establishment pattern does not differ radically from that of the nation: in the nation, 68.5 per cent of the establishments employ less than 20 persons; in the New York Area the proportion rises to but 70 per cent.

Apparel production in the New York Area is marked by a kind of organization which can be best described as amorphous. There are no "sizes" of firms as such. The International Ladies Garment Workers Union, a prominent labor organization in this field, functions virtually as the industry's personnel department and in a sense as its financial director; it trains employees, keeps a watchful eye on markets and monitors a large number of small entrepreneurs and on occasion helps them

TABLE 4. CAPITAL EXPENDITURE AND VALUE ADDED IN THE MANUFACTURING INDUSTRIES IN THE NEW YORK AREA AS SHARE OF NATIONAL TOTAL: 1947–1958

| | New York Area as Percentage of Nation | | | |
| | Capital Expenditures | | Value Added | |
	1947	1958	1947	1958
All industries	7.0%	6.7%	12.5%	10.9%
Food products	7.5	7.3	9.6	9.3
Tobacco products	2.8	0.8	4.7	3.1
Textiles	6.1	10.0	8.5	9.6
Apparel	25.8	45.8	45.9	39.4
Lumber, wood products	0.8	0.9	1.8	2.1
Furniture, fixtures	5.5	8.0	10.4	9.6
Pulp and paper products	4.9	3.6	9.3	8.2
Printing and publishing	14.5	15.2	25.6	24.3
Chemicals	11.0	7.8	17.9	14.8
Petroleum and coal products	5.2	6.1	10.5	4.1
Rubber products	5.5	2.3	5.2	3.3
Leather and products	9.6	16.1	13.4	13.4
Stone, clay, glass products	3.6	2.2	5.1	4.3
Primary metals	2.6	1.7	4.0	3.2
Fabricated metals	7.3	7.6	8.8	9.3
Machinery (except electrical)	3.7	4.7	6.2	5.6
Electrical machinery	12.8	10.8	13.1	12.7
Transportation equipment	3.6	4.5	6.6	6.8
Instruments	15.1	13.7	20.9	16.9
Miscellaneous manufactures	17.3	17.3	26.6	18.0

out of financial difficulty. The contractor functions as the purchasing department and bears the cost of materials and supplies. Wholesalers and the buying officers of chains and department stores function as the sales department and perform important warehousing and agent functions. One might characterize the garment center as one gigantic establishment housed in a number of buildings.

If we exclude New York City from the Area totals of manufacturing establishments, again aside from apparel industry, the proportioning in the rest of the Area veers toward the larger size groups. This is especially true of the New Jersey sector, where the proportion of establishments employing 100 or more persons is considerably higher than that of the nation, 12.2 per cent and 9.8 per cent, respectively.

Manhattan alone accounts for 48 per cent of the 34,768 small firms (less than 20 employees) in the Area. The other boroughs in the city are either slightly below the national level or slighty above it. The number of large firms as a proportion of total establishments is generally highest in the suburban counties. This is true especially of Nassau, Westchester, Middlesex and Union counties. In Union County, over 14 per cent of all establishments employ more than 100 persons.

The influence of the central city as the home of small industry is most pronounced in the apparel trades. In New York City 62 per cent of the apparel firms employed less than 20 persons, and this proportion rises to almost 68 per cent in Manhattan. Outside of New York City in the New York sector of the Area the percentage of small apparel firms declines to 42 per cent.

The growth in the number of small firms in the New York Area during the postwar period has been slight, a net increase of about a thousand establishments in 1958 over 1947, when there were 33,792,

an increase of less than 3 per cent. The primary cause may be traced to the apparel trades, which suffered a decline of 2,719 firms between 1947 and 1958, but declines occurred in other groups, marked typically by a fairly high percentage of small firms, in tobacco, textiles and leather goods. On the other hand, there was an increase of almost 1,200 small firms in printing and publishing, and substantial gains took place in fabricated metals, machinery and electrical goods.

As for the geographic distribution of gains in small establishments within the

TABLE 5. GAINS IN NUMBER OF SMALL INDUSTRY ESTABLISHMENTS (LESS THAN 20 EMPLOYEES) IN THE METROPOLITAN AREA BETWEEN 1947 AND 1958

Metropolitan Area	976
New York sector (S.M.S.A.)	− 844
New York City	−2,263
Bronx	
Kings	− 114
New York	−2,536
Queens	364
Richmond	23
Other New York	1,419
Nassau	804
Rockland	26
Suffolk	325
Westchester	264
New Jersey sector	1,820
Jersey City S.M.S.A. (Hudson)	170
Newark S.M.S.A.	661
Essex	184
Morris	142
Union	335
Paterson-Clifton-Passaic S.M.S.A.	876
Bergen	640
Passaic	236
Middlesex	106
Somerset	7

Area, the New Jersey sector, with 1,820 more small firms in 1958 than in 1947, appears to have taken over the role of incubator for small industry, with Bergen and Union as the most active counties. The whole New York sector declined, due largely to the apparel establishment losses in Manhattan. Outside of New York City but within the New York sector, there was a net gain of 1,419 small firms, about 60 per cent of it in Nassau County (Table 5).

Growth Trends in Manufacturing

The past 60 years have seen the gradual diffusion of manufacturing among the major regions making up the nation. At the close of the century, New England and the Middle Atlantic Region accounted for more than half of the nation's manufacturing employment. At present their share is less than 35 per cent. The Middle Atlantic Region — New Jersey, New York and Pennsylvania — dropped from 34 per cent to slightly less than 26 per cent. But the national total of manufacturing employment has also expanded, and manufacturing jobs in the Middle Atlantic Region rose during this long period from 1.7 million to almost 4.2 million.

Three groups of states — New England, Middle Atlantic and East North Central — still constitute, as they did at the turn of the century, the manufacturing belt of the nation. This may be seen in Appendix Table 8, which shows the importance of manufacturing jobs relative to the population base in each region as measured against the national norm. Even in the Pacific States, the growth of manufacturing jobs has not kept pace with population expansion, and as a result industrialization is at a slightly lower level than in 1919. The important inference to be drawn is that there is still a marked contrast in industrialization among the regions of the nation, a sharp divide between those which consume more than they produce, and vice versa.

During the postwar period, 1947 to 1958, manufacturing employment in the New York Area relative to the nation tended to decline slightly, but more than held its own in the Middle Atlantic States (Table 6).

Distribution of Manufacturing Activity Within the New York Area

Thirty years of industrial development have brought about relatively few major changes in the geographic distribution of manufacturing within the area (see Table 7). The gain in manufacturing employment during 1929–1958 was large, roughly 750,000, an increase of 80 per cent. Yet the locational pattern of this employment

Table 6. Manufacturing Employment in the New York Area,
The Middle Atlantic Region and the Nation Compared, 1929–1958
(in thousands)

	Nation	Middle Atlantic	New York Area		
			Number	As Per Cent of Nation	As Per Cent of Middle Atlantic
1929	9,660	3,003	1,111	11.5	37.0
1939	9,527	2,758	1,117	11.7	40.5
1947	14,294	3,954	1,599	11.2	40.4
1954	15,651	4,106	1,732	11.1	42.2
1958	15,394	3,882	1,660	10.8	42.8

TABLE 7. TRENDS IN DISTRIBUTION OF METROPOLITAN AREA
MANUFACTURING EMPLOYMENT
(per cent of total)

	1929	1939	1947	1954	1958
Metropolitan Area	100.0	100.0	100.0	100.0	100.0
New York sector (S.M.S.A.)	63.8	62.4	64.2	64.7	64.9
New York City	60.0	58.6	58.4	54.7	54.1
Bronx	2.7	2.1	2.6	3.3	3.2
Kings	15.6	15.5	14.4	13.6	13.6
New York	34.9	34.3	34.6	30.0	28.7
Queens	5.9	6.0	6.1	7.2	8.0
Richmond	0.9	0.7	0.7	0.6	0.6
Other New York	3.8	3.8	5.8	10.0	10.8
Nassau	0.4	0.5	1.6	4.1	4.8
Rockland	0.4	0.5	0.5	0.6	0.7
Suffolk	0.3	0.4	0.8	2.4	1.9
Westchester	2.7	2.4	2.9	2.9	3.4
New Jersey sector	36.2	37.6	35.8	35.3	35.1
Jersey City S.M.S.A. (Hudson)	9.7	9.9	9.1	7.6	7.1
Newark S.M.S.A.	13.5	13.3	13.9	14.0	13.6
Essex	9.8	8.9	8.9	8.3	7.6
Morris	0.7	0.7	0.8	1.0	1.3
Union	3.0	3.7	4.2	4.7	4.7
Paterson-Clifton-Passaic S.M.S.A.	8.7	9.5	8.2	9.0	9.5
Bergen	2.5	3.0	3.3	4.8	4.9
Passaic	6.2	6.5	4.9	4.2	4.6
Middlesex	3.8	4.1	3.7	3.8	3.8
Somerset	0.5	0.8	0.9	0.9	1.1

has exhibited surprising stability. The New York sector commands about the same share today of Area manufacturing that it did in 1929.

There have been changes, of course, but they have been changes in the subregional distribution of employment rather than sweeping shifts between the two major sectors of the Area.

In the Newark subarea,[1] manufacturing employment as a per cent of Area employment in manufacturing has remained vir-

[1]Essex, Morris and Union counties.

tually constant, but there have been shifts among its component counties. The fairly steep rate of relative decline in Essex County has been offset by large gains in Union and Morris counties. Similarly, Bergen County in the Paterson-Clifton-Passaic subarea has developed so rapidly, especially after 1947, that its growth has more than compensated for shrinkages in Passaic County. When the data are analyzed in more detail they reveal decline — in some cases relative, in most cases absolute — in the older industrial centers within these subareas, and growth in the surrounding territory.

The Paterson-Passaic locale exhibits precisely this course of development.[2] Around the almost archaic assemblage of plant in Paterson there has developed in Clifton and Fair Lawn, for example, much new industrial plant, with firms drawing largely from the Paterson-Passaic pool of skilled and semiskilled labor. We can infer from other knowledge that expanding industry in open land in the Newark subarea draws extensively from the labor supply that is resident in and adjacent to the older, tightly knit industrial clusters.

The most striking feature in the redistribution of manufacturing employment in the New York side of the Area since 1947 is the decline, relative as well as absolute, of Manhattan. To Manhattan we may ascribe the shrinkage in New York City's share of industrial jobs in the Area. Most of the industrial growth in the New York sector has originated in its "inner ring" counties, Nassau County particularly.

It appears that industry has passed over eastern Queens, where residential land use has thwarted the spread of manufacturing out of the intensively developed centrally located industrial areas. Case studies of industrial firms relocating in Nassau, made in 1951 when the pace of relocation was at its height, reveal their motivations. High among the factors cited was scarcity in the city of strategically located land. This suggests that, other factors being favorable, the Narrows Bridge linkage to the major source of the Area's labor supply may bring about industrial expansion in Staten Island similar to the

[2]James B. Kenyon. Industrial Localization and Metropolitan Growth; the Paterson-Passaic Locale, Dept. of Geography, University of Chicago, 1960.

[3]The values cited here are based on the April 1961 revision and adjustment of the N.Y.M.R.S. forecast.

growth that took place in Nassau County between 1947 and 1958.

FUTURE GROWTH

The New York Metropolitan Region Study forecast a 30 per cent gain in manufacturing employment by 1985. This amounts to an absolute gain of about 590,000 manufacturing jobs for the 22-county New York Metropolitan Region, and a gain of 490,000 for the 17-county New York Metropolitan Area.[3] That study arranges the constituent industries in the Area into five broad groups designed to reveal their *locational* orientations. The changes foreseen in the distribution of manufacturing employment are shown in Table 8.

Employment in the production of women's and children's apparel, which now provides about 260,000 jobs in the Area,

TABLE 8. PROSPECTIVE CHANGES IN THE PATTERN OF MANUFACTURING EMPLOYMENT

All Industries	1956 100.0%	1985 100.0%
Communications-oriented	35.7%	33.5%
Women's and children's apparel	14.0	8.4
Printing and publishing	8.7	8.7
Electronic	6.0	8.0
Other communications-oriented	7.0	8.4
Nuisance, raw materials, water transport oriented	8.1	7.6
Local market industries	13.2	15.0
National market— large plant	18.0	16.4
National market— small plant	25.0	27.5

mostly in Manhattan, is expected to decline. This will bring about a reduction in the communications-oriented group of manufactures.

Unlike the rest of the United States, which showed an employment gain of 15 per cent during the postwar period, apparel manufacturing in the New York Area has remained virtually static. A number of forces lie behind New York's relative loss, but three of decisive importance emerge: (1) shortage of skilled labor; (2) space costs; and (3) changing fashion trends.

With the virtual drying-up of immigration as a source of skilled labor in the needle trades, apparel manufacturers in the Area have resorted to the "section shop," in which the less skilled operations are farmed out to outlying production centers and returned to Manhattan for tailoring. The section shop, to be efficient, requires a larger layout and work force than the traditional New York tailor shop, and suitable space is not available in Manhattan, or elsewhere in the Area at a price the industry can bear. The tendency has been to locate shops in areas such as Scranton and Wilkes-Barre, which lie within economical trucking distance of Manhattan, and which have an abundant supply of semiskilled labor.

The trend in dress has been away from fashion apparel toward more simple and casual attire. Not only are women spending a smaller proportion of the family income for apparel, but a smaller portion of the apparel dollar is spent for fashion items of the type dominated by New York. On the basis of these trends, the New York Metropolitan Region Study estimates that apparel employment may be expected in 1985 to be about 10 per cent below current levels. Manhattan as a center for apparel design and apparel marketing is, nevertheless, expected to maintain its preeminent position.

In the "nuisance, water transport, raw materials-oriented" industries — basically heavy industry — the absolute gain expected in employment is slight, with a resultant drop in relative importance. Although the growth rate of large-plant industries oriented to national markets is projected to be somewhat higher than in the foregoing group, it too should decline in relative importance. Two major groups of manufacturing, one oriented to local markets, the other comprising small plants geared to national markets, are expected to expand at a fairly rapid rate, and to account for about 18 per cent and 32 per cent, respectively, of the Area's net gain in manufacturing employment.

The Geographic Distribution of Future Growth within the Area

The gain to be expected in manufacturing employment between 1958 and 1985 in the major geographic divisions of the New York Metropolitan Area and its effect upon the future distribution of such employment is shown in Table 9. The New Jersey sector is expected to account for the bulk of the Area's gain, and in 1985 its portion of the Area's industrial employment is expected to reach 42.4 per cent, compared with 35.2 per cent in 1958.

The prospect of a strong shift toward New Jersey in the future marks a break with the historical trend noted earlier, a stable proportioning of employment between the two sectors of the Area between 1929 and 1958. The New York Metropolitan Region Study concludes that locational trends point toward the New Jersey side as more favorable for those industries having the highest potential for growth in the Area. New Jersey is expected to absorb two-thirds or more of the employment gains in "local-market" and in "national-market" oriented plants. In the communications-oriented industries, New Jersey is expected to account for more than half of the employment gain in electronics, and over a third of the gain in

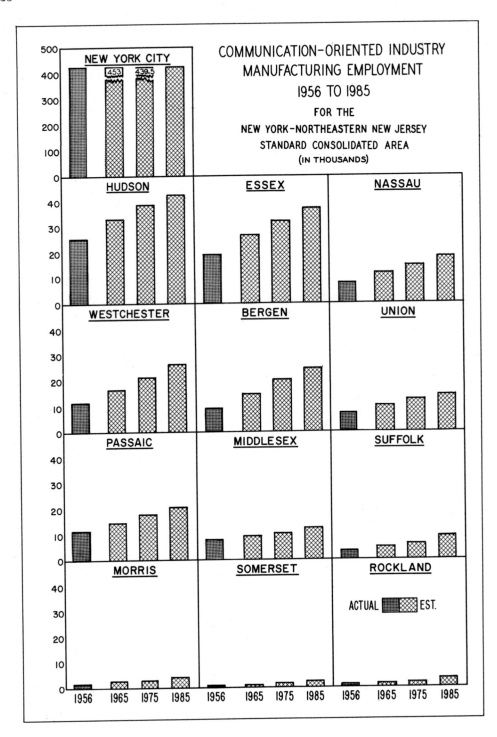

Fig. 3

the other communications-oriented group. The slight growth expected in the nuisance, water transport, raw materials industry group is also expected to accrue principally to New Jersey.

The communications-oriented industry group (Fig. 3), includes the apparel trades, printing and publishing, electronics, apparel accessories, "apparel parts," giftware, toys, jewelry and advertising displays. The marketing influence is deemed of paramount importance: designer, purchaser and seller must remain in close physical proximity. Employment, it is expected, will remain highly concentrated in New York City. Nevertheless a decline

is forecast, though small in relationship to the total magnitude of employment, to result from losses in the manufacture of women's and children's apparel. The growth outside of New York City is expected to be contained within the nearer counties. Rises are foreseen in Essex, Hudson and Westchester counties, associated with the availability of much semimodern plant vacated by other industries. This is the industry group which is expected to counteract the long-range employment decline in Hudson County.

Almost without exception, the industries in the "nuisance, water transport and raw materials" group fall within the heavy

TABLE 9. METROPOLITAN AREA MANUFACTURING EMPLOYMENT: 1958 AND 1985
(in thousands)

	Employ-ment in 1958	Estimated Gain or Loss 1958–1985	Estimated Employ-ment in 1985	Per Cent Distribution of Total Employment 1958	1985
Metropolitan Area	1,660	510	2,170	100.0	100.0
New York sector (S.M.S.A.)	1,075	172	1,247	64.8	57.5
New York City	896	−20	876	54.0	40.4
Other New York	178	193	371	10.8	17.1
Nassau	79	51	130	4.8	6.0
Rockland	11	10	21	0.7	1.0
Suffolk	32	59	91	1.9	4.2
Westchester	56	73	129	3.4	5.9
New Jersey sector	585	338	923	35.2	42.4
Jersey City S.M.S.A. (Hudson)	121	− 1	120	7.3	5.5
Newark S.M.S.A.	227	116	343	13.5	15.8
Essex	126	28	154	7.4	7.1
Morris	22	18	40	1.3	1.9
Union	79	70	149	4.8	6.8
Paterson-Clifton-Passaic S.M.S.A.	156	149	305	9.4	14.0
Bergen	82	75	157	4.9	7.2
Passaic	75	73	148	4.5	6.8
Middlesex	64	54	118	3.9	5.4
Somerset	18	19	37	1.1	1.7

range. They consume raw rather than semiprocessed materials, much of which is brought in by water, and they use large amounts of fuel and power. Access to deep water and prevailing zoning restrictions limit these industries to areas fringing the harbor and its navigable channels. All of the counties expected to show appreciable growth — Hudson, Essex, Union, Middlesex — are in New Jersey where most of the suitable undeveloped sites are to be found.

Some of the industries in the national-market large-plant group could well be classified in the foregoing group, such as coke and by-products, paving and roofing materials, foundries, nonferrous metals. Aside from these, there is the production of industrial and other machinery, electrical apparatus and equipment, motor vehicles, aircraft and parts, measuring instruments and photographic equipment. In accommodating this group the core areas are expected to decline — New York City, Hudson and Essex counties, where structural obsolescence as well as lack of sites for new plants inhibit growth. All counties with open land, on the other hand, are expected to gain. The increase in Passaic County is expected to take place in Wayne Township, beyond the older, settled portion of the county.

"Local-market" industries represent primarily the manufacture of dairy and bakery products, beverages, building materials, and containers of various types. Future population distribution will exert the major influence on location and is expected to yield a rise in employment in plants located in counties just outside the core (Fig. 4).

The "national-market small-plant" industry group includes food products, tobacco, textile specialties, men's apparel, furniture, leather products and footwear, luggage, fabricated metal products, spe-

cial industry machinery and machine parts, supplies and apparatus for medical professions, clocks, watches, musical instruments, notions, and office and artists' material. Employment in these industries is expected to decline in the core area (New York City and Hudson County); the growth is expected to take place in the counties surrounding it (Fig. 5).

THE INDUSTRIAL ENVIRONMENT

The addition of a half-million manufacturing jobs in the Metropolitan Area over the next 20 years implies a vast program of expansion of physical plant, calling for new capital investment aggregating perhaps $3 or $4 billion. Structural as well as site obsolescence will force relocation to new sites of much of the existing industrial base. The half-million new jobs foreseen for the Area is merely an arithmetic increment and does not reflect the shift in industrial composition which the future is expected to bring, with its attendant problems as to the suitability of existing industrial structures.

Role of the Loft Building in Manhattan

An inventory of New York City's commercial and industrial floor space, the first since 1934, was completed in 1957 through the joint efforts of the Department of City Planning and its consultants for the rezoning of New York City. This inventory, based on the records of the city's Tax Department, provides a valuable basis for determining present and future floor space requirements in the city.

In terms of floor space, it was found that the loft was the leading nonresidential building type in New York City, with about 190 million square feet. About 181 million square feet of this space was located in the 6,530 loft structures in Manhattan at the time of the survey.

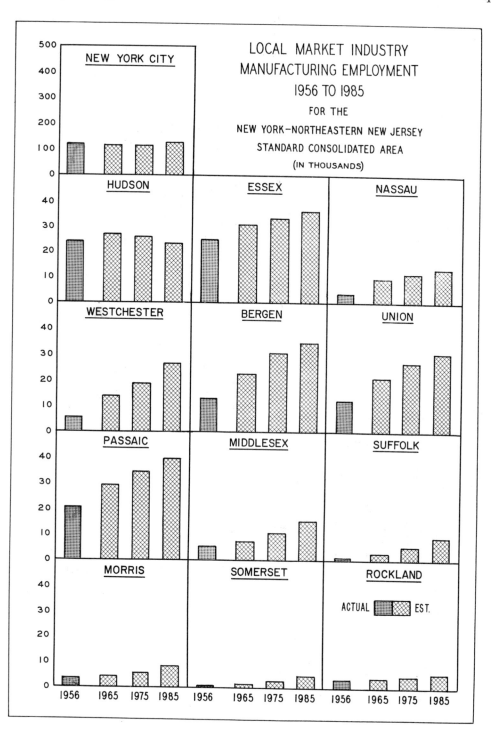

LOCAL MARKET INDUSTRY
MANUFACTURING EMPLOYMENT
1956 TO 1985
FOR THE
NEW YORK–NORTHEASTERN NEW JERSEY
STANDARD CONSOLIDATED AREA
(IN THOUSANDS)

Fig. 4

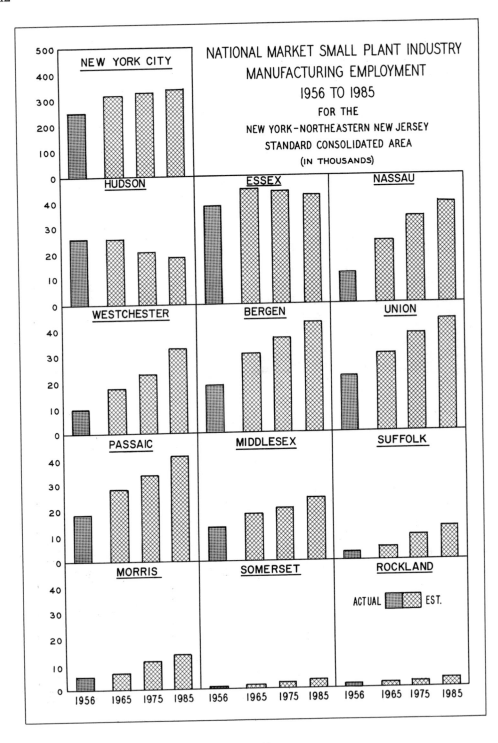

NATIONAL MARKET SMALL PLANT INDUSTRY
MANUFACTURING EMPLOYMENT
1956 TO 1985
FOR THE
NEW YORK-NORTHEASTERN NEW JERSEY
STANDARD CONSOLIDATED AREA
(IN THOUSANDS)

Fig. 5

Classification as a loft building by the Tax Department does not necessarily mean that the space is actually used for manufacturing. It may contain office functions and wholesale activities as well.

The loft building is a type of commercial structure prominent in New York. It may be described as a multistory multitenanted building generally occupied by manufacturing and related activities. Although most of New York's loft buildings are outdated, they make a major contribution to the city's economy and continue to house the bulk of the city's manufacturing industries. It has been estimated that nearly half a million manufacturing workers in Manhattan are located in multitenanted buildings, and represent some 86 per cent of Manhattan's work force engaged in manufacturing. According to an occupancy survey of competitive loft buildings in Manhattan conducted by the Real Estate Board of New York in 1961, 78 per cent of the space was used for manufacturing while the rest was used for showrooms and office space.

By and large, lofts are occupied by small firms that cannot plan far ahead, either for space or materials requirements. For these firms, lofts provide a wide range of choice with respect to size of quarters, with short-run commitments.

Almost 174 million square feet of Manhattan's loft space is in the Central Business District (Table 10). The garment trades, which are especially suited to loft

TABLE 10. LOFT SPACE IN MANHATTAN'S CENTRAL BUSINESS DISTRICT 1956-1957
(millions of square feet)

South of Chambers St.	11.8
Chambers to Houston St.	36.4
Houston to 23rd St.	36.8
23rd to 42nd St.	74.5
42nd to 60th St.	14.3

operation, absorb at least 22 million square feet.

Unfortunately most of the existing loft structures are obsolescent and unsuitable for efficient handling of goods; they are deficient in permissible floor loadings, elevator capacity, and off-street loading facilities. An analysis of Manhattan's loft space is shown in Table 11. A preponderance of the older structures is south of 14th Street.

TABLE 11. LOFT SPACE BY AGE GROUPS CENTRAL BUSINESS DISTRICT (MANHATTAN SOUTH OF 60TH STREET) 1956-1957
(millions of square feet)

Since 1945	0.3
1944-1930	8.3
1929-1914	43.7
Before 1914	40.5

Nevertheless, the Real Estate Board of New York's 1961 loft building survey disclosed a vacancy rate of only 3.6 per cent, which suggests that there is still a strong demand for available loft space in Manhattan.

Postwar Trends in Loft Capacity

Although for the Region as a whole the total amount of space available for multiple tenancy by manufacturers has probably increased in recent years, it is clear that there has been an absolute decline in the total amount of loft space in Manhattan that is used for manufacturing. The loss has been especially marked in the postwar period. The cause has been the absence of any new loft construction, the demolition of loft structures for various public improvement projects, and the change in usage of much loft space from manufacturing to nonmanufacturing activities.

There has been virtually no new loft construction in Manhattan for over two decades, due largely to the high cost of acquisition and the difficulty of assembling an adequate site in the Central Business District. The New York Metropolitan Region Study reports that a typical nine-story loft building located near the Garment District if built in 1957 would require a rental of about $3.75 per square foot, more than twice that now paid by the highest paying apparel manufacturer.

In recent years various public works projects have reduced Manhattan's inventory of loft space. A striking illustration of this is the Washington Square Southeast redevelopment project. Built in what had been a commercial and industrial area, it eliminated 2,285,000 square feet of loft space in providing some 2,000 dwelling units and several institutional buildings. Less dramatic are the demolitions here and there of miscellaneous structures, including lofts, which take place each year. New York City's Tax Department has reported a decline in the number of loft buildings in Manhattan from 7,418 in 1945 to 5,964 in 1960.

Additionally, the inventory of loft space available for manufacturing purposes in Manhattan is reduced further through increasing occupancy by nonmanufacturing activities. Many of the loft buildings in the Garment District, between 34th and 42nd Streets, are being converted to office and showroom activities.

A few steps have been taken to stabilize or to add to the supply of manufacturing loft space. The Bush Terminal buildings illustrate the stabilizing influence of systematic conservation measures. Named "Industry City," this complex comprises 16 buildings providing 6 million square feet of loft space. The tenant firms employ about 20,000 people. The structures have both railroad sidings and truck loading berths. Although this industrial complex had its beginning in 1906, obsoles-

cence has been kept in check by careful maintenance and a continuous program of improvements, including the installation of new boilers, modernization of electrical equipment, and the like. The current occupancy rate is about 97 per cent. Some of the tenants have been in occupancy almost from the time that the buildings were completed.

There also have been several cases in the Region during the past few years where large, multistory industrial buildings, heretofore owner-occupied, have been converted to multiple-tenant use through large-scale subdivision. The prominent instances are the National Biscuit Company and St. Johns Terminal Building on the West Side of Manhattan, the Mergenthaler Linotype Company near the Brooklyn Navy Yard, and the Singer Sewing Machine Company in Elizabeth, New Jersey. In each of these cases, the vacated building or group of buildings was subdivided into rental units of various sizes. Although considered obsolescent for the former occupant, the structures are endowed with assets that make them attractive for private real estate investment. In the aggregate, these subdivisions when completed will add almost 5 million square feet of loft space to the Region's supply.

A final instance is an effort to meet the needs of Manhattan manufacturers through physical consolidation and modernization of adjoining buildings. It is proposed to remodel and to consolidate into one operating property three buildings in the heart of the apparel center to provide a large center for the production of infants' and children's wear. The proposed changes will include a common lobby that will be air conditioned, a new façade at the main entrance, and interconnected floors of the three buildings where possible.

The Outlook for Loft Buildings

Manhattan's loft buildings play a dominant role in providing space for its manufacturing. Yet, most of this 181 million square feet of loft space is old by any reasonable standard, and in the older loft districts there are now consistently high vacancy rates. There has also been a substantial decline in the total amount of manufacturing loft space in Manhattan during the postwar period, and the prospect for new building construction is remote.

In the years ahead, a further decline in the available supply of manufacturing loft space and in the number of manufacturing employees in Manhattan may be expected. Although the emigration of large plants may contribute from time to time to the loft space inventory, these additions will probably be overbalanced by attrition of loft buildings through demolition and conversion.

Tenants in highly specialized districts, such as the Garment District, will probably continue in their present locations despite relatively high rentals, unless technological forces dictate a change. Other small industrial firms can be expected to seek low-cost, short-term space suitable to their needs in (1) the miscellaneous loft districts, (2) the older areas outside the Central Business District, such as those in Brooklyn, Queens, Jersey City and Newark, or (3) quarters abandoned by the out-moving large firms.

Industrial Renewal

A provision designed to arrest the decline of older areas and which possesses the potential to facilitate industrial redevelopment was included in the federal urban redevelopment program, authorized by Title I of the Housing Act of 1949.

Under this legislation, the federal government for the first time was in a position to make loans and capital grants to localities to help clear slums and blighted areas and make the land available for redevelopment. But coming from a housing parentage as it did, the Housing Act of 1937, it is not surprising that industrial redevelopment was given a secondary role. Over the years, however, there has been gradual but steady progress in the broadening of urban renewal powers to facilitate industrial renewal. By 1961, the original legislation had been so broadened that virtually all of the restraints against the use of urban renewal to foster industrial redevelopment had been eliminated from the program, and practically all of the states, including those of the New York Metropolitan Region, had acquired the necessary authority to use the urban renewal process.

From 1949 to 1961, Congress authorized about $2 billion in capital grants for about 900 projects in 500 cities. With practically all of the funds reserved, and a current backlog of applications amounting to $200 million, fewer than 40 projects were completed. Moreover, only 25 of the 500 well-advanced federally assisted urban renewal projects were exclusively for industrial re-use. These 25 projects totaled 477.3 acres, approximately the size of one large industrial district. There are, however, about 150 more projects throughout the nation in which part of the land will be made available for industrial re-use. In all, the nation's 180 industrial renewal projects would provide about 4,500 acres for industrial development. This represents 17 per cent of all the land in clearance sections of the nation's urban renewal projects which were in advanced planning by the middle of 1960.

During the same twelve-year period, 13 industrial re-use projects in the New York Metropolitan Region reached the stage where final plans were authorized.

Six of these projects were located in the New Jersey sector of the Region, four in the New York sector and three in Connecticut. All told, the industrial re-use portions of these projects amount to 115 acres, ranging in size from 0.1 acres in Asbury Park to 24.6 acres in Paterson.

In its first decade of operation, the Region's industrial renewal program was extremely slow-moving. Only one of the 13 industrial re-use projects has been completed so far, and only 2 per cent of the federal grant reservations have been disbursed. New York City, a leader in the urban renewal program, with 16 projects in the "execution stage," had no industrial re-use projects under way by the end of 1962.

In recent years, however, New York City has departed somewhat from its housing-oriented program and has actively promoted industrial development projects. An example, which relies upon the city's power of condemnation for site acquisition, and which is not renewal but initial development, is the Flatlands Industrial Park in Brooklyn. This pilot project comprising some 95 acres of underdeveloped lowlands is being acquired under a new section of the State General Municipal Law, which empowers the city to condemn and assemble blighted, largely vacant land and sell it to industrial users.

Elsewhere in the Region, industrial renewal projects are planned in Mount Kisco and Sloatsburg in New York, in Englewood, Newark and Jersey City in New Jersey, and in South Norwalk, Connecticut. These projects, all in built-up areas, would add about 100 acres to the Region's supply of industrial land outside of New York City.

Although Congress between 1949 and 1961 authorized about $2 billion in capital grants for urban redevelopment, the nation's experience with the program has actually been limited — in spite of its recent acceleration. The great bulk of the present program is still in the planning or execution stage.

Some communities have found that centrally located land prices are prohibitive for industrial re-use projects, even with a two-thirds federal sharing of the write-down.

Cincinnati's Kenyon-Barr project, on the other hand, provides an example of an undertaking designed to accommodate renters of manufacturing space in a close-in location. It will yield a total of 170.8 acres of marketable industrial land in high density, investment-type buildings. In this case, the peculiarities of the city's industrial community, namely, an economy based on a multiplicity of small manufacturing establishments, served as a guiding factor in the formulation of the redevelopment plan.

The Housing Act of 1961 provides an additional $2 billion urban renewal grant authorization, some of which can be employed for industrial renewal purposes. The amount available, when prorated among the industrial centers of the nation, cannot, within any given region, create new sites sufficient to alter substantially the distribution of jobs.

Until now the latent potential and hope that urban renewal offers to the older urban areas, in creating modern industrial sites, has been largely underdeveloped. Whether or not the potential of industrial renewal can be developed to provide efficient urban sites for employment in manufacturing is uncertain.

Factory Obsolescence Outside the Urban Core

Around Manhattan, on both sides of the Hudson River, there is an extensive industrial zone, much of it featured by multistory buildings. Large portions of this zone originated as industrial clusters around secondary urban concentrations at a time when urbanization had not yet filled in the land area between them and the central city. Jersey City, Hoboken, Newark and Paterson-Passaic are representative of cities that were industrialized at an early date. Much of industrial Brooklyn and parts of Queens are basically a product of the same development.

The Paterson-Passaic area reveals a pattern of successive occupancies, of growth and decline, from cotton to locomotives, from locomotives to textile spinning, weaving and finishing, particularly silk, to the production of aircraft, and finally, the last phases of textiles are seen as disappearing. Some of the plant still in use dates from the mid-nineteenth century. Much of it is obsolescent, at least for particular industries. Nevertheless, the structures are still useful.

Obsolescence of industrial plant is accompanied by the gradual withdrawal of manufacturing activity. As a company grows and improves its financial condition, it sets out to improve its competitive position, to increase its production and to lower its costs. When room for expansion at the factory site is not available, congestion hampers movement of goods. Modern methods of materials handling and mechanization of plant operation may be inhibited by structural limitations. At this point, the firm may move.

Typically, as a firm moves out, the plant is bought or leased by another firm, or subdivided for use of a number of firms. Perhaps it is used for warehousing or other non-manufacturing activities. Frequently, the new firm in this process is smaller and financially weaker than its predecessor. In this sense the old buildings may serve as industrial incubators.

Few of the older mills in the Paterson-Passaic area, for example, have been abandoned. Their obsolescence has been reflected in lower rent levels. Thus through much of the history of the city, the older buildings have functioned as a favorable industrial environment for the embryonic or the marginal industrial firm.

The Organized Industrial District

The organized industrial district as an area reserved for industrial use, usually at a low land coverage, and developed by a single firm according to a preconceived plan for the provision of utilities, streets and other transportation services, is a relatively new development in the industrial scene, although the basic idea dates back more than a half century. It was essentially the idea behind the development of the New York Dock Company in 1900 and Bush Terminal in 1906. There were 1,012 such districts in the United States in 1958, most of which were established after World War II. The Urban Land Institute reports that "over 80 per cent of the developments . . . were established after 1949, and 60 per cent date from 1955 or later."

TABLE 12. NUMBER OF INDUSTRIAL DISTRICTS AND ESTABLISHMENTS IN THE METROPOLITAN AREA

	Districts	Establish-ments
Metropolitan Area	47	500
New York	11	116
Kings	1	12
Nassau	9	99
Suffolk	1	5
New Jersey	36	384
Bergen	13	171
Essex	4	57
Middlesex	4	8
Morris	1	1
Passaic	7	42
Union	7	105

TABLE 13. ACTIVITIES IN INDUSTRIAL DISTRICTS
(number of firms)

	Total	Manu-facturing	Distri-bution	Office	Research	Other
Metropolitan Area	500	288	150	26	20	16
New York	116	81	22	1	6	6
Kings	12	5	6	0	0	1
Nassau	99	73	15	1	6	4
Suffolk	5	3	1	0	0	1
New Jersey	384	207	128	25	14	10
Bergen	171	87	67	5	4	8
Essex	57	33	10	6	6	2
Middlesex	8	4	1	2	1	0
Morris	1	1	0	0	0	0
Passaic	42	24	17	1	0	0
Union	105	58	33	11	3	0

The development of industrial districts has proceeded more slowly in the New York Area than in many other metropolitan areas. In 1960 there were 47 postwar industrial districts in the New York Metropolitan Region (Table 12), counting all those that contained at least one industrial occupant.

Although they are not great in number, nor imposing in area, it is clear that the industrial districts have made an impact on the suburban settlement of industry in the New York Area. In 1960 these 47 districts accommodated 500 establishments, 384 in New Jersey and 116 in New York. They accounted for almost 30 per cent of the industrial buildings constructed in the New Jersey portion of the Area during the past five years.

Typically, the firms established in these districts are small, with a median employment of less than 50. Their contribution to industrial capacity is thus smaller than the number of firms would suggest.

While the rail service is a location requirement for all but the smaller industrial districts, access to major arterial highways is a necessity. Routes 3, 17, 27 and U. S. 1 and 22 in New Jersey are favored zones for the establishment of industrial districts in that state.

Usually the industrial district becomes the site for distribution, office and research activities as well. Manufacturing, however, is dominant most frequently (Table 13). The manufacturing firms attracted to the districts usually fall within the broad categories of national market small-plant and local market industries, as defined in the New York Metropolitan Region Study. A high proportion of the manufacturing plants in the Region's industrial districts represents the larger and better-known American manufacturing companies, producing primarily for the northeastern section of the country as well as for the metropolitan area. Most of the other plants are for the supply of the metropolitan area itself, either the consuming public directly, as in the bottling of beverages, or other industries, as in tool and die-making.

CHAPTER 4

WHOLESALE TRADE IN DOMESTIC MARKETS

Trade, the transference of ownership of goods, has been of central importance to the economic growth of the Port of New York. In Colonial days, the initiative and commercial acumen of the merchant community made the most of the geographical and physical advantages of the port and laid the groundwork for what soon became the primacy of the New York Area among American cities. Trading in the simple products of a Colonial economy was followed by the assembly and fabrication of raw materials as the national economy matured, stimulated by the marketing facility the Area's trading institutions afforded. Financing the trading operations led to the Area's dominance in the nation's financial activities. A vast complex of business service, brokerage, trade promotion and management activities was brought into being. The Area's economic history is based on trade. As a trading center it is also a transportation center.

Today, wholesale trade is probably second only to manufacturing in its importance to the economic base of the Area. Its importance derives not only from the employment attributable to it and its net contribution to the Area's income, but also from the importance of its linkages with and influence upon other categories of economic activity: finance, brokerage, insurance, warehousing, shipping, manufacturing. Its importance in the generation and routing of the goods of commerce and industry is profound and far-reaching. The transportation tasks of the future will depend in part upon the prospective strength of wholesale trade.

ORGANIZATION OF WHOLESALE TRADE

In assembling business statistics relating to wholesale trade the Census Bureau recognizes five major types of establishments: merchant wholesalers, manufacturers' sales branches and sales offices, merchandise agents and brokers, petroleum bulk plants and terminals, and assemblers of farm products. For the New York Metropolitan Area, for purposes of this study, the three classes of major importance are: merchant wholesalers, manufacturers' sales branches and sales offices, and merchandise agents and brokers.

Merchant Wholesalers

The merchant wholesaler group consists of establishments usually known as wholesalers, distributors, jobbers and foreign trade merchants primarily engaged in buying, taking title to, and physically storing and handling goods produced by others. They sell these goods at wholesale to retailers and industrial and commercial users.

Manufacturers' Sales Branches and Sales Offices

Owned by manufacturers or mining companies, their primary function is the wholesale selling or marketing of the parent company's product.

A *sales branch* usually maintains facilities for the physical storage, handling and delivery of at least a portion of the merchandise sold. Sales branches frequently install machinery and apparatus sold by them and sometimes maintain repair and service facilities.

Sales offices are, as the title implies, restricted to the sales function.

There is considerable overlapping of the merchant wholesaler and manufacturers' sales branch categories. Some branches, despite the fact that they operate under a company name, may have the preponderance of their sales in goods produced by other manufacturers. In such cases, the Census Bureau classifies them as merchant wholesalers.

Merchandise Agents and Brokers

Dealers in this group are primarily engaged in selling and buying products owned by others; they negotiate sales but do not, as a rule, take title to merchandise. They include merchandise brokers, commission merchants, export and import agents, selling agents, resident buyers and auction companies. "Agents and brokers" in wholesale trade are engaged in the marketing of merchandise, and do not include dealers in futures, options, real estate or securities.

Wholesale trade does not lend itself to the kind of precise measurement characteristic of manufacturing. The values that are presented should be viewed as measures of a central tendency, always with the reservation that there is implicit a high degree of variation from such central values. The scope of investigation does not cover the entire range of wholesaling *functions* but is limited to wholesaling *establishments* or institutions.

IMPORTANCE IN THE NEW YORK METROPOLITAN AREA

Sales of wholesaling establishments in the New York Metropolitan Area amounted to $54.4 billion in 1958. As

about 8 per cent of this sum, $4.4 billion, was absorbed in operating costs incurred in the Area, if a 1 per cent allowance is made for profit, the net contribution of the activity to the Area's income may be estimated at $4.9 billion. Something less than $2 billion was expended for the salaries and wages of the 400,000 persons employed in the 38,000 wholesaling establishments located in the Area. The remainder was used to defray other operating expenses such as local delivery, warehousing, insurance, office rental, supplies and a host of services.

Between a third and a half of the sales of New York's wholesaling institutions are generated in dealings with markets lying beyond the confines of the Metropolitan Area. A substantial portion, $5.9 billion, represents sales to buyers in foreign countries, and another large portion, $4.5 billion, represents wholesalers' purchases from foreign sources of supply.[1] The largest portion of the New York Area's extra-regional trade is with domestic markets.

Reaching out for distant markets, domestic as well as foreign, has long been of singular significance to the New York Area. In 1925, Dr. George Filipetti in *The Wholesale Markets of New York*[2] noted that "New York appears to owe its economic supremacy primarily to certain fundamental advantages it possesses as an assembly point for goods produced over a very wide area." This advantage, he pointed out, grew out of the presence of a large population and a heavy concentration of industry, in whose service wholesalers developed skills and facilities for far-ranging marketing operations.

Marketing centers where the wholesaling function is prominent, such as Atlanta, New Orleans, Dallas and Denver, show dramatic strength as generators of travel. Trade by its very nature requires constant communication with other

---

[1] This aspect is dealt with in Chapter 5.

[2] Monograph 11 in the *Regional Plan of New York and its Environs*, 1925. The reference to assembly is in the transactional as well as the physical sense.

marketing centers and with sources of production, and fosters an awareness and curiosity even among those people in the community who may not be directly connected with trade. Cities with a strong trade base are less vulnerable to the devastation of major economic contractions, which is manifest in severe depletion of personal and business resources. Wholesale trade employment also fluctuates, of course, with the business cycle but the swing between crest and trough is less violent than it is in other fields.

During the Depression of the 1930's such employment declined less and recovered earlier than in other major sectors of economic activity. Real estate values in marketing centers tend to be higher than elsewhere and much less subject to fluctuation. Retail sales per capita are also higher. In the New York Area, employment in the wholesale trades declined less than in the nation and in 1939 exceeded the predepression level by 10 per cent. During the postwar period, 1948–1958, the gain in employment was a substantial 8 per cent. Significantly, this growth was marked by a smooth year-by-year course of development, which was scarcely interrupted by the recession of 1954.

In recent years marketing practices other than those found in wholesale trade for linking producers and buyers have come to the fore. These are sales negotiated with producers by volume buyers and are among the expansive forces in the growth of corporation offices in Manhattan. The entry of producers into direct marketing has displaced wholesalers' functions in some fields but has in all probability extended New York's trading sphere. New York's early primacy in wholesaling probably paved the way for primacy in direct distribution. Both share a common marketing environment and, although the wholesaling point of view has some limitations, it affords insights into the total of trade potential of the Metropolitan Area.

Wholesale trade ranks next to manufacturing as a generator of freight. It brings into the Area an extensive array of goods which are not manufactured locally but which are nevertheless essential to the well-being of the community, and it is still a powerful instrumentality in the distribution of goods produced locally into national and foreign markets.

CHANGING ROLE OF THE WHOLESALER

If national wholesale sales volumes are adjusted for price changes and compared with measures of total national production, it appears that wholesalers do not now participate in the total scheme of distribution to the degree evident 20 or 30 years ago. On the other hand, wholesale trade presents few outward symptoms of an industry in decline. Wholesaling compares favorably with other activities in employment growth, outstripping in growth rate even manufacturing and retail trade, the two ranking sources of employment (Table 1).

TABLE 1. WHOLESALING AND OTHER EMPLOYMENT COMPARED

	National Employment in 1957 (in thousands)	Gain Over 1939 (per cent)
Wholesale Trade	3,199	64.7
Retail Trade	9,754	51.4
Manufacturing	16,783	55.7
Transportation and Utilities	4,151	42.5
Finance	2,348	67.8
Mining	809	−9.6
Construction	2,808	144.2
Services	6,336	90.7
Government	7,626	91.8

Changes in the Pattern of Patronage

There is a popular idea that the bulk of wholesale trade is concerned with the supply of retailing establishments and that with the rise of chain stores and other retailer organizations purchasing directly from producers, wholesaling has suffered large absolute declines in business vol-

as 1935, the retailer as a patron of the wholesalers accounted for less than half (45.4 per cent) of the total wholesale trade.

If we assume that the retail trade margin (operating expenses plus profit) has been maintained around the 30 per cent level of retail sales during the period un-

TABLE 2. DISTRIBUTION OF WHOLESALE SALES BY CLASS OF CUSTOMER
(per cent of total)

Class of Customer	Nation			New York Area		
	1939	1948	1954	1939	1948	1954
Industrial and commercial	32.2	40.5	41.7	33.8	36.8	41.4
Consumers and farm	1.2	1.0	1.9	0.4	0.4	0.7
Retailers	41.4	33.9	32.8	30.4	26.2	23.0
Other wholesale firms	20.9	19.7	19.4	25.5	23.2	23.0
Export	4.3	4.9	4.2	9.9	13.4	11.9

umes. But industrial and commercial concerns have supplanted the retailer as the prime customers of the wholesaler both in the nation and in the New York Area, as is shown by Table 2. In terms of absolute volumes, sales to each class of customer have expanded enormously.

Sales to Retailers. A summary of the changing relationship between wholesalers' and retailers' sales since 1935 is given in Table 3. It may be noted that as early

der consideration and apply it to the retail trade series, the percentage of retailers' goods originating in wholesale trade channels has declined from 85 per cent in 1935 to about 60 per cent in 1954. The decline appears to have slowed down markedly, however, during the period 1948–1954.

Sales to Other Wholesalers. Least amenable to analysis is the category of sales by wholesalers to other wholesalers which

TABLE 3. NATIONAL WHOLESALE SALES TO RETAILERS
(millions of dollars)

	1935	1939	1948	1954
Wholesale sales[a]	42,803	51,458	163,259	218,936
Per cent of wholesale sales to retailers	45.3	41.4	33.9	32.8[b]
Estimated wholesale sales to retailers	19,400	21,300	55,300	71,811
Retail sales	32,791	42,042	128,849	169,968
Retail sales less retailers' margin[c]	22,954	29,429	90,194	118,978
Retailers' purchases as per cent of wholesale sales	85	72	61	60

[a]Excepting sales by petroleum bulk stations.

[b]Census provides per cent estimates for most lines. Missing lines in 1954 (e.g., food products) have been estimated on the basis of the 1935–1948 trends.

[c]Retailers' margin assumed to be 30 per cent of retail sales.

assumes more importance in the New York area than elsewhere. In part, such sales reflect cross-trading to cover shortages and to fill gaps in lines. The practice is especially prominent in Manhattan where, among dealers highly specialized with respect to commodities handled, it virtually assumes a form of communal wholesaling. In food lines, machinery, gift and art goods, for example, the interchange is especially lively. Functionally, it cannot be dismissed as wasteful, for in the end, it promotes efficient use of inventories and enhances the value of the dealers' services. The bulk of this type of intertrading takes place among merchant wholesalers.

Trade among wholesalers within the Area is highly important in the export phase of wholesaling. Export agents and export merchants draw extensively upon stocks held in inventory by merchant wholesalers and manufacturers' sales branches. These basic suppliers to export dealers usually perform the entire goods-handling function. In the New York Area, this practice has been developed to the point where export dealers specialize in sales and order-processing. As a result, only a small portion of the exporters' transactions involves goods handling in their own establishments.

For the most part, sales among wholesalers are between large wholesalers and smaller distributors located outside of the immediate trading area.

Sales to Industrial Customers. During the past 20 years, industrial and commercial users have become the prime customers of the wholesalers. A number of influences have contributed to the rapid growth of sales to industrial users. In the production of goods, the dependence upon specialty manufacturers for components flowing directly into assembly and manufacture has grown rather than declined. Many of these producers of special components fall into the medium- and small-size business category and, aside from negotiated agreements with large customers, they must depend upon wholesalers for distribution among low-volume customers or customers in remote locations. Also, the range of goods required in plant and office maintenance and operation has expanded enormously, and a large portion of sales in this category, too, involves small-lot trading.

Changes in the Organization of Wholesale Trade

Among the three major types of operation in the nation's wholesale trade, sales branches and offices of manufacturers have shown the sharpest rate of growth (Table 4). Their rise was noted in the first Census of Wholesale Trade, taken in 1929, and a persistent pattern of expan-

TABLE 4. DISTRIBUTION OF SALES BY TYPE OF WHOLESALING OPERATION
(per cent of total)

Type of Operation	Nation				New York Area			
	1939	1948	1954	1958	1939	1948	1954	1958
Merchant wholesalers	49	48	48	48	43	45	46	47
Manufacturers' branches and offices	28	32	33	34	26	30	31	53
Merchandise agents and brokers	23	20	19	18	31	25	23	

sion has prevailed to the present time. Merchandise agents and brokers have declined in relative importance, while merchant wholesalers have maintained a relatively stable share position.

In the New York Area manufacturers' wholesale sales have risen but not to the same relative degree as in the nation,

below that of the nation (Table 6). As a consequence, New York's share of the nation's wholesale sales has declined. The trend was under way by 1939, and has continued through the postwar period, dropping from a 22.1 per cent share in 1948 to 19.2 per cent in 1958. To some extent, this trend has been influenced by

TABLE 5. NEW YORK AREA'S WHOLESALE SALES BY MAJOR CLASSES OF CUSTOMERS
AND BY TYPE OF WHOLESALING OPERATION
(per cent of total)

	Industrial and Commercial Sales		Sales to Retailers		Sales to Other Wholesalers	
	1939	1954	1939	1954	1939	1954
Merchant wholesalers	38.5	35.4	57.9	59.4	23.5	46.2
Manufacturers' branches and offices	33.1	45.8	19.6	19.6	33.3	18.6
Merchandise agents and brokers	28.4	18.8	22.5	21.0	43.2	35.2

while merchant wholesalers have steadily increased their share of the trade.

The various types of operators in the New York Area have not participated equally in the redistribution of patronage (Table 5). In sales to industrial and commercial customers, manufacturers' sales branches and offices have captured a commanding share of trade, displacing the merchant wholesaler. Merchant wholesalers have gained slightly in sales to retailers; they have become the dominant figures in sales to other wholesalers. Merchandise agents have experienced declines in all three sectors of the market. Manufacturers' sales branches and offices have fallen sharply in sales to other wholesalers.

COMPOSITION OF NEW YORK'S TRADE

Wholesale trade in the New York Area has grown over the years, but at a rate

[3]Bureau of Labor Statistics of Wholesale Price Index: (1947–49 = 100)

TABLE 6. WHOLESALERS' SALES
(billions of dollars)

	1948	1958	Per Cent Gain
New York Area	42.2	54.4	28.9
Nation	188.7	283.8	50.4

the composition of the trade in the New York Area, which is heavily weighted by nondurable goods and therefore more resistant to inflationary pressures. The application of a price deflator would narrow the disparity between the growth rates in New York and the nation.[3]

Changes in Trade Shares
  Among Commodity Lines

However, the same basic pattern of growth at a rate lower than in the nation prevails in most of the commodity lines that make up the bulk of New York's trade. As a result the New York Area's share has declined in most of these lines. In the seven groups listed in Table 7,

TABLE 7. NEW YORK AREA'S SHARE OF THE NATION'S WHOLESALE TRADE
(per cent)

	1948	1958
Dry goods and apparel	75.2	67.8
Groceries and related products	19.0	15.6
"Other wholesale trade"	28.4	33.6
Metals and minerals	22.0	20.4
Machinery and equipment	14.9	13.9
Drugs and chemicals	33.2	26.8
Electrical goods	16.3	15.1

which accounted for 64 per cent of New York's wholesale trade in 1948, only "other wholesale trade" scored a gain in trade share.

Dry Goods and Apparel. The most significant change took place in dry goods,

predominantly textiles, and apparel, including footwear.

The dry goods phase suffered a steep decline in 1948–1958 amounting to an absolute loss of $2 billion in sales. New York handles about 80 per cent of the national total of this trade, and New York and the nation declined at the same rate. A number of factors have been instrumental in bringing about the absolute decline. Contrary to the general price trend, wholesale prices of textiles actually declined during this period, and this accounts for some of the shrinkage in dollar volumes. More important, however, the structure of the textile trade has changed since the war. Sales of textiles to other than the cutting trades have declined appreciably. In part, this represents a displacement of conventional

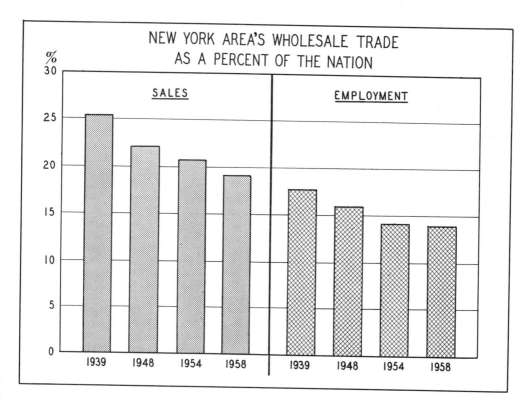

Fig. 1

textiles by plastic fabrics. In addition, there has been a growth of direct sales by textile producers to industrial users, bypassing the wholesale trade channels. Although New York's textile sales are still at a high level (about $6.3 billion annually), the effect of changes in technology and trade practices upon the Worth Street area has been far-reaching. Selling agents of textile producers and textile converters in that area once occupied over 3 million square feet of space; the current level of occupancy is estimated at less than 300,-000 square feet.

In the apparel lines, New York's gain during the postwar decade has lagged behind that of the nation (Table 8). As a result, New York's share of the apparel trade has dropped from 64.5 per cent in 1948 to 53.0 per cent in 1958.

The forces behind this change have been analyzed in detail in the New York Metropolitan Region Study. The change in wholesale trade shares reflects basically a loss in the region's strength in apparel *production,* a phenomenon of the postwar period. Resort and casual wear production centers have developed in Florida and California, and production in St. Louis of junior misses' outer wear and in San Antonio of infants' and children's garments has also had its impact.

Other Commodities. Among the other major commodity groups making up the Area's wholesale trade, the trends are mixed.

The net effect of gains and losses, however, has altered the structure of New York's wholesale trade. Operationally, and in commodity composition, the New York Area has moved closer to the national pattern (Table 9).

The performance of wholesale trade during 1948–1958 indicates a trade structure in transition. Except for the dry goods and apparel lines, commodity by commodity analyses afford no reliable

TABLE 8. WHOLESALE SALES IN APPAREL
(millions)

	1948	1958
New York	$2,613	$3,273
Nation	4,052	6,175

TABLE 9. DISTRIBUTION OF WHOLESALE SALES BY COMMODITY LINES
(per cent of total)

Commodity Lines	New York Metropolitan Area		The Nation
	1948	1958	1958
Automotive	3.3	5.7	8.3
Drugs, chemicals	5.0	8.2	5.8
Dry goods and apparel	25.6	17.6	5.0
Groceries	17.3	13.8	17.1
Farm products (raw)	3.6	4.5	9.8
Electrical goods	3.7	4.6	5.8
Hardware, plumbing	1.6	1.7	2.8
Machinery	5.4	6.6	9.1
Metals	7.0	8.3	7.8
Scrap and waste	2.5	0.8	1.1
Paper	2.6	2.9	3.1
Furniture, furnishings	2.1	2.5	1.7
Lumber, construction	1.8	2.0	3.7
Other	18.5	20.8	18.9

basis for projecting New York's future. Although the data are far from definitive, a changing market base can be detected. The lines which appear stable when compared with the national rate of growth are those marked by increased sales to industrial and commercial customers. This may be seen in sales of chemicals, office furniture, printing paper, automotive equipment, electronic goods and machinery. Wholesalers' sales to retailers are generally shrinking, relative to the national pattern, but there are some important exceptions in the leisure and luxury goods lines.

Users Considered as Markets

The industrial market now absorbs almost 42 per cent of all of the wholesale trading activity in the New York Area, as well as in the nation. New York's share of this market is strong, and although it has declined slightly from its position in 1939, New York has maintained a stable and even somewhat increasing share during the postwar period, amounting to about 22.2 per cent in 1954. The merchant wholesaler's participation in industrial sales has tended to decline slightly, but this has been offset by continued gains on the part of manufacturers' sales branches and offices. The other major element lending strength to New York's wholesaling position is continued participation in the export market. Sales to exporters constitute about 12 per cent of New York's total wholesale trade, and New York handles almost 65 per cent of the nation's trade in this market.

Relative declines are taking place in sales to retailers and in sales to other wholesalers. During the past 20 years, New York's share of the national market in sales to retailers has declined from 19 per cent to slightly below 16 per cent. This, of course, is the sector of the market which has felt the impact of direct sales to the greatest extent, more acutely in the New York Area than elsewhere. In sales to other wholesalers, New York's trade volumes, while showing absolute increases, have also steadily declined as a percentage of the nation.

TRADE TRENDS IN THE NEW YORK AREA AND IN THE MIDDLE ATLANTIC REGION

The radius of trade in wholesaling varies widely with the nature of the commodity. It tends to be fairly short in highly standardized commodities in common use and much longer in specialty items with a sparse pattern of consumption. In automotive supplies, New York's share of the nation's sales indicates a trading territory conforming to the boundaries of the metropolitan area. In other lines, such as textiles and apparel, the magnitude of the share of the national total indicates an almost national penetration.

The Middle Atlantic and Other Regions Compared

In comparing the wholesale trade of the Middle Atlantic States with that of the nation and with that of New York, two central facts emerge: (1) There has been a long-range decline of wholesale trade activity in the Middle Atlantic Region as a percentage of the nation's and (2) New York's participation in the Middle Atlantic trade, the primary marketing area for New York, has been shrinking.

The Middle Atlantic Region's share of the nation's wholesale trade has shown a long-range decline from 33.9 per cent in 1929 to 28.0 per cent in 1958. The East North Central Region, whose hub is Chicago, appears to have stabilized its share of the nation's trade, while the South Atlantic and Pacific Regions have shown extraordinary growth (Table 10).

Differential population growth does not

appear to have been the decisive element in the shifting of wholesale trade volumes among the regions. In those regions showing the greatest gain in wholesale trade, trade expansion has outpaced population growth. In the Middle Atlantic Region, for example, with the relative loss of

manufacturing employment, and population, as shares of the nation, have about stabilized. Wholesale trade over this same period appears to have stabilized also. In the South Atlantic Region there was a gain of 3.2 percentage points in the share of personal income and 2 percentage points

TABLE 10. TRENDS IN THE DISTRIBUTION OF WHOLESALE TRADE, MANUFACTURING EMPLOYMENT AND PERSONAL INCOME AMONG THE REGIONS OF THE NATION
(per cent of total)

	Wholesale Trade Sales		Manufacturing Employment		Personal Income	
	1929	1958	1929	1958	1929	1957
New England	6.0	4.8	12.2	8.7	8.3	6.6
Middle Atlantic	33.9	28.0	29.5	25.9	29.6	22.7
E. North Central	20.1	20.8	28.9	26.4	23.6	22.5
W. North Central	12.6	9.8	5.6	6.0	8.9	8.1
South Atlantic	6.7	10.0	9.8	11.8	8.5	11.7
E. South Central	3.7	4.2	4.1	4.9	4.0	4.4
W. South Central	7.1	7.9	3.3	5.0	6.1	7.8
Mountain	1.7	2.8	1.2	1.5	2.5	3.4
Pacific	8.2	11.8	5.4	9.8	8.5	12.8
United States	100.0	100.0	100.0	100.0	100.0	100.0

wholesaling position noted above, the relative decline in population has been slight, from 21.3 to 19.1 per cent of the nation's population during 1930–1960. Other factors have influenced the shift in trade.

Since wholesalers' two principal customer groups are the retailers and the manufacturers, shifts in personal buying power (personal income) and in manufacturing employment should bring about corresponding shifts in wholesale trade. This relationship is supported by trade statistics.

In the North Central Region, income,

in manufacturing employment. There was a gain of 3.3 percentage points in trade. Similarly in the Pacific Region, gains of 4 percentage points in these factors were accompanied by an almost equal uplift in the wholesale trade share. In the Middle Atlantic Region these factors have been in relative decline and have exerted a negative influence. Personal income, when computed as a share of the nation, has declined by almost 7 percentage points and manufacturing employment has declined by 3.5 percentage points. The decline in wholesale trade has been just under 6 percentage points.

Trends within the Middle Atlantic Region

Wholesale trade in the New York Metropolitan Area as a share of Middle Atlantic trade volumes has also declined, dropping from 75.0 per cent in 1939 to 68.6 per cent in 1958.

Thus the Middle Atlantic States have become a progressively weaker force in the nation's trade, and New York's participation in this shrinking sector has also gradually declined. Until 1954, New York's loss of position seems to have resulted from greater relative growth of the other large wholesaling centers in the Middle Atlantic Region, especially Pittsburgh and Philadelphia. During the most recent period, however, 1954–1958, a new factor emerged, the growth of secondary wholesaling centers.

In contrast to the New York Area's gain of 12 per cent in sales between 1954 and 1958, Buffalo, Rochester and Syracuse all gained in excess of 20 per cent. As may be seen in Table 11, the secondary centers in the Middle Atlantic Region grew at more rapid rates than did New York, some at double the rate prevailing in the Area. There is little evidence to suggest that this intraregional shift resulted from economic growth rates greater than that of the New York Area, and the inference is that much of it is diversionary in character and represents a partial displacement of New York by secondary wholesaling centers.

In the latest period, 1954–1958, most of the gain in wholesale trade in the New York Area was attributable to gains in the merchant wholesaler type of operation. In the secondary centers of the Middle Atlantic Region, the bulk of the gain stemmed from growth in maufacturers' sales offices and branches.

Explanations tend to be speculative. In the growth of wholesale trade outlets of manufacturers there are some basic and far-reaching changes in marketing and distribution strategy. Formerly, it was a general rule in locating sales branches to

TABLE 11. INCREASE IN WHOLESALE SALES VOLUMES
IN THE MIDDLE ATLANTIC REGION 1954–1958
(per cent)

Metropolitan Areas	Merchant Wholesalers	Other Operating Types[a]	Total
New York Metropolitan Area	15.5	9:8	12.1
New York sector	13.7	5.3	9.0
New Jersey sector	30.1	56.1	42.5
Albany–Schenectady–Troy	14.1	17.0	15.5
Binghamton	23.8	42.1	32.9
Buffalo	10.5	29.8	21.4
Rochester	19.9	23.3	21.7
Syracuse	15.5	51.5	38.4
Utica–Rome	23.6	8.4	16.5
Trenton	19.8	38.7	29.4
Philadelphia	9.4	34.5	24.4
Harrisburg	23.4	20.9	22.0
Pittsburgh	28.4	26.6	27.3
Wilkes-Barre	32.8	38.7	35.3

[a]Mainly manufacturers' sales branches and offices.

concentrate on major cities, and the usual form of organization was a sales department operated in conjunction with a warehouse. More and more of these sales outlets have been converted from branches to offices so that sales without stock now account for roughly 60 per cent of all manufacturers' sales. Basically, this has been a trend toward dispersing sales transactions while concentrating goods handling; and one major distributing branch may now handle the orders originating in a half-dozen sales territories. Generally, this has had the effect of shrinking the territories covered by the larger sales centers and expanding the sales scope of those of lesser rank.

SHIFTING OF WHOLESALE TRADE WITHIN THE NEW YORK AREA

In 1929, the New York sector of the Metropolitan Area accounted for 95 per cent of the Area's sales and 94 per cent of the Area's employment in wholesale trade. The dominance of Manhattan was overwhelming: it accounted for 88 per cent of the Area's sales and 80 per cent of its employment.

The subsequent pattern of dispersal may be seen most clearly by comparing the New York and New Jersey sectors of the Metropolitan Area with respect to their shares of area sales and employment in three key years (Table 12).

In the prewar period, employment showed a tendency to shift but the distribution of sales showed little change. Both sales and employment have shifted markedly during the postwar period, and sales have developed in the New Jersey metropolitan counties at a rapid rate.

Manhattan is the pivotal county in this pattern of change. Over the course of 30 years, its share of Area sales has declined from 88 per cent to 71 per cent, and employment has dropped from 80 per cent to 57 per cent. In the case of sales, this decline has been only relative, with Manhattan falling behind the Area in its growth rate. With respect to employment, however, the decline has been absolute and represents a loss of 12 per cent in the number of jobs in wholesale trade during the postwar period. As a result, the New York side of the Metropolitan Area has steadily lost ground.

Although the proportions in 1958 were still impressively in favor of the New York sector — 82 per cent of the employment and 87 per cent of the sales — the growth rate in New Jersey is significant and must be reckoned as a potent factor in future developments. In terms of sales, the New Jersey sector, during 1948–1958, rose by 235 per cent compared with a gain of 137 per cent for the New York sector; in employment the gains were 52 per cent and 1.5 per cent respectively.

The most meaningful perspective, how-

TABLE 12. TREND IN THE SHARES OF WHOLESALE TRADE SALES AND EMPLOYMENT
IN NEW YORK AND NEW JERSEY SECTORS
(per cent of total)

| | Sales | | | Employment | | |
	1929	1939	1958	1929	1939	1958
New York sector	95	94	87	94	90	82
Manhattan	88	85	71	80	73	57
New Jersey sector	5	6	13	6	10	18

ever, may be gained by looking at how much of the Area's growth in wholesaling has been accounted for by the New Jersey counties during successive time periods (Table 13).

TABLE 13. NEW JERSEY'S SHARE OF
AREA GROWTH IN WHOLESALE TRADE
(per cent)

Census Period	Sales	Employment
1939–1948	7.9	19.4
1948–1954	22.0	32.6
1954–1958	34.5	30.1

New Jersey's share of employment gains, while still high, shows some signs of tapering off, but participation in sales appears to be gathering momentum. In 1930, with a population of 2.9 million northern New Jersey represented 26.6 per cent of the Area's population, yet it accounted for only 5 per cent of the Area's wholesale trade. In 1958 it represented 12.7 per cent.

There has been no major shift in population to account for its rise in the wholesaling function. The rise of wholesaling in New Jersey appears to have resulted from the development of trans-Hudson vehicular crossings and connecting highway routes. These, along with the coincident development of motor truck transport, were decisive in the major expansion in northern New Jersey. The first wave of wholesale trade development in northern New Jersey was evident in the mid-thirties and may be detected in the rise of wholesaling employment in Hudson, Essex and Union counties. This was followed by an upswing in Passaic and, more recently, in Bergen counties (Appendix Tables 9 and 10).

The development of trans-Hudson crossings, each opening large segments of northern New Jersey, allowed for a greater degree of freedom in distribution strategy. The linkages across the Hudson River allowed a New Jersey wholesaler to participate in the New York market and, by the same token, allowed a New York wholesaler to relocate in New Jersey and to participate in its trade without sacrificing his prime market.

MANHATTAN AS A TRANSACTION CENTER IN WHOLESALE TRADE

The average employee in wholesaling, taking the nation as a whole, handles about $95,000 of trade annually. This is an aggregative value and varies considerably from one type of wholesaling operation to another. Volume of sales per employee is highest among merchandise agents and brokers, slightly over $300,000 per annum, for this type of operation offers the narrowest range of wholesaling services and is least concerned with goods handling. The sales per employee is lowest among merchant wholesalers, $66,000, for this type of operation offers the widest range of services — from sales and credit through delivery of goods — and dealers engaged in it are frequently and appropriately termed "service wholesalers." Manufacturers' sales branches and offices as a group occupy an intermediate position between these extremes, $130,000 of sales per employee annually.

Sales per employee have tended to rise, owing to gains resulting from increased efficiency in goods handling and from the practice of direct routing of goods by the wholesaler from the producer to the customer. This latter development, especially, has yielded significant reductions in labor requirements and has had the effect of building up the sales per employee ratio. However, the contrasts among the types of operations noted above have persisted and sales per employee, in the aggregate and in the specific branch of the trade, are a useful indicator of the basic character of wholesaling in the major trade centers of the nation. Table 14 compares New York and the next ranking wholesale trade areas with respect to sales per employee. Aside from the New York

brokers in Manhattan. These dealers, whose stock in trade is a knowledge of supply and demand, have shown a negligible tendency to locate anywhere else in the Area. Manhattan's 3,600 establishments in this category of wholesaling establishments account for 95 per cent of

TABLE 14. INDEX OF SALES PER EMPLOYEE IN WHOLESALE TRADE IN RANKING
METROPOLITAN AREAS AND IN THEIR RESPECTIVE CORE COUNTIES
(Nation = 100)

Standard Metropolitan Areas	Index	Core Counties	Index
New York	137	New York	170
Chicago	124	Cook	126
Los Angeles	91	Los Angeles	92
Philadelphia	98	Philadelphia	102
Boston	108	Suffolk	114
San Francisco	109	San Francisco	121
St. Louis	103	St. Louis	98
Cleveland	110	Cuyahoga	111
Pittsburgh	113	Allegheny	107

and Chicago areas, most of the important trade centers do not differ materially from the national average. The New York Area clearly emerges as the trade center most heavily weighted by the transaction phase of wholesaling.

The value for the New York Area's business core, Manhattan, stands in sharp contrast not only to the New York Area and other metropolitan areas but also to their respective business cores as well. Indeed, the Area's primacy in wholesaling stems from the influence of Manhattan, for the rest of the Metropolitan Area, with an index of 92, is rather much like the rest of the nation. The strong attraction of Manhattan to dealers in what might be called "transactional wholesaling" is evident in each of the major types of operation.

Most striking is the extreme concentration of the Area's merchandise agents and

all of the Area's agents' and brokers' sales. Manhattan agents' and brokers' sales, aggregating slightly under $10 billion annually, account for more than 25 per cent of the nation's total transactions in this type of operation. Employment is of modest proportions, however, 23,000. Hence, the volume of sales per employee is high, over $400,000 annually.

The same emphasis on transactions may be observed in the operations of manufacturers' sales branches and offices in Manhattan. Among these, the sales per employee is about $214,000. In contrast, the ratio in the rest of the Metropolitan Area is about half this value, $105,000. We may infer that manufacturers' wholesaling in Manhattan is predominantly of the office type and almost purely transactional.

In merchant wholesaling, also, we can

perceive the preponderance of transactional wholesaling in Manhattan — sales per employee, $170,000 a year. The rest of the Metropolitan Area, at $57,000, is somewhat below the level of the nation.

Manhattan is also clearly the hub of wholesaling in commodity lines where the Area's share indicates participation in a national market. In commodity lines, where the share implies trade activity geared primarily to local demand, the sales function is more widely dispersed within the Area. With few exceptions, Manhattan is preponderant in all lines.

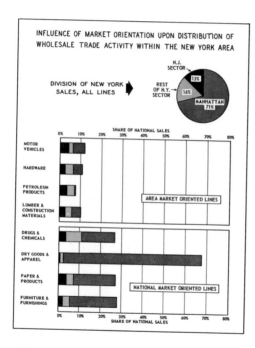

FIG. 2

OUTLOOK IN THE NEW YORK AREA

How important will wholesaling be in the New York Area's economic base in 1980? How much of the Area's employment will it account for? How important will the Area's trade be in relation to the national total?

Historical Relationship Between Wholesale Trade and the Gross National Product

Wholesale trade volumes in themselves exhibit only a general sort of relationship to the national economy as a whole. Goods flowing through a wholesaler's establishment represent a vast accumulation of values, an accumulation which begins in the mine or field, gains substantial additions in each stage of processing or manufacture, and ends with the participation of the wholesaler when he delivers goods to his customers.

The value added to goods by the wholesaler varies with the type of operation. It is high in merchant wholesaling, where a full range of service is provided, and low among merchandise agents and brokers, where the wholesaler's contribution is almost purely transactional. Since the distribution of trade among the various types of wholesale operations has changed materially in recent years, total wholesalers' sales no longer provide a meaningful measure of the role of wholesale trade in contributing to the nation's economy.

The concept of "value added" overcomes this difficulty, for it reflects the contribution made to the value of goods in each type of wholesaling operation. Basically, value added is the difference between the costs of goods to the wholesaler and to the wholesaler's customer. It is, for practical purposes, equivalent to the markup: the cost of the wholesaler's operation plus an allowance for his profit.

So defined, the proportion of national income attributable to wholesale trade, expressed as a percentage of the gross national product, has been fairly constant. In this sense, it is certainly not a declining economic function. In 1929 it amounted to 4 per cent; since 1947 it has fluctuated between 4.8 and 5.1 per cent, with a tendency to rise. If this relationship prevails in

TABLE 15. PROJECTION OF WHOLESALE TRADE EMPLOYMENT IN THE NATION
AND IN THE NEW YORK AREA: 1955–1980

	Gross National Product[a] (billions of 1955 dollars)	Value Added in Wholesale Trade[b] (billions of 1955 dollars)	Value Added per Employee[c]	Estimated National Employment (thousands)	New York's Area Share of Employment[d] (per cent)	Estimated N. Y. Area Employment (thousands)
1955	$398	$19.9	$ 7,400	2,690	14.0	377
1960	473	23.7	7,970	2,974	13.7	408
1965	561	28.1	8,590	3,271	13.4	439
1970	667	33.3	9,250	3,600	13.2	475
1975	792	39.6	9,970	3,972	12.9	514
1980	945	47.3	10,700	4,421	12.7	561

[a]The estimate of gross national product in the future is based on a 3.5 per cent annual rate of growth and conforms closely to the forecast of the U. S. Bureau of Labor Statistics. The National Planning Association and the Joint Economic Committee have assumed growth rates somewhat over 4 per cent. Others, such as the National Industrial Conference Board, have estimated future growth at a rate in conformance with the long-range trend, which is roughly 3 per cent.
[b]Five per cent of GNP.
[c]Based on 1929–1954 trend.
[d]Based on 1929–1958 trend.

the future, at 5 per cent as a round value, it is a basis for forecasting the portion of the nation's income to be accounted for by wholesale trade (Table 15, Column 1).

Effect of Productivity in Employment Projections

Future employment in wholesale trade, however, cannot be expected to rise proportionately to the increase in national income originating in wholesaling. During the 25 years 1929–1954 the productivity of labor engaged in wholesaling (value added per employee) rose by about 44 per cent. A similar gain during the forecast period (1955–1980) would raise productivity (value added per employee), for the nation as a whole, from $7,400 in 1955 to about $10,700 in 1980. The value added per employee divided into the projected national income originating in wholesale trade yields an estimate of 4.4 million employees in the nation's wholesale trade in the terminal year of our forecast, 1980.

Future Employment in the New York Metropolitan Area

The Area's employment in wholesaling, as a percentage of the nation's, has declined much less than has its share of national sales. Whereas the Area's share of the nation's sales dropped from 24.9 per cent in 1929 to 19.2 per cent in 1958, employment in the same period declined only from 15.6 per cent to 14.1 per cent.

The New York Area's future share of national employment is likely to conform with its historical trend. This involves a decline from 14.0 per cent to 12.7 per cent and yields a total of 557,000 employees in the New York Area in 1980.

Distribution of Future Employment Within the Area

What is Manhattan's future? The employment trends do not give any clear clue. After a sharp drop in employment following 1948, Manhattan gained slightly in number employed during 1954–1958 (Table 16).

TABLE 16. AREA AND MANHATTAN
WHOLESALING EMPLOYMENT

	Area Employment (thousands)	Manhattan (thousands)	Manhattan's Share (per cent)
1939	277	204	73
1948	364	253	70
1954	369	224	61
1958	392	225	57

The 1948 peak for Manhattan may have represented a brief period of supersaturated employment arising out of the peculiar conditions prevailing after World War II. High trade volumes, with ample profit margins, fostered high levels of employment in an era of replenish-ment prosperity. The period immediately thereafter witnessed the construction of new warehouse plant on a large scale in other areas, especially in Queens, and this pulled large blocks of employment out of Manhattan. The subsequent stabilization of employment in Manhattan stands out as an important bench mark.

We may assume, therefore, that the New York Area and Manhattan may be declining relative to the nation. In absolute terms, however, Manhattan's employment in wholesale trade may be expected to remain at approximately its most recently reported level, 225,000. Wholesale trade employment in the Area as a whole should total between 500,000 and 600,000 by 1980.

CHAPTER 5

WHOLESALE TRADE IN EXPORTS AND IMPORTS

The Port of New York has been a center of foreign trade sales transactions, as well as the nation's leading port. Commercial transactions and port activity have supported each other. When the nation depended upon foreign sources for a large portion of its manufactured goods scarcely a hundred years ago, the ties between New York's mercantile houses and the maritime activity of the port were obvious. Even though wholesaling institutions since that time have adopted new practices and have retreated from their close association with the water front, the presence of the nation's most important wholesale market for commodities entering into foreign trade has encouraged the routing of import and export shipments through the port, and the availability of extensive port facilities in the most populous section of the eastern seaboard has enlarged the wholesale marketing activity.

This mutual relationship is of strategic importance in estimating New York's future as a shipping center. A favorable outlook for the Area's share of the nation's foreign trade transactions presents a favorable influence on its port activities of the future. Conversely, if the prospect should be one of declining importance of the Area as a marketing center for import and export commodities, a negative factor could be expected to operate on its export and import tonnages.

Of course, not all foreign trade transactions flow through wholesaling channels. There are the direct purchases of raw materials by domestic manufacturers from foreign producers, and the direct sales of domestic producers to foreign companies, manufacturers or distributors. There are imports, such as crude rubber, which may come from plantations owned by domestic tire manufacturers, and exports, such as automotive parts, which go to a domestically owned factory abroad. There are commodities, such as petroleum, ores and grains, which, for the most part bypass the wholesaler in the process of transferring ownership, in either import or export trade. Nevertheless, more than half the national foreign trade volume does involve the wholesaling function. The trade intermediary between the producer, whether foreign or domestic, and, the user, manufacturer or distributor is a vital cog in the wheel of foreign commerce.

Over the years, the trade volumes of export and import intermediaries have exhibited a greater degree of stability than the total export and import flows into and out of the nation. The intermediaries' share of the nation's foreign trade rises during a period of recession and declines during periods of trade expansion. Since the New York Area's intermediaries command about 70 per cent of the nation's sales in foreign trade wholesaling, their presence has had an important stabilizing effect on the import and export commodity flows through the port.

Quite aside from the maritime interest, New York has a high stake in the foreign trade segment of the wholesaling business. The New York Area's foreign trade intermediaries accounted for $10 billion in transactions during 1954. This amount represented slightly over 70 per cent of the nation's foreign trade flowing through wholesaling channels and 20 per cent of New York's *total* wholesale trade, domestic and foreign. If we make allowance for the cross-trading which takes place among the domestic wholesaling institutions, foreign trade in wholesale channels is probably equivalent to about 30 per cent of the Area's unduplicated domestic wholesale trade.

As employers, or as purchasers of supplies for the maintenance of their establishments, New York's middlemen in foreign trade do not represent an important element in the economy of the region. However, as specialists in foreign trade transactions almost entirely divorced from goods handling, they lean upon the services of the metropolis and draw heavily upon its sources of supply. It is possible that the demands which these intermediaries make on service wholesalers alone may account for as much as a quarter of the Area's 400,000 employment in wholesale trade.

The Nature of Foreign Trade Wholesaling

Paralleling the classification of domestic wholesalers discussed in the preceding chapter, three basic types of middlemen are to be identified in foreign trade wholesaling. These are merchant wholesalers, merchandise agents, and manufacturers' sales branches and offices.

Merchant wholesalers and merchandise agents are the traditional intermediaries in wholesale trade. The merchant wholesaler takes title to goods, deals on his own

[1]The statistical basis of this study is the Census of Wholesale Trade. The published series covers 1929, 1935, 1939, 1948, 1954 and the preliminary returns for 1958. Data for the New York Area were prepared for The Port of New York Authority by the Census Bureau from unpublished materials. None of the 1958 data for the New York Area were available for the preparation of this report.

account and sells to industrial and commercial users, as well as to retailers and other wholesalers. If the source of his goods is foreign, he is known as an *importer* or *import merchant*. If he sells into foreign rather than domestic markets, he is known as an *exporter* or *export merchant*.

The other traditional middleman, the merchandise agent, negotiates purchases or sales for others. Normally, he does not take title to goods, but works on a fee or commission basis. He is known as an *import agent* if he specializes in representing foreign sellers in the domestic market or if he acts as a purchasing agent buying foreign goods for domestic firms. An *export agent* specializes in the purchase of goods for or the sales of goods to foreign buyers.

The third type of intermediary, the manufacturer's sales branch or office, an instrumentality of relatively recent origin in wholesale trade, is a producer-owned establishment for export marketing of the producer's goods at wholesale. A manufacturer's sales branch sells from stock in its custody, and the manufacturer's sales office sells primarily from sample or specification. While these sales branches and offices may be geared primarily to distributing domestic goods in domestic markets, their participation in foreign trade, especially in the export phase, is large and is growing in importance.

Focus on Transactions

The Census of Wholesale Trade, the primary source of information on foreign trade wholesaling, emphasizes the transaction phase of the distributive process.[1] The transaction data are expressed in terms of the dollar value of sales and are related to the place where the sales are made and recorded. The place of transaction may or may not be the place where the goods involved are shipped or received.

Study of these wholesale trade data reveals the high degree to which the transaction phase of the nation's foreign trade is concentrated in this Area, particularly in Manhattan. The data furnish a statistical linkage between foreign trade so measured and the Area's total marketing structure, whose buying and selling activities involve merchandise probably worth well in excess of $75 billion annually.

WHOLESALERS' PARTICIPATION IN FOREIGN TRADE

There is a widely held belief that middlemen, as factors in the conduct of the nation's foreign trade, are waning in importance. Dr. E. E. Pratt, in the *Foreign Trade Handbook* of 1952, stated, "Unfortunately for American export business, the race of export commission houses and export merchants seems to be approaching extinction."

The statistics covering foreign trade wholesaling do not support this conclusion for either the import or the export aspects of the trade. Even if we consider only the activities of the traditional intermediaries in foreign trade — the import and export merchants and the import and export agents — and compare their combined sales with the nation's total foreign trade, there is nothing to indicate a weakening in their position; the ratio has been virtually stable over many years. Their sales in 1958 were equal to 43 per cent of the nation's foreign trade volumes, somewhat higher, in fact, than the proportion in 1929 (see Table 1). If we add the foreign sales of producer-owned wholesaling establishments — they came to the fore in 1935 — the level of participation is raised further, and the maintenance of unimpaired strength in the trade is even more evident.

In one business census year, 1939, the ratio of sales of foreign trade middlemen to total foreign trade was considerably higher. This may have been due in part to a relative decline of trade in certain kinds of raw materials which do not involve a middleman, during that war-

TABLE 1. NATION'S FOREIGN TRADE IN WHOLESALE TRADE CHANNELS COMPARED WITH NATION'S TOTAL FOREIGN TRADE

(in billions of dollars)

	Value of Total Foreign Trade in Merchandise[a]	Sales of Foreign Trade Merchants and Agents	Ratio to Total Trade	Foreign Trade Merchants and Agents plus Foreign Sales of Manufacturers[b]	Ratio to Total Trade
1929	$ 9.6	$ 3.8	.39	$ —	—
1935	4.3	2.1	.48	2.5	.57
1939	5.5	3.2	.58	3.8	.69
1948	19.8	8.6	.43	11.5	.57
1954	25.3	10.3	.40	13.7	.55
1958	30.4	12.9	.43	17.1	.56

[a]Based on Tables #1120 and #1175 of *The Statistical Abstract of the United States*, 1956 and 1959 issues, respectively. Foreign trade in merchandise excludes gold and silver and, of course, payments for services.
[b]Sales of manufacturers' sales branches and offices; estimated value for 1958.

preparation year in Europe, and in part to the greater use of middlemen by producers during periods when their sales volumes did not warrant maintaining their own foreign trade departments. Whatever the underlying causes may be, trade volumes of intermediaries do not expand as much as total foreign trade in times of prosperity nor contract as much in times of recession.

Intermediaries located in the New York Area command about 70 per cent of the national total of foreign trade in wholesaling channels, somewhat more than 60 per cent in export wholesaling and almost 80 per cent in import wholesaling. Participation in imports has been maintained at a high level over a period of 30 years, but the rise of New York to a commanding position in export wholesaling is relatively recent.

EXPORT WHOLESALING: 1929-1958

Expansion of the nation's export trade after its low level during the early thirties was accompanied by a dramatic rise in trade volumes of export wholesalers (Table 2). From 1935 on, they have consistently handled more than 50 per cent of the nation's export trade. A high point was reached in 1939, and thereafter the level of participation stabilized around 58 per cent.

Between 1929 and 1954 New York's share of the nation's export trade in wholesaling channels grew from about 40 per cent to 64 per cent. Data for measuring the degree of participation at the time of the most recent census, 1958, are not yet available, but from other evidence it appears likely that New York has maintained a trade share between 62 per cent and 64 per cent.

The rise in New York's share of the nation's export wholesaling resulted from a

TABLE 2. UNITED STATES MERCHANDISE EXPORTS IN WHOLESALING CHANNELS RELATED TO TOTAL MERCHANDISE EXPORTS

	Total Merchandise Exports	Exports in Wholesale Trade Channels	Per Cent
	(billions of dollars)		
1929	5.2	1.9	37
1935	2.3	1.2	52
1939	3.2	2.1	66
1948	12.7	8.0	63
1954	15.1	8.7	58
1958	17.7	10.3 (est.)	58

number of influences. Shrinkage in the nation's export trade volumes during the Depression forced many of the other trade centers out of competition. The increasing importance of manufactured products in export trade following the depression of the 1930's gave New York an advantage over competing centers. Changes in the structure of the nation's wholesaling system, especially the rising emphasis on manufacturers' sales branches in marketing at home and abroad was an important factor in the Area's forward surge. Finally, New York's export intermediaries, by specializing in the transaction function, were able to effect economies in their operations that could not be matched in the smaller marketing centers handling a narrower range of commodities.

Effect of Trade Shrinkage

Sharp declines in the nation's export trade during the early thirties had the effect of reducing export wholesaling volumes almost to the vanishing point in marketing centers outside of New York, with telling repercussions upon their financial services essential to the conduct of foreign trade. The extremely low level of foreign trade during the thirties in Philadelphia, a typical case, induced bankers there to close out their foreign departments rather than continue unprofitably in low-volume business. As a result, New York banks by 1940 handled all but a small fraction of the nation's foreign trade finance; not until the late forties did this activity resume on a significant scale in other trade centers.

Rise of Manufactures in Export Trade

Between 1935 and 1954, the nation's exports of finished and semifinished goods grew from 65 per cent to 82 per cent of total exports, and the shift in commodity composition was manifest in the trade volumes of wholesalers engaged in export operations.

In 1929, the bulk of the trade in export wholesaling channels was made up of raw materials. Agricultural raw materials alone accounted for 58 per cent of the sales transactions, and these together with lumber and petroleum constituted about three-quarters of all wholesale trade to export. Since most of the export transactions in these commodities at that time were centered at ports of assembly near producing areas, New York's share of the trade was correspondingly small, about 40 per cent. By 1948, the situation was almost completely reversed. Manufactures accounted for over 70 per cent of export wholesalers' sales, and raw materials less than 30 per cent. New York, the primary handler in 1929 of the smaller segment of the trade, reaped vast benefits from this shift.

Changes in Trade Structure

In the years following 1935 there was rapid growth of export sales originating in sales branches and offices of manufacturers. Statistically insignificant in 1929 they now account for at least 30 per cent of the nation's exports in wholesaling channels.

Equally marked has been the steady shrinkage in the part played by export agents, whose shares appear to have stabilized at about the 15 per cent level (Fig. 1). Merchants' sales have remained remarkably stable over the long run. In all cases, it should be emphasized, these are shares of an expanding trade.

The pattern of trade sharing among the export intermediaries in the nation differed materially from that in the New York Area in 1935, but the subsequent course of development has been such as to erase these differences, as may be also seen in Figure 1. Although 1958 data for the New York Area are not yet available, they are likely to reveal a still closer agreement between New York and the nation and will emphasize the decisive role of the export merchant and the manufacturers' sales outlets in the future of New York as a center of export wholesaling.

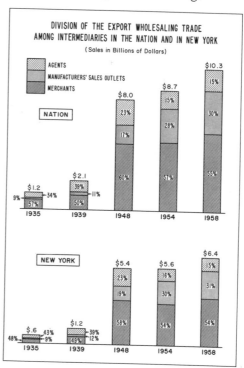

FIG 1

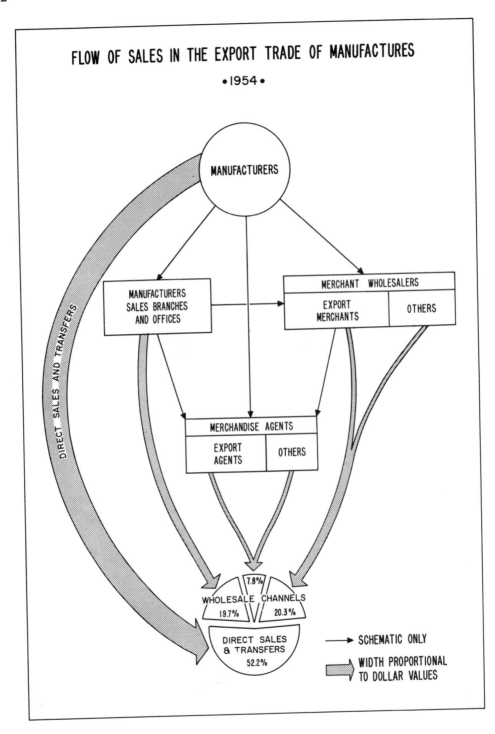

FIG. 2

The Manufacturer in Export Wholesaling

Figure 2 portrays in schematic form the flow of transactions underlying the movement of manufactured goods to buyers in foreign countries in 1954. The greater portion of this flow, 52.2 per cent, does not involve any intermediary whatsoever, for it represents transactions concluded by principals, and sales by firms operating branches in foreign countries. Also included in the main flow are shipments of components for assembly in foreign locations — these may be regarded as interplant transfers, and as such are part of the manufacturing activity rather than a flow in wholesale channels of distribution. The remainder, 48 per cent, flows through wholesaling channels.

In 1954, manufacturers' export sales from their branches and offices amounted to about $2.4 billion and the New York Area accounted for 69 per cent of it. Most of the national sales volume was concentrated in four major commodity groups: primary metal products, chemicals, transportation equipment and machinery. The same commodities constitute the bulk of the Area's wholesale trade in this category. Electrical machinery, textiles, fabricated metals, instruments and food products made up most of the remaining portion.

New York's share of exports in the various commodity lines appears to be influenced by the strength of these lines in the regional market. Where New York's share of national sales in the wholesale market is larger than would be accounted for by its share of the population, the share of export sales is also larger (Table 3). Conversely, where New York's position in the domestic market is weak, as it is in the case of leather and rubber products, the share of export sales is also weak.

A manufacturer's sales branch, by definition, maintains stocks, whereas manu-

TABLE 3. New York's Share of Nation's Wholesale Trade, Domestic and Export (per cent)

	Domestic Market	Export Sales
Primary metals	22	86
Chemicals	25	52
Transportation equipment	12	94
Textiles	59	87

facturers' sales offices sell almost exclusively from sample or specification. Inventories maintained by manufacturers' sales branches in the Area were valued at almost $800 million in 1954, a level vastly higher than in any other market in the nation and one whose magnitude is influenced primarily by regional consumption requirements. It is probably no chance association that more than 50 per cent of New York's export sales by manufacturers' sales outlets originate in sales branches. In the rest of the nation, the greater part of export sales in this category originates in manufacturers' sales offices. The ability to fill orders from stock as the occasion may require, combined with frequency of sailings, are twin aspects of the advantage of *availability* which had enabled New York to capture a large portion of manufacturers' sales to export.

The Changing Function of the Export Merchant

Despite the tremendous thrust of manufacturers' sales branches, export merchants are still the dominant figure in export wholesaling. However, the effect of the manufacturers' entry into export is reflected in a decline in sales of manufactured goods by export merchants. The evolution of a new mode of operation, with lowered cost, first developed in the New York Area, has enabled New York's export merchants to maintain a firm grip on specialty wholesaling and invade the agents' domain in nonmanufactured goods.

Changes in Commodity Pattern. During 1948–1954 a profound change took place in the basic commodity lines handled by export merchants. Most of the sales gain, 11.5 per cent, stems from a sharp rise in agricultural raw materials, chiefly grain, which increased by approximately $1 billion, doubling 1948. Had it not been for the increase in their trade in farm products, export merchants' sales would have declined by about $600 million. In contrast, there were declines in export merchant transactions in manufactured and semifinished goods all along the line.

Although there are some differences between the reporting schedules of manufacturers' sales arms and those of export merchants, there is statistical comparability in four major commodity lines. Table 4 shows that strong gains by manufacturers were made at the expense of the merchants during 1948–1954.

TABLE 4. CHANGE IN EXPORT SALES
VOLUMES, 1948–1954
(per cent)

	Manufacturers' Branches and Offices	Export Merchants
Chemicals	+138	−28
Primary metals	+161	−28
Machinery	+ 27	+ 4
Electrical goods	+141	− 7

As a result of these recent trends, New York's share of national sales in almost all

TABLE 5. CHANGE IN SALES VOLUMES OF EXPORT MERCHANTS AND CHANGE IN
NEW YORK'S SHARE OF NATIONAL EXPORT MERCHANT SALES, 1948 AND 1954

	Change in Sales Volumes (per cent)		Area's Share of National Sales (per cent)	
	Nation	New York	1948	1954
All lines	11.5	− 4.3	71.7	61.5
Groceries	− 9.3	− 46.3	80.1	47.4
Farm products (edible)	26.6	72.0	30.9	42.0
Beer, wine, spirits	− 67.0	− 87.5	61.4	23.3
Tobacco	− 39.6	− 57.4	96.8	68.2
Drugs, chemicals	− 28.0	− 38.6	90.1	76.9
Dry goods, apparel	− 39.9	− 37.2	94.2	98.4
Furniture, furnishings	− 10.4	32.6	60.9	90.1
Paper, paper products	− 24.1	− 28.3	95.0	89.7
Farm products (raw materials)	99.8	146.4	37.4	46.1
Automotive goods	− 52.3	− 66.5	80.2	56.3
Electrical goods	− 7.2	− 9.3	94.2	92.0
Hardware, plumbing, heating	− 69.2	− 77.1	88.6	65.9
Lumber, construction materials	− 22.2	− 34.9	15.2	12.7
Machinery, equipment	4.4	− 20.1	77.3	59.1
Metals, metalwork	− 27.9	− 28.3	96.6	96.0
Scrap, waste materials	266.6	190.1	75.4	59.7
Other export	− 24.1	− 21.2	83.5	86.7

Sales in most lines composed of manufactured goods declined, but New York's declines have been generally greater than in the nation. As a result, New York's shares of the trade have declined in almost all categories.

lines made up of manufactured goods sold by merchant wholesalers declined appreciably.

In aggregate sales, manufactures and nonmanufactures combined, the trade volume of export merchants in the New York Area shrank by 4.3 per cent during 1948–1954. This relatively modest decline in the aggregate conceals losses in lines made of manufactured goods. With the exception of two lines, New York's trade shares in manufactures declined appreciably during this same period. In the case of dry goods and apparel, as may be seen in Table 5, New York's trade share increased; its shrinkage in sales was less than that of the nation. In furniture and furnishings, New York's trade share advanced appreciably because of absolute gains in the face of national decline.

It is not to be assumed that the Area's decline between 1948 and 1954 represents a trend. The evidence in the 1958 Census of Wholesale Trade shows sharp gains nationally in export merchants' sales over 1954 levels. Data for the New York Area for that year are not yet available, but the strength of the national gain was so great that it is unlikely that the New York Area did not share in it materially.

Changes in Mode of Operation. The export merchant, as revealed in the first Census of Distribution in 1929, was a far cry from his predecessors, and the changes which have taken place during the past 25 years have further widened the distance between him and the merchant entrepreneur of an earlier era. Two statistical series (Table 6), dealing with inventories and operating expenses, provide the key to an understanding of this development.

The export merchant is no longer a handler of goods on an appreciable scale, for the goods-handling function would, under current standards, result in at least a

TABLE 6. INVENTORIES AND OPERATING EXPENSES OF EXPORT MERCHANTS

| | Year-end Inventories as Per Cent of Annual Sales | | Operating Expenses as Per Cent of Sales | |
	Nation	New York Area	Nation	New York Area
1935	13.2	8.2	9.0	11.7
1939	12.0	6.9	7.7	5.9
1948	6.1	–	7.6	7.2
1954	9.0	4.8	5.6	5.2

doubling of inventories and a threefold increase in operating expenses. New York's export merchants have been the leading force. Inventory levels of export merchants in the New York Area represent only "pipeline" stocks or goods in transit — less than 6 per cent of transactions in this field involve direct goods handling by the merchant.

Sources of Supply. The export merchant in the New York Area now functions primarily as an assembler, taking title to goods and assuming responsibility for their delivery to the customer without, however, engaging in actual goods handling. The goods-handling function is shifted to service wholesalers who perform it on a much larger and more efficient scale. New York with its highly developed domestic wholesaling structure, strong in all types of operations and in all commodity lines, and supported by extensive volumes of goods in inventory, has been ideally suited to this division of function.

Aside from inventories of manufacturers within the Region there also are the stocks maintained in the warehouses of merchant wholesalers' establishments and in manufacturers' sales branches. The value of these in 1954 amounted to $2.1 billion. Chicago, the next ranking wholesale center in the nation has less than $0.7 billion in merchandise in wholesale inventories. Nevertheless, New York's inven-

tories, as a percentage of sales, are maintained at considerably lower levels than
Chicago's. This is an advantage resulting
from the scale of operation and implies a
degree of efficiency not matched elsewhere in the nation.

Forces Adverse to New York. In view
of these advantages, why is the principal
segment of New York's export wholesale
trade vulnerable to inroads from other
centers, particularly with respect to manufactures, which have long been the trade
specialty of the region? If shrinking trade
volumes during the Great Depression favored the concentration of export trade in
the New York Area, expanding trade volumes by the same token should favor the
entry of competing trade centers. However, the rather late entry of these competing centers implies the presence of
other forces of a more specific character.
Export merchants in the rest of the nation
exhibited gains in sales of manufactures.
Manufacturers' sales also grew in the rest
of the nation and at a rate even greater
than in the New York Area.

Within the Middle Atlantic States secondary centers such as Pittsburgh, Buffalo
and Philadelphia have gained in various
types of wholesaling operations at a rate
greater than New York. This is consistent
with the national trend in the postwar
period toward greater relative growth of
wholesaling in the smaller trading centers.
In effect, the gap in trading advantage between the larger and smaller marketing
centers appears to be closing. The implication is that pricing advantages are no
longer to be assumed for large-scale operations. Rising transport costs have encouraged decentralization of wholesaling
as well as manufacturing.

In wholesaling in the New York Area
in recent years there have been progressive declines in sales of highly standardized items, while the share of national

sales has held up or even gained in
highly specialized lines. It seems probable that the New York Area export merchants' trade opportunities that stem from
the ready availability of regional stocks
have become restricted to trade situations
where quick assembly and speed of dis-
patch override pricing considerations, or
where sheer availability of high-value
specialty lines favors New York above
other trading centers.

Given a weakening of the domestic
wholesale trade base, other restrictive influences, formerly held in check, come to
the fore. If the New York Area has lost
the pricing advantage in certain lines, the
export merchant must look beyond the
region to more advantageous sources of
supply. When he completes a transaction
calling for the shipment of goods by a producer located in an area which enjoys a
preferential freight rate over New York,
the routing of the shipment may be likely
to avoid the Port of New York, unless
there are offsetting advantages of services
and schedules.

There is nothing new in the practice of
New York's export merchants turning to
external sources of supply, or in routing
goods through ports benefiting from differentials in overland transportation rates.
New York has long lived with this transportation handicap, but living with such
a disadvantage in a less favorable trade
context is quite another matter.

New York cannot hold the transaction
function in export wholesaling at a high
level if the routing of the shipment increasingly drifts away. The export statistics in wholesale trade show that it is precisely in the sphere of transaction-making
that competitive inroads are taking place.

Trends in the Export Agency Field

Like the export merchant, the export
agent has become more and more a dealer

in manufactured goods. Such goods in the agency trade rose from 60 per cent in 1935 to 72 per cent in 1954. In the New York Area, the export agency trade has been even more heavily weighted by manufactures, 86 per cent in 1954. Consequently the agent has had to face the competition of both the merchant and the manufacturer, and his share of the export trade in wholesaling channels has declined. Nationally, as a result of this dual squeeze, export agents' share of the total export wholesale trade declined from 34 per cent in 1935 to 15 per cent in 1954. The agent in New York has fared somewhat better in sales of manufactures than have agents elsewhere (Table 7). In the nonmanufactures trade, he has weakened more drastically than have agents in other trading centers.

TABLE 7. EXPORT AGENTS' SALES AS PER CENT OF EXPORT WHOLESALERS' SALES

	Manufactures		Nonmanufactures	
	Nation	New York	Nation	New York
1935	38	37	30	64
1948	19	23	30	20
1954	13	19	16	9

National trade volumes in the export agency field have been erratic. During 1948–1954 agents in the New York Area, and in the nation as well, showed a decline of 20 per cent in transaction volumes. The limited data now available on 1958 show that, nationally, there were gains of a high order during 1954–1958. New York clearly commands all lines representing manufactured goods. In the "other exports" category, made up of mixed-lot exports, fine goods, and an array of miscellaneous items, including what is left of the petroleum-products trade in wholesaling channels, New York's dominance is overwhelming.

IMPORTS IN WHOLESALING CHANNELS

Although the ratio of imports in wholesale trade channels to total merchandise imports of the nation has varied considerably over the years, at no time has it fallen below 40 per cent (Table 8). During the postwar period, this relationship appears to have become stabilized at slightly below the 50 per cent level.

TABLE 8. IMPORTS IN WHOLESALING CHANNELS RELATED TO TOTAL MERCHANDISE IMPORTS

(billions of dollars)

	Merchandise Imports	Import Wholesalers' Transactions	Importers' Wholesale Sales as Per Cent of Total Imports
1929	$ 4.4	$1.9	42
1935	2.0	1.3	63
1939	2.3	1.7	74
1948	7.1	3.5	49
1954	10.1	5.0	49
1958	12.7	6.2	49

The higher ratio of imports in wholesale trade channels to total imports during the thirties probably reflected the relatively greater decline in direct imports for industrial consumption when compared with imports of finished and semifinished goods. It is also likely that some industrial firms during that period of retrenchment switched from buying directly from foreign sources of supply to buying through import intermediaries, as was observed in export wholesaling during this period.

Direct and Wholesalers' Imports Compared

There is a fairly consistent pattern in the kinds of commodities handled by import intermediaries and those handled directly. As long ago as 1929 wholesalers' imports in mineral raw materials —

ores, earths, petroleum — were insignificant. Since then, the wholesale import
trade in this field, with the exception of
a few commodities, has been minuscule,
and the presumption is strong that the
great bulk of mineral raw materials is imported directly by industrial firms, probably in large part from captive sources of
supply. Direct purchasing by industrial
and other large volume consumers is
dominant in such lines as industrial chemicals, utility paper including newsprint,
automotive goods, and lumber and construction materials.

By contrast, wholesalers command more
than half of the trade in drugs, pharmaceuticals, toiletries, fine paper including
stationery and wallpaper, electrical goods,
machinery and scientific instruments.
Wholesalers account for almost all of
the trade in an extensive array of consumer goods, ranging from bicycles and
books to jewelry and musical instruments.

In other lines the pattern is not as clear-
cut. Wholesalers handle about a third of
the coffee-tea-spice trade, an equally high
share of sugar imports, and over half the
commerce in fibers, skins, hides and forest
products other than lumber. Wholesalers
handle a surprising 25 per cent of the
nation's iron and steel imports and about
40 per cent of the commerce in nonferrous
metals.

The wholesaler, in short, dominates the
import trade in consumer goods and in
high-value commodity lines destined for
industrial, professional and commercial
purchasers. While he has long ceased
to function as a prime supplier of mineral
raw materials, he commands more than
a respectable portion of the import
trade in food-base materials, and in a
large number of miscellaneous raw materials whose sources are not easily
reached for direct purchase.

Trends in Commodity Composition and in the Division of Trade

The commodity composition of the import wholesale trade has not undergone
the sweeping changes during 1929–1954
noted in export wholesaling. Agricultural
raw materials have declined in relative
importance and gains have taken place in
transactions involving food products and
semiprocessed food bases, in metals and
in specialty goods.

Import merchants have long been preponderant in the import wholesaling trade,
and since the war their share of the trade
has increased at the expense of the agents.
In 1954–1958, the decline in the agents'
transaction volumes was absolute as well
as relative (Table 9).

TABLE 9. DIVISION OF TRADE BETWEEN
IMPORT MERCHANTS AND IMPORT AGENTS

	Merchants' Share	Agents' Share
1948	80%	20%
1954	85	15
1958	90	10

A functional specialization of the agent
has come about, however. Whereas merchants are entrenched in all lines and
dominate the trade in finished goods, almost 80 per cent of the agents' transactions by 1954 were concentrated in agricultural raw materials, fresh fruits and
vegetables, food bases and metals. This
narrowing of the import agents' sphere of
participation in commodities is reflected
in a progressive shrinkage in their portion
of the total import trade.

In the New York Area, where the import trade is more heavily weighted by
manufactures, the sphere of the agents
has become even more restricted. By 1954,
the agents' share of the Area's import
trade had dropped to 12 per cent, com-

pared to their 15 per cent share of the nation's total.

These changing relationships in the division of the trade by type of operation in New York and in the nation are shown in Figure 3. New York has increased its share in the merchant field, the expanding segment of the trade. These gains have more than offset New York's decline in agency sales. The basis of New York's strength in the merchants' sphere is explored in a later section. The reasons for New York's decline in the agency operation are not entirely clear. It may be due in part to the national shift noted earlier of some commodity transactions, especially in manufactures, from the agency to the merchant operation. The residual activity, because it is heavily weighted by trading in such commodities as edible agricultural products, is more highly dis-

persed among secondary import centers serving regional markets.

Although the import agent is declining in importance in the New York Area, his trade volumes — a half billion dollars in 1954 — are worthy of notice. Since the war there has been a drastic decline in agent trade in agricultural raw materials but a gain in food products and metals. The net effect has been to diversify agents' sales in the New York Area over a somewhat broader range of commodity lines than in the rest of the nation.

Import Merchants

Since import merchants are of crucial importance in the New York Area, it is worthwhile to examine their gains and losses in the component commodity lines. Although the New York Area increased its share of the trade in the import mer-

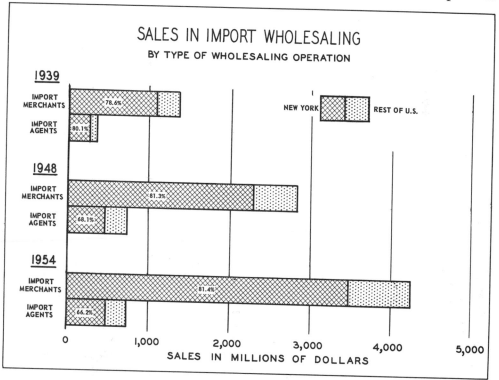

FIG. 3

chant field during the 1948–1954 period, the gains were concentrated in a few commodity lines. The bulk of the gain is accounted for by gains in sales of food products (the groceries line), "other imports," and metals. In 1954 these three lines accounted for 74 per cent of merchant import sales in the New York Area and 70 per cent in the nation. Furthermore, these three key lines accounted for 85 per cent of the $1.4 billion gain reported by New York's import merchants over 1948 levels.

Most of the increase in New York's import wholesale sales of groceries was concentrated in coffee, tea, spices, refined sugar and cocoa. The bulk of the "other imports" category consists of food base materials: malt and malt extracts, hops, raw sugar and molasses, beverage bases and chocolate coating materials, although it also includes fine manufactures such as cameras, sporting goods, art goods and semifinished goods. New York's merchant importers have enjoyed the lion's share of the nation's trade in metals and metalwork, but between 1948 and 1954 their sales increase was a rate slightly less than that of the nation. Most of the trade is in nonferrous metals in which New York's share of the nation's sales was slightly over 98 per cent.

As in export wholesaling, import wholesaling shows a tendency away from full-service wholesaling and toward specialization in the transaction phase of the trade. However, goods handling in the import phase has remained at a much higher level than in exports. Only 5 per cent of export transactions are accompanied by goods handling, but the proportion in importing is still around 23 per cent. Goods handling in the import merchant field is confined to finished goods for household and industrial consumption. Semifinished goods and raw materials are consigned directly to industrial users without any handling by the import intermediary.

In contrast to export trade, the import merchant trade shows no sign of relative decline in the New York Area. In many important commodity lines the Area's share of the nation's trade is overwhelming.

The adoption of new practices undoubtedly has increased the over-all efficiency of the import wholesaling operation, but these efficiencies, growing out of specialization, could not have been effected without the presence of two important predisposing conditions: (1) New York is the nation's largest and most highly concentrated market for consumer and industrial goods, and (2) New York has within its confines an elaborate marketing organization with an identifiable sales aggregate of $54 billion. The services of supply and distribution provided by this complex reach far beyond the confines of the Region. Not only in size but in depth of commodity detail — and hence highly developed services in marketing specialization — this wholesaling structure has but one rival in the country, Chicago; there are none on the eastern seaboard of sufficient strength to intercept commerce originating overseas. Import wholesaling is highly conducive to concentration, whereas the export phase is not nearly so subject to an orientation favorable to New York.

Considering first the regional demand for imported commodities, the New York Area is the nation's largest single market for consumer goods. Then there is the huge concentration of food industries in the New York Area, serving a far more extensive market area. The coffee roasting, sugar refining and confectionery industries, together with the breweries and bakeries, absorb vast quantities of raw and semiprocessed food materials, such as coffee, tea, spices, sugar, malt, chocolate. In 1954 New York's merchant importers sold more than $1.5 billion worth of these materials.

Next, the strength and magnitude of the New York Area's domestic wholesaling structure exert a powerful influence on the Area's import trade. With few exceptions, where there is strength in the Area's domestic wholesaling activities, import wholesaling achieves a commanding position in the nation's trade. For example, the Area's share in the domestic wholesale trade in industrial chemicals was some 38 per cent in 1954; its share of import trade was almost 90 per cent. In nonferrous metals, the Area's share of domestic trade was 72 per cent, and of the import trade 98 per cent. Similar situations can be cited in connection with consumer goods: in wines and distilled spirits there is a 21.5 per cent share of the domestic wholesale volume and 90 per cent of the sales of imports, and in dry goods and apparel, with practically a 50 per cent share of the domestic market and 95 per cent of the import market.

THE OUTLOOK

Export intermediaries in the New York Area may be expected to increase their business volumes by 75 per cent during 1955–1980. Their level of transactions in 1980 will probably be about $9.3 billion. Transaction volumes of import wholesalers in the Area will probably be slightly higher, about $9.4 billion.

Of the two forecasts, the estimation of New York's export wholesale volumes is the less firm, for it is assumed that the restrictive influences discussed above will continue in force. Removal or reduction of these influences would augment the estimate.

Export Wholesaling

This forecast involves three stages of estimation: (1) the future level of the nation's export trade, (2) the degree of participation in this trade by wholesale intermediaries, and (3) New York's share of the wholesale component. These stages in the forecast are developed and identified in Table 10.

With respect to foreign trade, it is believed, on the basis of historical trends, that the nation's exports as a percentage of the gross national product will decline from 3.9 per cent in 1955 to 3.4 per cent in 1985. The resultant volumes of trade to export would increase from $16 billion to $33 billion in that period.

As to the degree to which export wholesalers will participate in the trade, summary census data for 1958 reveal some unlooked for developments. Whereas the data for 1948–1954 pointed toward a future weakening of trade shares of export middlemen, the data for 1958 indicate a different prospect, for during this most recent period, the value of U. S. exports gained by 18.1 per cent. The combined trade volumes of export merchants and export agents during the same period gained by 25.7 per cent, a reversal of the trend in the earlier period.

If we assume that between 1954 and 1958 export sales of manufacturers through their own sales branches and offices gained at the same rate as sales through middlemen, wholesale sales in 1958 may have been as much as 60 per cent of total exports.

It may be stated, conservatively, that exports in wholesale channels relative to total merchandise exports of the nation will decline gradually from 58 per cent in 1955 to 53 per cent in 1980. In terms of 1955 dollars, wholesalers' export sales would then climb from $9.3 billion to $17.5 billion.

In the absence of 1958 data on export wholesale trade volumes for the New York Area, an estimate of future volumes must rely mainly on earlier trends. However, in the light of the national trends revealed in the census of 1958, a continuance of the 1948–1954 decline in New York's trade share, especially with respect to the shares of export merchants and manufacturers' sales outlets, would imply a disproportionate and improbable trade gain for these intermediaries in the rest of the nation. Furthermore, it would appear that the large national increases recorded by export agents, as noted above, would have rebounded in considerable measure to the benefit of export agents located in New York, for they have been traditionally strong.

Three factors, singly or together, could raise New York's trade shares above these levels: (1) A downward revision of rail rates on manufactured goods would enlarge New York's wholesale trading area and raise the level of domestic wholesale transactions, thereby making the region more attractive as a center for the assembly of goods from regional stocks for export in competition with other market centers. (2) Equalization of export rates from inland points would pull through the Port District a large proportion of the flow of goods resulting from export transactions concluded in New York and strengthen the position of New York's export middlemen. (3) The physical coordination of services allied to export wholesaling in the proposed World Trade

TABLE 10. PROJECTION OF EXPORT SALES IN THE NATION AND IN THE
NEW YORK AREA: 1955–1980

(in billions of 1955 dollars)

	Gross National Product[a]	Exports as Per Cent of G.N.P.	Exports	Export Wholesaling as Per Cent of Total Exports	Estimated Wholesale Sales to Export	New York's Share of Export Wholesaling (per cent)	Estimated New York Export Wholesale Sales
1955	$398	3.9	$16.0	58	$ 9.3	63	$5.9
1960	473	3.9	18.4	57	10.3	61	6.3
1965	561	3.8	21.3	56	11.9	59	6.8
1970	667	3.7	24.7	55	13.6	57	7.8
1975	792	3.6	28.5	54	15.4	55	8.5
1980	945	3.5	33.1	53	17.5	53	9.3

[a]The estimate of gross national product in the future is based on a 3.5 per cent annual rate of growth; conforming to the forecast of the U. S. Bureau of Labor Statistics. The National Planning Association and the Joint Economic Committee have assumed growth rates somewhat over 4 per cent. Others, such as the National Industrial Conference Board, have estimated future growth at a rate in conformance with the long range trend, which is roughly 3 per cent.

Taking these broad influences into account, New York's share of export wholesaling should decline from an estimated 63 per cent of the trade in 1955 to about 53 per cent in 1980. This means that the volume of trade during this period should grow from $5.9 billion to $9.3 billion, about 75 per cent over 1955 trade volumes.

Center should increase the efficiency of export intermediaries and could provide a telling advantage over competing trade centers.

Import Wholesaling Forecast

If we assume the same gain in gross national product and that imports will be maintained at a more or less constant 3 per cent of the G.N.P., the value of the nation's imports should rise to $28.4 billion by 1980 (Table 11).

The most recent statistics on the volume of import transactions generally parallel those observed for export wholesaling. During 1954–1958 the reckoned share of imports flowing through wholesale trade channels increased from 48.8 per cent to 49 per cent. It is difficult, therefore, to expect any sharp reduction in this rate of participation in the future. Rather, a gradual decline from 49 per cent in 1955 to 44 per cent in 1980 is deemed a reasonable allowance for increases in the imports of raw and semifinished materials for industrial consumption which would bypass wholesaling institutions.

With respect to New York's share of the import wholesale trade, the only ground for discounting New York's future trade levels in import wholesaling would be that as national foreign trade volumes expand, competing centers will find it feasible to enter more actively into the trade. New York's share of this trade has persistently stayed near the 80 per cent level.

New York's strength in import wholesaling stems from the region's position as the prime marketing center in the nation's domestic wholesale trade for the distribution of manufactured goods, and from its stature as a consumer of semifinished and raw materials. With respect to the first factor, the most recent statistics on domestic wholesaling (1958) show that New York's share of the nation's wholesale trade is declining more slowly than are the shares of the other large wholesale centers. New York's relative advantage over Chicago, for instance, is probably greater today than it was in 1954 or in 1948. The World Trade Center may be expected to enhance the institutional strength of New York as the focal point for pricing, marketing and distributing imports entering as finished goods.

On the other hand, it is expected that New York's industrial consumption of import raw materials, much of which involves trade intermediaries, will grow at a lower rate than the rest of the nation's. Again, to be conservative, it may be estimated that the shrinkage in this sector of the trade will result in an over-all trade share decline of New York's import wholesalers from 80 per cent of the nation's trade in 1955 to 75 per cent in 1980. This should result in a growth of import wholesaling in New York from $4.5 billion in 1955 to $9.4 billion in 1985.

TABLE 11. PROJECTION OF IMPORT SALES IN THE NATION AND IN THE
NEW YORK AREA: 1955–1980

(in billions of 1955 dollars)

	Gross National Product[a]	Imports as Per Cent of G.N.P.	Imports	Import Wholesaling as Per Cent of Total Imports	Estimated Import Wholesale Sales	New York's Share of Import Whole-saling (per cent)	Estimated New York Import Wholesale Sales
1955	$398	2.9	$11.5	49	$ 5.6	80	$4.5
1960	473	3.0	14.2	48	6.8	79	5.4
1965	561	3.0	16.8	47	7.9	78	6.2
1970	667	3.0	20.0	46	9.2	77	7.1
1975	792	3.0	23.8	45	10.7	76	8.1
1980	945	3.0	28.4	44	12.5	75	9.4

[a]See footnote to Table 10.

CHAPTER 6

WAREHOUSING AS AN ADJUNCT TO WHOLESALE TRADE

In the report of the *Regional Plan of New York and its Environs,* issued during the 1920's, it was noted that Manhattan suffered from severe vehicular congestion, much of it resulting from the handling of goods flowing into and out of wholesale markets, then highly concentrated in that borough. Manhattan's inability to provide essential services of supply to a growing metropolis was manifest in an expansion of warehousing along the Brooklyn water front.

The development of a similar warehousing complex was also under way at that time on the New Jersey side of the area, but at a much slower rate. It was believed that with the construction of vehicular tunnels, warehousing in New Jersey would expand as in Brooklyn. The permissive condition, as pointed out in the 1920 report, was that the growing standardization of manufacture would allow the further development of wholesale trade by inspection of samples rather than of lots. Manhattan would, it was believed, develop as a transaction center, and the surrounding counties and boroughs would be the locale for the receipt, storage and physical distribution of goods.

Succeeding events have proved this to have been a generally accurate forecast. Manhattan has developed as a center of transactional wholesaling, but the outward drift of goods handling did not take place on the schedule or on the scale anticipated. A major depression intervened, and slack trade volumes during that time may have dampened the urgency for relocation. More important, the pressure for wholesalers to relocate was eased by

developments in the trade not foreseen when the *Regional Plan* report was prepared.

It was then assumed that the physical volume of goods handled by wholesalers would expand in more or less direct proportion to the growth of transaction volumes, but subsequently progressive declines in the level of inventory held in wholesalers' warehouses were revealed. In many commodity lines, the wholesaler has pushed back the goods-handling function to the producer, reducing the relative importance of the wholesaler's warehouse. The full-scale entry of manufacturers into distribution, with their own wholesaling establishments and their emphasis on sales to volume buyers, has vastly stepped up the practice of direct shipment from the mill or factory to the customer, and this too has contributed diminishing importance of filling orders from stocks maintained in warehouses. Nor could the authors of the *Regional Plan* foresee the revolutionary role of truck transport in shortening the path of physical distribution, and in thus easing the pressure for increased storage capacity in the wholesaler's plant.

Much of the "rundown warehouse and old loft building" referred to in that early report is still in use by many Manhattan wholesalers. While the prospects are that, barring vast demolition and redevelopment for other uses, some of this ancient plant will continue in the service of Manhattan's wholesalers during the next 20 years or so, it will be overshadowed by the continued rise of new and more efficient plant outside of Manhattan.

Inventories and Warehousing

Inventories of wholesalers are commonly thought of as goods held in place on wholesalers' property, and as a corollary that wholesalers' warehouse space must be adequate to accommodate these inventories. But not all of a wholesaler's inventory is stored in his own warehouse. Goods owned by wholesalers are held by others, chiefly retailers on a consignment basis. A significant amount of inventory is represented also by wholesaler-owned goods in transit. Still another part is to be found in public warehouses, in bond or in producers' warehouses awaiting delivery.

Nevertheless, there are nationally about 1.3 billion square feet of *net* occupiable warehouse space in wholesalers' establishments for accommodating stocks at hand.[1] Wholesalers' warehouses are generators of freight and freight-handling activity of an unusually high order. Where warehouses exist in clusters, they are the locale of intensive freight handling in receiving goods from distant points and in distributing them within a particular trade territory. If wholesalers' warehouses should exhibit a tendency toward locational dispersion rather than concentration, this would be an important influence in the shaping of and the planning for future transportation demands.

The bulk of wholesalers' warehousing, about 80 per cent, is found in the merchant wholesaler branch of the trade. About 13 per cent is found in manufacturers' sales branches, and 7 per cent is divided almost equally between merchandise agents and assemblers of farm products. The latter are of limited importance in the New York Area.

[1]As defined in the U. S. Census of Business: Excluded is auxiliary space such as that occupied by stairways, loading platforms, office space, and circulatory area contiguous to but not within the main storage system.

Sales and Goods Handling in the New York Area

As recently as 1929, goods handling and sales transactions, insofar as these activities are reflected in the ratio of inventories to sales, appear to have been carried on in about the same proportions in the New York Area as in other large wholesaling centers. By 1939, the preponderance of transactions in the New York Area was clearly evident. For the nation as a whole there was at that time approximately one office or clerical worker for every warehouse employee. Assuming that office and clerical workers (excluding street and floor salesmen) were engaged primarily in processing orders and that warehouse employees were engaged in filling orders out of stock, the proportioning of jobs in these activities should indicate their relative importance in the major trade centers. Using this ratio as a measure, the ascendancy of the transaction function over the warehousing function was marked in New York when compared to the other ranking wholesale market centers. Chicago appeared as a strong transaction hub, but scarcely bore comparison with New York.

TABLE 1. OFFICE AND CLERICAL WORKERS PER HUNDRED WAREHOUSE WORKERS IN WHOLESALE TRADE: 1939

New York	160
Chicago	106
Cleveland	87
Los Angeles	91
Philadelphia	93
St. Louis	92

There is no current measure of this sort but warehouse space related to sales volumes affords a suitable substitute. New York's wholesale establishments in 1954 accounted for 10 per cent of the warehouse space maintained by the nation's wholesalers, but 20 per cent of the nation's wholesale sales. This is the most recent evidence of the New York Area's strength as a transaction center relative to its importance as a center of physical distribution.

IMPORTANCE OF WHOLESALERS' WAREHOUSES TO THE NEW YORK AREA

It should not be inferred that wholesalers' warehousing in the New York Area is of minor importance. The amount of space maintained by wholesalers in 1954 is of an imposing magnitude: 130 million square feet of net warehousing space.[2] It is by all odds the nation's largest concentration of space for the storage of goods moving in wholesale trade channels (see Table 2).

TABLE 2. NET OCCUPIABLE SPACE IN WAREHOUSING MAINTAINED BY WHOLESALERS: 1954

(millions of square feet floor space)

	Merchant Wholesalers	Manufacturers' Branches	Total[a]
Nation	1,016.0	136.4	1,152.4
New York	116.0	10.9	126.9
Chicago	53.9	10.4	64.3
Los Angeles	36.3	7.1	43.4
Philadelphia	32.0	4.6	36.6
Detroit	19.9	3.8	23.7
San Francisco	23.0	5.4	28.4
Boston	23.8	3.9	27.7
Cleveland	15.0	2.7	17.7
St. Louis	18.8	3.6	22.4
Pittsburgh	15.1	2.6	17.7

[a]Does not include warehouse space maintained by merchandise agents and by assemblers of farm products. In New York space occupied by these dealers amounted to 6.0 million square feet.

Source: U. S. Census of Business: Wholesale Trade 1954.

A comparison with other trade centers reveals that this superiority is manifest in all commodity lines composed of finished goods and semimanufactures. The utility of this space is immense. The availability of goods from wholesalers' stocks, in the form of parts, components and semifinished goods, is of decisive value to New York's specialty manufactures. Typically, these specialties are produced in short production runs, they are subject to frequent change in style and design, and are highly dependent upon a wide range of supplies and materials which can be priced and obtained within a short time. Value here is the value of immediate availability. Within the trade, wholesalers' warehouses also play an important role; stocks in them are cross-traded to fill out dealer shortages and from them are assembled a wide array of goods for export.[3]

If wholesalers' inventories in the New York Area, however, were maintained at the level relative to sales that prevailed in 1929, the amount of warehousing space required today would be at least double. Or, if the New York Area maintained the amount of warehouse space per dollar of sales that prevails now in Chicago, the space needed in the New York Area would be increased by about 40 per cent. If national proportions prevailed, New York's space might well be doubled.

The prime factors in this situation, sales volumes out of proportion to inventories, are, first, the long-term trend toward the reduction of inventory levels by both merchant wholesalers and manufacturers' sales branches, and, second, the greater relative growth of the wholesaling activity originating in manufacturers'

[2]As pointed out later in this discussion, about 45 per cent of this space is of modern construction; this represents addition to capacity as well as replacement of old plant, mainly loft structures. A discussion of loft structures, which house manufacturing as well as trade, is given in Chapter 3.

[3]Immediate availability is of particular value in the assembly of many kinds of goods for shipment by air, especially to overseas points. This asset probably ranks next to service density in New York's supremacy in the generation of air cargo.

sales offices involving virtually no inventories whatever.

Warehousing by Merchant Wholesalers

Inventories maintained by merchant wholesalers as a percentage of sales have been in gradual decline since 1929, more so in the New York Area than in the nation (Table 3). Merchant wholesalers account for about 90 per cent of the 127 million square feet of warehousing space maintained by wholesalers in the New York Area, yet extensive selling from stock in this branch of the trade is by no means

TABLE 3. MERCHANT WHOLESALERS' INVENTORIES AS PER CENT OF SALES

	1929	1954
Nation	11.4	9.4
New York Area	11.3	8.1

the universal practice. Merchant wholesalers who maintain less than 500 square feet of warehousing space in their establishments account for almost 57 per cent of the merchant wholesalers' sales in the New York Area.[4] Annual sales per establishment among them are higher on the average than the sales of merchant wholesalers who maintain large areas of warehouse space, and their inventories in relationship to sales are appreciably lower, 6.1 per cent compared with 10.8.

Generally, where the sales volume in a commodity line indicates a regional rather than a national market, the proportion of sales originating in merchant wholesalers' establishments with stock is fairly high. Thus in the cases of edible farm products, beer and liquor, tobacco, automotive goods, electrical goods, lumber, machinery and scrap and waste mate-

rials, New York's share of national sales ranges from but 9 to 16 per cent. The proportion of sales stemming from establishments with stock ranges from 45 to 76 per cent.

By contrast, in those commodity lines where New York commands a large share of the nation's trade, the proportion of sales originating in establishments with stocks tends generally to be rather low.

There are, however, some important exceptions to this generalization. For example, New York handles 66 per cent of the nation's merchant wholesale trade in apparel and dry goods. Yet almost half of the sales originate in establishments with warehouse space. In fact, dealers in dry goods and apparel rank next to those handling machinery and industrial equipment as the largest users of warehouse space in the area — about 13 million square feet each. In the furniture and house furnishings line, where New York also commands a large share of the nation's trade (31 per cent), 63 per cent of the sales originate in establishments with warehouse space. In both of these broad groups, much of the product originates in small manufacturing establishments within the city for whom the wholesaler is the agent as well as the distributor and the warehouseman.

These exceptions aside, the amount of merchant wholesalers' warehouse space appears to be governed largely by the level of stocks required to meet regional consumption. Future warehouse requirements will be influenced primarily by the growth of population, commerce and industry in the metropolitan area.

Warehousing by Manufacturers' Sales Branches and Offices

Manufacturers' sales branches deal mainly with industrial and commercial customers. Volume transactions by direct shipments from the parent producer to

[4]The cut-off point adopted by the Census Bureau represents a rather low minimum for warehousing space. The average residential double-garage occupies approximately 500 square feet of ground space.

the customer are the general rule, and, as a consequence, inventories for filling orders from stock are maintained at relatively low levels. Manufacturers' branches in the New York Area occupy 10.6 million square feet of warehouse space compared with 112 million square feet by merchant wholesalers.

In 1929, the great bulk of manufacturers' sales appears to have originated in sales branches. Beginning with 1935, when the "sales office" was identified statistically, we can trace a progressive increase in the sales volumes originating in offices relative to sales by branches. The most recent census, 1958, disclosed that offices now dominate sales of manufacturers' wholesaling outlets. A similar trend is evident in the New York Area. Here, as in so many of the phases in wholesale trade, the trend from branch to office wholesaling took place in New York at an earlier date than in the nation. Basically, it represents an acceleration of selling from sample rather than from stock.

If we regard manufacturers' wholesaling operations as a whole and relate inventory to sales volumes, we can measure the drastic changes which have taken place in manufacturers' practices in goods handling in their wholesale outlets. Between 1935–1954, inventories as a per cent of sales dropped from 5.4 to 3.1 for the nation as a whole. In the New York Area, the decline was sharper, from 6.0 to 2.2.

As in the merchant wholesale trade, although less pronounced, where the Area share of the nation's trade in a commodity line indicates a regional market, inventories are relatively high in relation to sales volumes, and the proportion of the sales which originates in manufacturers' establishments maintaining warehouse space is high. Where the Area's share indicates a strong degree of national market support, the level of inventory is clearly below the service level characteristic of sales branches. Hence, it appears that future growth of manufacturers' sales will lead to but moderate increases in warehouse space requirements. Thus, in view of the declining trends in inventories generally, and the narrowing function of inventories, future warehousing growth in manufacturers' wholesaling activities will be influenced by local rather than by extraregional consumption requirements.

The Rise of Single-Story Warehousing

The advantages and circumstances that have attracted large segments of the manufacturing industries into single-story facilities have also exerted their influence in wholesale trade. There are a number of facets to this development, and while they are shared to some extent by both manufacturing and wholesaling, their impact upon wholesaling has been more selective.

Substantial operational economies may be gained in manipulating goods within a single-story structure, as opposed to the multistory loft. Studies conducted by the Department of Agriculture show that unit handling costs in warehousing operations are from 30 to 40 per cent lower in single-story than in multistory structures. Since the cost of demolition and the assembly of parcels for a sufficient portion of land virtually prohibit the replacement of multistory by single-story warehouse plant within the older established wholesale districts, those wholesalers engaged extensively in the handling of goods have sought new locations in order to reap the benefits of rationalized materials-handling.

Obsolescence of plant is by no means the only factor encouraging the migration of private warehousing in the wholesale trade out of central business districts. Poor access has also been a potent factor. The rise of industry as the prime customer of the wholesaler and the outward growth of industry have also influenced the wholesaler's distribution strategy, so that the wholesaler must follow the trade axiom of arranging himself for maximum service to the customer.

However, the pattern of survival in the older wholesaling districts differs substantially from that in the older manufacturing centers. The process of change has been slower. Since wholesalers in many branches of the trade can operate with limited inventories, the retention of the residual goods-handling function in the older, high-cost locations can be offset by the ease of communication. In some cases, the goods-handling function has been split off, leaving the office or showroom in the prime sales area, but with the warehouse located at a site having superior access to transportation services, and with sufficient space for achieving the maximum efficiency in the handling of goods.

The function of the wholesaler's warehouse has also changed considerably. The practice of amassing stores seasonally has been replaced by continuous inventory replenishment, which has increased the importance of efficiency of goods handling. The modern warehouse has become, in effect, a transit shed, in which the inbound flow of goods is closely phased with stock depletion. This requirement has not only altered drastically the internal layout of the warehouse and enhanced the demand for ground space to secure the necessary planning freedom, but has put a premium on a site with adequate supporting transportation services.

Examination of some of the more recently developed distributing facilities of wholesalers reveals that space occupied by stocks in place is less than that devoted to processing orders, receiving and shipping docks, aisleways for self-propelled vehicles, and space held in reserve. The relocation of warehousing from traditional multistory into single-story plant results in more ground space required.

Single-Story and Multistory Space in the New York Area

More than 43 per cent of the warehouse space maintained by wholesalers is in single-story structures (Table 4), in the New York Area.

Wide differences may be observed in the degree to which single-story buildings are employed in the warehouse function. In the merchant wholesale trade, less than 22 per cent of the space maintained by dealers in dry goods and apparel is single-story, as compared to almost 75 per cent for dealers in metals and metalwork. The range is even more extreme among manufacturers' sales branches.

Three factors, singly or in combination, appear to determine the degree to which single-story warehousing is employed. (1) Where the product is bulky or heavy, and the sheer cost of physical manipulation is high, the tendency is to employ single-story warehousing. (2) Where the commodity line is composed of high value, fairly compact goods, there appears to be no strong urge to abandon the warehousing function in multistory structures. (3) Where the source of goods is highly concentrated geographically, or where the bulk of the customers of the wholesaler are located in a restricted locale, warehousing space must be strategically located, even though the cost of goods handling in a multistory structure might be high.

Warehousing in Manhattan

Concentration of the warehousing function in a particular commodity line in mul-

Rank		Per Cent of Warehouse Space in Single-Story Structures
	Total Merchant Wholesalers	43.7
1	Metals, metalwork	74.9
2	Automotive goods	69.6
3	Lumber, construction materials	56.9
4	Tobacco	56.8
5	Farm products (edible)	56.0
6	Beer, wine, spirits	55.3
7	Scrap, waste materials	54.6
8	Groceries	52.6
9	Machinery, equipment	48.6
10	Hardware, plumbing, heating	44.3
11	Drugs, chemicals	43.8
12	Electrical goods	33.9
13	Other products	32.3
14	Furniture, furnishings	27.8
15	Farm products (raw materials)	26.5
16	Paper, paper products	26.3
17	Dry goods, apparel	21.5
	Total Manufacturers' Sales Branches	41.8
1	Transportation equipment	82.5
2	Fabricated metals	56.1
3	Primary metals	53.2
4	Stone, clay, glass	48.4
5	Rubber products	42.2
6	Machinery	40.3
7	Food products	38.2
8	Apparel	37.7
9	Chemicals	36.0
10	Other products	34.9
11	Electrical machinery	33.6
12	Furniture and fixtures	31.5
13	Instruments	28.8
14	Paper and allied products	26.7
15	Textiles	14.2
16	Leather and products	2.7

tistory space, inferred in Table 4, implies that a large portion of the warehousing will be found in Manhattan, where single-story space is virtually nonexistent. Among lines for which multistory warehousing is predominant — furniture and home furnishings, paper and paper products, and dry goods and apparel — the sales volume of the Area is highly concentrated in Manhattan. The extreme is dry goods and apparel; over 95 per cent of the Area's transactions are credited to establishments in Manhattan. In paper and paper products, and furniture and home furnishings, Manhattan's share of Area sales approaches 75 per cent. Proximity to the production area and to the sales hub has been a powerful force in restraining the migration of warehousing out of the midtown district.

The paper and paper products group is in a class by itself. Here the prime market of the dealers is the job printing industry in Manhattan. Now, as in 1924, when the comprehensive plan report was prepared by the Regional Plan Association, the need to be close to customers has tended to keep stocks as well as sales showrooms within the Central Business District. While there has been a large-scale migration of segments of the printing trade out of Manhattan into the New Jersey portion of the Metropolitan Area, the migration has been primarily of volume printers for periodicals and the book publishing trades. Many of these purchase their paper and printing supplies directly from producers or from captive sources of supply. When they do purchase through wholesalers the size of the shipments is such that direct delivery from producer rather than sales out of stock at hand accounts for the major part of the purchases.

Some lines, such as agricultural raw materials, exhibit only a slight use of single-story warehousing. Unfortunately, this product line is statistically so broad and the information on its components is so lean that it is difficult to draw any precise conclusions. Some portions of it, such as the hide and fur trade, make extensive use of warehouse space. Some of this trade is highly seasonal, and much of it probably flows through public warehouse facilities. Other portions of it, especially the fur component, are of extremely high value and can be readily absorbed by existing structures in Manhattan. This branch of the trade retains one of the characteristics common to much of wholesaling in an earlier era, the function of pricing based on inspection of each item in any given lot. Proximity to the fur garment manufacturing industry (over 60 per cent of the nation's production originates in Manhattan) compels the continuance of the close association between warehousing and marketing.

Of the 71 million square feet of multistory warehouse space in the New York Area, it is estimated that about half is found in Manhattan loft buildings. While wholesalers' warehousing activity is ubiquitous in Manhattan, most of it is concentrated in the older loft buildings lying below 23rd Street.

For the New York Area as a whole, if modernization of warehousing plant should take place to the degree already evident in other trade centers, it would require the replacement in single-story structure of 33 million of the Area's 71 million square feet of multistory space. If we assume that New York will follow the national trend, at least 50 million square feet would be involved in replacement by single-story structure during the next 20 years.

With respect to Manhattan, it is likely that as much as 50 per cent of its warehouse space ultimately will be abandoned in favor of more efficient plant. The at-

trition of loft space in Manhattan will also be a strong factor, for between 1945 and 1960 the number of loft buildings in Manhattan declined from 7,418 to 5,964. Over 40 per cent of Manhattan's lofts are now more than 50 years old and are especially vulnerable to demolition in urban renewal projects. The decline of warehousing in Manhattan will be a product, therefore, not only of the pull toward locations affording greater operational advantages, but also from the push resulting from the declining availability of loft structures.

FUTURE DEVELOPMENTS

A number of developments are expected to exert a strong influence on the location of the goods-handling phase of wholesale trade.

The population of the Region is expected to grow by about 37 per cent between 1960 and 1985. This gain, at current levels of consumption, spells a large absolute increase in the volume of goods flowing into the Region for supplying its householders, factories and commercial establishments. It is more than likely that, if past trends are a guide, this increase will be compounded by per capita gains in consumption. Distributing systems will, therefore, be sized to handle greater volumes of goods and shaped to handle a greater variety of goods. This development implies an expansion and specialization of the existing distributive plant in the Region. It surely suggests that many wholesalers will be concerned with the problem of relocation.

Of particular relevance to the locational factor in wholesaling is the expected rise in population and manufacturing employment on the New Jersey side, and the further concentration there of freight transport services. New Jersey's share of the Region's population is expected to climb from 27.3 per cent in 1960 to 33.4 per cent in 1985 and to yield a corresponding increase in retail trade and thus to expand the market for wholesalers. More importantly, the forecast for manufacturing, the prime customer of wholesalers, also reveals a more rapid rate of gain for the New Jersey side, for its share of manufacturing employment in the Region is expected to rise from 33.8 per cent in 1956 to 40 per cent in 1985.

The further concentration of freight transport services on the New Jersey side has resulted from two influences: (1) development of new port facilities on the New Jersey side of the harbor and (2) the growth of a large truck terminal complex in northern New Jersey during the postwar period.

Among the various transportation factors which will influence the location of distribution activities, motor freight transport is of primary importance. It has the greatest locational freedom in establishing terminal facilities, and is in a distinctly superior position for responding to trade opportunity. The truck terminal itself functions as an arm of distribution to an unusual degree, for it breaks bulk of arriving truckloads and provides the essential link between over-the-road and local motor transport.

The growth of truck terminals in northern New Jersey during the postwar period has been imposing. In 1941, there was only a sprinkling of truck terminals on the New Jersey side of the river; the great bulk of the area's motor terminals was concentrated on the New York side. By 1960, a highly developed pattern of terminals was evident in New Jersey. Most significant is the tremendous shift in terminal capacity: of the 4,400 truck bays in the Area, 3,700 are dispersed among the New Jersey counties fronting the Hudson.

⁵*Architectural Record,* December, 1958, pp. 129-136.

Wholesale trade on the New Jersey side during the postwar period exhibits some singular characteristics. Whereas wholesalers' *sales* in New Jersey have shown only modest growth, *employment* has risen sharply: a gain of 52 per cent during 1948–1958 contrasted with a 1.5 per cent increase for the New York portion. New Jersey with its high absorption of wholesaling employment appears to be developing as a goods handler for many of the sales transactions conducted in Manhattan.

While population growth and industrial expansion are powerful positive factors in New Jersey's expansion in wholesale trade, another factor, availability of land in conjunction with transport services, is a decisive influence in attracting the goods-handling phase of the trade.

SPACE REQUIREMENTS IN SINGLE-STORY WAREHOUSING

According to a firm of architect-engineers that has designed about 100 large warehouses since 1945, "Pure warehouses are becoming scarce. The former concept of a warehouse as a dead storage area for out-of-season merchandise is fast disappearing. . . . Warehouses are now required to contain a number of additional functions. . . ."⁵ Among these functions, mention must be made of inventory control systems, workrooms, packaging facilities and, since new warehouses are located outside of central business districts, provision must also be made for food service and other employee amenities. It is also pointed out that structural layout of these new warehouses varies widely, depending upon the nature of the materials-handling equipment which, in turn, depends upon the nature of the commodities handled in the warehouse. There are, however, some common features; except for materials-handling systems depending upon gravity flows, the structure is almost invariably of the single-story type, and the space within the structure for goods in place is less than that allocated for other functions. Furthermore, the ground area is usually large enough to permit future structural expansion and to allow for off-street parking by employees and trucking services. Aesthetic consideration also frequently enters and this consideration adds to the ground space requirement.

Replacement of space in multistory by space in single-story structures involves the absorption of large amounts of land. For the same amount of net storage space the ground area covered by the single-story structure, of course, is much greater, but in addition the new structure typically occupies no more than 40 per cent of the total land. Furthermore, there is usually involved in any specific move a desire for more storage space immediately and also allowance for further expansion in the future.

The need for space in acreage units becomes a quest for land with a specific orientation. In those cases where distributors require access to all sectors of the metropolitan area, the choice of location east of the Hudson River is severely restricted. The New York City Planning Department estimates that about 400 warehouses have been constructed in Queens since 1945, and a field survey has disclosed that the majority of these are single-story structures in the service of merchant wholesale houses and manufacturers' sales branches. With approaching exhaustion of suitable land in Queens and Brooklyn, further expansion of the wholesaling function in the New York portion of the Metropolitan Area, except for Staten Island, rests upon development of commercial and industrial sites through renewal programs.

Development of Single-Story
Warehousing in New Jersey

A field survey in 1960 by the Port Authority of the 43 major industrial parks in the Metropolitan Area revealed that of the 385 establishments in the parks in New Jersey, 102 were engaged solely in distribution. The heaviest concentrations were found in Union and Bergen counties where distributing facilities accounted for 25 and 29 per cent respectively, of the establishments located in industrial parks. Only 18 of the 99 establishments in parks in the New York portion of the Area were distributors. Almost all of these parks have been established within the past ten years.

That distributors should have sought out the industrial park, is also noteworthy, for in these new developments the single-story structure prevails, and particular attention is given to an exterior layout for providing a maximum efficiency in loading and unloading of trucks. Most warehousing establishments noted in this field survey were of moderate size, with a gross area of less than 50,000 square feet and with an average far below that figure. Their limited size suggests that many of them are engaged in serving the New Jersey rather than the metropolitan market.

Larger facilities, designed for distributing throughout the entire Metropolitan Area, and beyond, also appear to be developing at a greater rate in the New Jersey portion. Although there is no complete enumeration of large wholesalers, the basic pattern is evident nevertheless. A distributor of drafting materials and supplies, after a careful evaluation of locational advantages, chose a site in Bergen County. The sales branch of a manufacturer producing pressed wood for industrial customers moved first to Nassau County from Long Island City, and then, after a few years, moved to Bergen County.

The case of a large producer of pharmaceuticals is of special interest. Company growth and increasing street congestion at the company's Brooklyn site seriously impaired the efficiency of distribution into the Metropolitan Area and into the Middle Atlantic states. After a careful consideration of a number of sites within and beyond the region, a distributing facility was established in northern New Jersey. This site met all of the classic specifications for a distributing center, including the availability of a rail siding. The decisive factor, according to the chairman of a company committee deciding on relocation, was the availability of a wide array of trucking service, long-distance as well as local, from nearby truck terminals.

DISTRIBUTING CENTERS

Warehousing complexes have long been established in the New York Area, and a number may be seen in various waterfront terminals. Typically, they comprise multistory structures, built during the first wave of the migration of goods handling out of Manhattan. At the time of their development they represented in part displacement of older facilities fringing the Central Business District and in part an expansion of existing capacity.

The only large-scale warehousing in the New York Area designed for multitenant occupancy is represented by the distribution facilities developed in connection with Port Newark, where the total structure contains over a million square feet of storage and cargo-handling space. In common with modern distribution centers built in other parts of the country, space is provided in single-story struc-

⁶See Chapter 5.

tures at a site convenient to all forms of transportation — rail, highway, air, and, as the prime focus, water transport.

Noteworthy in this development at Port Newark is the variety of goods handled and of organizations found among its tenants. There are a number of small mail-order houses which have typically been found in Manhattan's loft buildings. Also there are firms handling a wide range of imported consumer goods who have found it entirely feasible to relocate their goods-handling functions while retaining their showrooms in Manhattan. As noted in an earlier chapter,[6] goods handling in specialty importing has long been wedded to the sales function. This and other reported relocations in the same field represent a sharp and highly significant break away from an established practice.

Indeed, these exceptions and other developments in the area put many assumptions as to the affinity between transactions and goods-handling to test in a number of lines. A recent announcement of plans for a 21-story office and showroom building for the furniture trades (Lexington Avenue and 33rd Street), indicates a further sundering between transactions and stock.

Least susceptible, apparently, to the attractions of single-story warehouse sites are the wholesalers and buying organizations in the apparel and dry goods trade. Nevertheless, some of these firms have been showing concern over goods-handling costs in multistory structures and there are instances of rather heroic efforts, involving the use of elaborate equipment, to achieve goods-handling economies.

CONCLUSION

Wholesale trade is a prime generator of wealth in the New York Metropolitan Area. Its trade resembles that of other large market centers in that it provides essential services of supply, but its value to the area's economy is not limited to this function. It is an important instrumentality in foreign trade, particularly in the assembly of goods for export, and in the marketing of imports over broad areas in the nation. It has developed unique marketing mechanisms and has grown as a center of transactional wholesaling outstanding in magnitude and scope.

A vital element in the Area's trade supremacy is the presence of wholesalers' inventories, extensive in kind and quantity and able to accommodate a varied demand. They are essential to a host of small-establishment producers of specialty manufactures, as sources of supply as well as for channeling their output into exterior markets.

New York's wholesalers also have led the way in exploiting market opportunities in fields other than the supply of retailers.

The analysis of wholesalers' operations in the goods-handling phase of the trade in the New York Area reveals a resourceful and dynamic business community. It has developed new methods, streamlined functions and taken advantage of the opportunities afforded by the flexibility of motor transport in combination with other modes of transport. Wholesalers in the New York Area appear to be well in advance of the rest of the nation in adopting direct shipment to the customer as a means toward the reduction of inventories held in warehouses, always a high cost element in distribution.

The ability of wholesalers in the New York Area to use direct shipments to a high degree results from deeper engagement than wholesalers in other areas in supplying distant markets. Here, logically, the transaction function divorced from goods-handling comes to the fore. Also,

the New York market itself contains an unusually high concentration of volume customers and these also absorb goods directly from the point of production.

The services of supply for the New York Area are supported by a large warehousing complex. The rise of single-story warehousing in the wholesale trades during the past 15 or 16 years probably represents an average annual addition of 3 million square feet to the Area's goods-distributing facilities. This expansion affirms the value of availability of goods in variety and depth.

The downward trend of inventories of wholesalers in the New York Area may be viewed as a measure of increasing efficiency of distribution. The sharpness of the decline in inventories during the most recent period, however, especially among manufacturers' sales branches, may not be viewed with equanimity. The 1958 Census of Wholesale Trade discloses only a modest rise in sales originating in manufacturers' sales branches and offices in the New York Area, in contrast to strong gains by them in other wholesaling centers in the Middle Atlantic Region as well as in the nation as a whole. This suggests that the downward shift of inventories may reflect a certain weakness of the New York Area as a goods-distributing center, and that the use of direct shipment to such a great degree may arise out of economic necessity rather than out of convenience or choice. In the end, direct shipment from producer to user may well become a costly method of distribution, particularly for small-lot shipments. If the costs must be absorbed by the producer, they will sooner or later be reflected in wholesale price differentials between New York and other markets. This could have two adverse effects: an increase in the cost of doing business on the part of enterprises heavily dependent upon wholesalers' services, and a restriction of New York's distributing radius.

There is an unmistakable trend toward splitting the goods-handling phase away from the downtown-located sales show-rooms and offices. The first burst of ware-house development in the postwar period quickly absorbed almost all of the avail-able land in Queens. More recently, case after case points to northern New Jersey as the area ideally suited to goods han-dling for supplying regional as well as extraregional markets. Although, in gen-eral, new transportation technology pro-vides greater locational freedom for com-merce and industry, the distributive phase of manufacturing and the intermediaries of distribution find their most effective lo-cations where there is close access not to just one but to all of the major elements of transportation service. This narrows the choice of location and places a high premium on open land in those parts of the region which afford space in quantity and which are at the same time provided with transportation services. Wholesale trade in an expanding region will seek such locations in its effort to achieve effi-cient services of supply.

CHAPTER 7

RETAIL TRADE AND THE SERVICE INDUSTRIES

A preponderant portion of the retail business in any metropolitan area is directed toward supplying the needs of the resident population. Retail trade, therefore, is an important generator of metropolitan travel. The geographic distribution of the trade within the metropolis determines the travel pattern of both customers and employees, and the prospective distribution is closely related to prospective metropolitan travel patterns. Certain components of retail activity have an affinity for a central business district location and therefore have a strong influence

TABLE 1. TRENDS IN DISTRIBUTION OF RETAIL SALES IN THE METROPOLITAN AREA
(per cent of total)

	1935	1939	1948	1954	1958
Metropolitan Area	100.0	100.0	100.0	100.0	100.0
New York sector (S.M.S.A.)	78.8	77.0	75.9	73.9	73.5
New York City	68.7	65.4	63.7	56.8	53.5
Bronx	7.5	7.2	7.3	6.5	6.3
Kings	16.3	15.8	16.0	14.0	13.4
New York	35.3	32.5	30.0	25.5	23.5
Queens	8.5	8.9	9.4	9.8	9.2
Richmond	1.1	1.0	1.0	1.0	1.1
Other New York	10.1	11.6	12.2	17.1	20.0
Nassau	3.0	3.7	4.7	7.9	9.4
Rockland	0.5	0.5	0.5	0.6	0.7
Suffolk	1.5	1.8	2.0	3.0	3.8
Westchester	5.1	5.6	5.0	5.6	6.1
New Jersey sector	21.2	23.0	24.1	26.1	26.5
Jersey City S.M.S.A. (Hudson)	4.0	4.4	4.1	3.8	3.5
Newark S.M.S.A.	10.8	11.2	11.5	12.2	12.1
Essex	7.5	7.9	7.5	7.5	6.9
Morris	0.8	0.9	1.1	1.3	1.5
Union	2.5	2.4	2.9	3.4	3.7
Paterson-Clifton-Passaic S.M.S.A.	4.7	5.3	6.1	7.4	7.8
Bergen	2.2	2.6	3.2	4.4	4.8
Passaic	2.5	2.7	2.9	3.0	3.0
Middlesex	1.3	1.6	1.8	2.1	2.4
Somerset	0.4	0.5	0.6	0.6	0.7

on core-focused travel, the mainstay of the common carriers.

In 1958, according to the Bureau of the Census, there were 160,000 retailing establishments in the New York Area. During that year, their sales amounted to $18.5 billion. The number of customers approximated the population beyond the infant age. Total full-time employment was just under 600,000; irregular and part-time workers probably swelled it to well over 800,000.

Among the activities making up the Metropolitan Area's economic structure, none is so sensitive to regional growth and population redistribution as retail trade. The changing distribution since 1935 of retail trade among the major sectors and individual counties which make up the Metropolitan Area is shown in Table 1.

New York (Manhattan) County's sales relative to the total for the Area began to decline as early as 1935. Two other counties of New York City, Bronx and Kings (Brooklyn), have also shown a relative decline over recent years, as the suburban counties have taken more and more of the Area's retail function. There have been

TABLE 2. TRENDS IN DISTRIBUTION OF GAINS IN RETAIL SALES IN THE METROPOLITAN AREA
(per cent of total)

	1935–1939	1939–1948	1948–1954	1954–1958
Metropolitan Area	100.0	100.0	100.0	100.0
New York sector (S.M.S.A.)	66.8	75.2	66.7	70.6
New York City	47.3	62.6	31.5	33.8
Bronx	5.1	7.4	3.5	5.6
Kings	12.6	16.1	7.0	9.9
New York	17.3	28.5	8.6	11.3
Queens	11.5	9.6	11.3	5.8
Richmond	0.8	1.0	1.1	1.2
Other New York	19.5	12.6	35.2	36.8
Nassau	7.9	5.3	19.6	18.1
Rockland	0.5	0.5	1.0	1.2
Suffolk	3.4	2.1	6.6	8.7
Westchester	7.7	4.7	8.0	8.8
New Jersey sector	33.2	24.8	33.3	29.4
Jersey City S.M.S.A. (Hudson)	5.8	4.0	2.5	1.6
Newark S.M.S.A.	13.9	11.7	14.5	11.7
Essex	10.5	7.3	7.0	3.7
Morris	1.2	1.2	2.4	2.1
Union	2.2	3.2	5.1	5.9
Paterson-Clifton-Passaic S.M.S.A.	9.0	6.5	12.3	10.6
Bergen	5.0	3.5	9.1	7.6
Passaic	4.0	3.0	3.2	3.0
Middlesex	3.7	1.9	3.2	4.2
Somerset	0.8	0.7	0.8	1.3

important growths, on the other hand, in Nassau and Suffolk counties, and, to a smaller degree in Westchester County, reflecting expansion of population.

The New Jersey side of the Metropolitan Area has steadily increased its share over a 25-year period. Expansion has been most evident in Bergen and Middlesex counties. Long-range shrinkage has been experienced in Hudson and Essex counties.

None of the counties exhibiting relative decline have lost in terms of total sales volumes, even after appropriate reductions are made for the inflationary factor in retail prices. Even the one county showing a long and consistently downward trend, New York County (or Manhattan), had a 1958 sales volume $300 million more than its $4 billion in 1954. Most importantly, even in 1958 Manhattan's share of the Area's sales was far out of proportion to its share of the Area's population, 23.5 per cent compared to 10.5 per cent.

Further insight into the effect of metropolitan growth upon retail trade in the individual counties may be gained from Table 2, which shows the distribution of the Area's gains in retail sales from one census period to the next.

As might be inferred from Table 1, in none of the time intervals listed in Table 2 did the older, established retailing centers, Manhattan, Brooklyn, Jersey City and Newark, account for shares of the total regional growth that matched their relative strengths in regional retailing. Consequently, their relative strengths continued to decline. Growth in most of the suburban counties, conversely, accounted for disproportionately large shares of the region's retail sales increase. It is interesting to observe, however, that during the last time period, 1954-1958, some reversals of trend appear to have occurred. Manhattan and Brooklyn, in

particular, seem to have regained some strength, while Queens appears to have lost momentum.

Retailing in Manhattan

Nevertheless, as we have seen, Manhattan has a striking share of the Area's total retail business, a share far out of proportion to its share of Area population. It probably reflects Manhattan's huge daytime population, swelled by workers residing in other parts of the Area and by transients from other parts of the country. Not only is their number great but their incomes are typically higher than average.

There is a basic difference between the pattern of retailing in Manhattan and in the rest of the Metropolitan Area (Fig. 1). In Manhattan there is a striking preponderance of sales by general merchandise stores, apparel stores, eating and drinking places, and a wide range of specialty stores grouped statistically under the heading "Other Retail Stores." In the rest of the Metropolitan Area sales are concentrated in householder convenience items, composed for the most part of standardized goods; outstanding is the prominent position of sales by food stores, automobile dealers, gasoline service establishments, and lumber and building materials dealers.

Extremely high proportions of retail sales in Manhattan are accounted for by men's and women's clothing stores. The share drops sharply in family clothing stores and in children's and infants' wear; it reaches its highest point, almost 52 per cent of the Area total, in sales of miscellaneous apparel, which includes, among other things, riding and sports apparel, beach wear and accessories. In the "Other Retail Stores," specialty establishments, high shares for Manhattan prevail in the entire group, with unusual concentrations in antiques, books, sporting goods, jew-

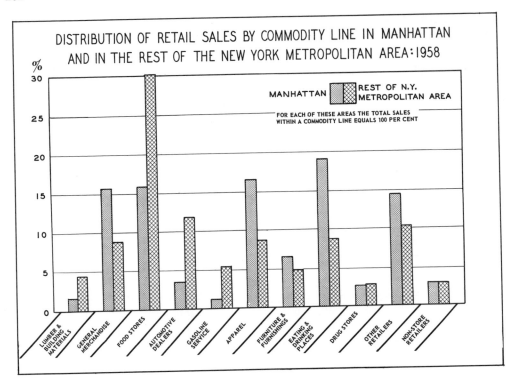

FIG. 1

elry, cameras, optical goods and luggage. In these categories of trade, Manhattan offers values which compensate the consumer for the time, expense or inconvenience involved in the journey to the Central Business District.

Manhattan's competitive strength in retailing is, to some extent, a function of its distance from residential neighborhoods and, as a rough estimate, in the suburban counties it can bid for no more than 15 per cent of the consumer dollar. It is therefore to be expected that as the distribution of population shifts, the distribution of retail trade must also shift; and as population increases faster in the outlying areas, retail sales in the Central Business District will not expand as rapidly as in those establishments located closer to the suburban population.

Manhattan owes some of its continued supremacy in retail trade to its volume of out-of-town visitors. It was estimated in the New York Metropolitan Region Study that 5 per cent of the Metropolitan Region's retail trade stems from this source. This estimate is difficult either to substantiate or to dispute. In absolute terms, it would amount to $900 million a year, and if it be assumed that it is principally Manhattan business, it represents almost 20 per cent of Manhattan's total retail trade.

A large, but undetermined, portion of Manhattan's retail trade is in purchases by people who work in Manhattan but reside elsewhere in the Metropolitan Area. Lunch-hour shopping is an important factor in Manhattan's retail business. The actual number of employees in Manhattan's Central Business District has not grown

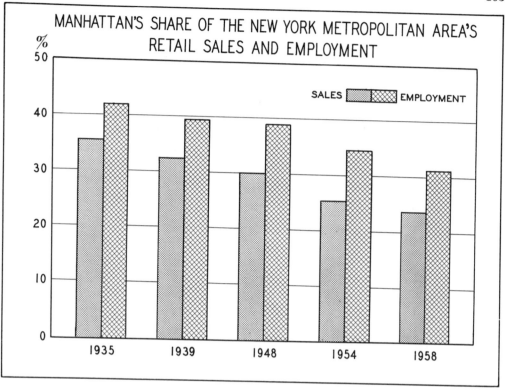

MANHATTAN'S SHARE OF THE NEW YORK METROPOLITAN AREA'S RETAIL SALES AND EMPLOYMENT

SALES ▨▨ EMPLOYMENT

1935   1939   1948   1954   1958

Fig. 2

appreciably in recent years, but their average income probably has. This is indicated by scattered statistics relating to the central administrative offices of large manufacturing companies, to wholesale trade and to a number of key service industries. Generally, there has been a tendency for the ranks of workers to become fewer in the less-skilled categories and greater in the skilled groups, thereby exerting considerable influence on the overall average income. In wholesale trade, for example, the progressive decline of goods handling in Manhattan has emphasized the role of transactional wholesaling; average annual compensation per employee in Manhattan is not only higher than wholesale trade employees in the rest of the Area, but higher than in all other major trade centers in the nation.

Also observed are a fairly sharp upswing in the well-being of lower-income groups in Manhattan and the steady increase in the number of high-income people who have been attracted to Manhattan's luxury-class residential development.

Employment in Retail Trade

The distribution of employment in the retail trades, among the metropolitan counties, has followed the same general trend observed in the distribution of sales: a relative decline in the older retailing centers, especially Manhattan and other boroughs in New York City, and growth elsewhere (see Table 3).

However, an important distinction must be made. Manhattan's share of employment has remained consistently higher than its share of sales (Fig. 2). For example, in 1958 Manhattan accounted for 23.5 per cent of the Area's retail sales, but 31.1 per cent of retail employment.

The contrast between the sales and employment shares indicates the kind of retailing dominant in Manhattan. It is "labor intensive" and stresses the service element in retailing, which is very prominent in apparel and in the specialty shops. Retailing in suburban areas is more emphasized in standardized goods. In this phase of retailing, supermarkets and other forms

of self-service have tended to reduce the amount of labor required in the sales function.

The employment trend from 1935 through 1958 indicates slowly rising employment in Manhattan, but at a rate considerably below the Area's rate of expansion. If we consider only the period since 1948, we are almost forced to the view that the future will bring about no rise in employment, and probably a decline.

As a reference point, 1948 reflects a

TABLE 3. TRENDS IN RETAIL TRADE EMPLOYMENT IN THE METROPOLITAN AREA
(employment in thousands)

	1939		1948		1958	
	Employ-ment	Per Cent	Employ-ment	Per Cent	Employ-ment	Per Cent
Metropolitan Area	490	100.0	635	100.0	723	100.0
New York sector (S.M.S.A.)	383	78.0	492	77.6	544	75.2
New York City	335	68.4	428	67.5	417	57.7
Bronx	26	5.4	38	5.9	39	5.4
Kings	66	13.4	88	13.9	85	11.8
New York	201	41.0	247	38.9	225	31.1
Queens	38	7.7	50	7.9	62	8.5
Richmond	4	0.9	5	0.9	6	0.9
Other New York	48	9.6	64	10.1	127	17.5
Nassau	15	3.0	25	3.9	60	8.3
Rockland	2	0.4	2	0.4	4	0.5
Suffolk	7	1.4	9	1.4	22	3.1
Westchester	24	4.8	28	4.4	40	5.6
New Jersey sector	107	22.0	143	22.4	179	24.8
Jersey City S.M.S.A. (Hudson)	19	3.9	23	3.5	22	3.1
Newark S.M.S.A.	56	11.5	72	11.4	86	11.8
Essex	41	8.4	50	7.8	52	7.2
Morris	4	0.9	6	1.0	9	1.3
Union	11	2.2	16	2.6	24	3.3
Paterson-Clifton-Passaic S.M.S.A.	23	4.8	34	5.3	52	7.1
Bergen	11	2.3	17	2.7	32	4.4
Passaic	12	2.5	16	2.6	19	2.7
Middlesex	7	1.4	11	1.7	16	2.2
Somerset	2	0.4	3	0.5	5	0.6

number of unusual conditions. The postwar population expansion into the outlying areas was just reaching its full force. Few of the major store relocations and expansion outside of Manhattan had yet taken place. (The shutdown of three or four major retailing establishments took place after 1948.) These relocations alone would have accounted for a large portion of a 24,000 decline in Manhattan's retail employment which took place in 1948–1954.

Also, data on employment in the retail trades must be used cautiously, for the nonfull-time component has become increasingly important and the uncritical use of *total* employment volumes, such as are presented in Table 3, tends to overstate the number of jobs which can, of themselves, support and maintain house-

holds. The ratio of part-time to total workers in retail trade in Manhattan has remained fairly stable, whereas the proportion in the other counties has increased considerably in recent years (Table 4). This reflects an important aspect of suburban retailing which, with its greater emphasis on shopping during the evening hours, draws heavily upon the services of part-time employees.

TABLE 4. PART-TIME EMPLOYEES AS PERCENTAGE OF TOTAL RETAILING EMPLOYMENT

	Manhattan	Rest of Metropolitan Area
1948	13.8	17.5
1954	14.6	18.4
1958	13.7	19.0

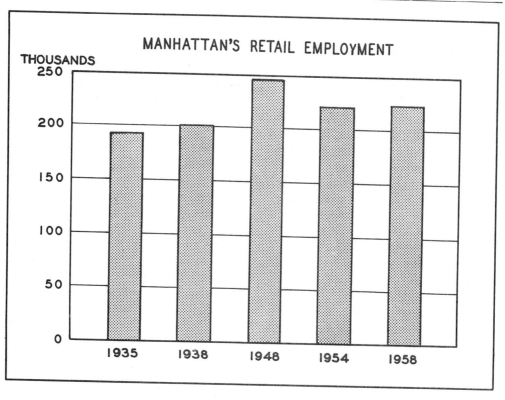

FIG. 3

In addition to the retailing employment analyzed in Table 3, there are, according to the 1958 Census of Business, 35,400 persons employed in the Area in central or administrative offices and other establishments engaged in the over-all management or supply of retail stores in multi-unit organizations. Since this represents 20 per cent of the nation's employment in such establishments, more than double New York's share of the nation's retail sales, it is evident that many of these establishments are engaged in functions which are national rather than regional in scope. The bulk of the Area's employment in this category, more than 60 per cent, is in Manhattan.

The kinds of employees represented in this aggregate are varied, ranging from warehouse workers to management personnel. The average wage of these workers is appreciably higher in Manhattan than in the other boroughs and counties, which suggests that the employment in Manhattan is mainly in central administrative functions. A large portion of the Manhattan employment consists of the personnel in buying offices of major chain organizations, many of whom have direct representation in the garment, house furnishings and housewares wholesaling districts, even though the executive offices of such buying branches may be located in other cities.

Warehousing by Retail Establishments

Warehouses maintained by multi-unit or chain retailers in the New York Area contain a total of 7.2 million square feet of net occupiable floor space (Table 5), slightly over 11 per cent of such space in the nation. In addition, chain retailers in the Area maintain about 3 million cubic feet of net cold-storage space.

The data in Table 5 are for 1954 and the amount today is probably somewhat

TABLE 5. WAREHOUSING FLOOR SPACE OF
CHAIN RETAILERS IN THE METROPOLITAN
AREA IN 1954

(thousands of square feet)

Metropolitan Area	7,242
New York sector	4,358
Bronx	674
Kings	377
New York	1,774
Queens	1,297
Nassau	236
New Jersey sector	1,884
Essex	572
Hudson	582
Middlesex	248
Union	482
Undistributed	1,000

larger. The figures do not include space rented by chains in public warehouses and cold-storage facilities.

As in wholesaling, there has been a general outward trend in the location of retailers' warehouses. This is especially true of chain food retailers, who alone account for about 40 per cent of this warehouse space.

Except for the retail organizations dealing in food lines, there has been little recent growth in retailers' warehouses. Instead, there has been a growing practice of routing furniture, appliances and other large household items directly from the factory to the consumer. In these cases, contract carriers handle consolidated shipments and either directly, or through affiliates, break bulk at and distribute out of their own terminals. There are indications that this trend is making itself felt in other lines. One large retailing chain has virtually eliminated its warehousing system and has substituted for it the direct routing of goods from point of production to individual stores.

Manhattan is probably still the largest single center for retailers' warehousing, and functions not only as a center of supply for stores located in the borough, but for others within New York's trading radius. The kinds of goods warehoused in Manhattan are closely related to the intense concentration of production and wholesaling there in dry goods, apparel, and general merchandise.

Impact of Shopping Centers on Surrounding Trade Areas

In the competitive contest with suburban shopping centers, few of the older retail districts in the Area have fared as well as Manhattan or Brooklyn. Both of these central-core retail centers showed renewed strength in the 1954–1958 period, but their smaller counterparts in the outlying parts of the Metropolitan Area were more vulnerable. There is strong evidence that the newer suburban shopping centers have arrested the development of the older shopping facilities within their own trading areas.

This may be seen in a number of communities in Nassau County; Freeport, Mineola and Rockville Centre had well-established retail shopping districts long before the major rush of population into the county following World War II. Growth of population stimulated the development of new stores and service establishments in these districts for a short period after 1945. In the middle 1950's, three major New York City department stores established branches in the county: Abraham and Straus in Hempstead, R. H. Macy in Garden City, and Gimbels in Valley Stream. The latter two became the star attractions of the Roosevelt Field and Valley Stream shopping centers, respectively. Abraham and Straus located beyond the established shopping district in Hempstead, but provided a facility es-

sentially like the large shopping centers, with extensive parking areas. An S. Klein branch store, also in Hempstead, developed along the same lines.

The results of these ventures were apparent by 1958 (Table 6). Although Hempstead, Garden City and Valley Stream enhanced their retail trading volumes by $30 million or more each, the older retail districts in the neighboring communities suffered. Freeport and Rockville Centre showed negligible gains between 1954 and 1958, while Mineola lost over $3 million in retail sales.

TABLE 6. RETAIL SALES IN SELECTED
LONG ISLAND COMMUNITIES
(thousands of dollars)

	1954	1958	Major Stores
Hempstead	$162,039	$192,931	A&S and
Garden			Klein's
City	32,287	70,814	Macy's
Valley			
Stream	47,009	82,369	Gimbels
Freeport	51,782	53,887	
Mineola	41,117	38,292	
Rockville			
Centre	53,348	53,887	

In Hempstead, the gain in sales from $162 to $192 million does not tell the full story. The gain in sales enjoyed by the Abraham and Straus and the S. Klein stores was more than $30 million, while the remainder of the shopping complex in the village of Hempstead showed declines. The older shopping sectors of Hempstead are now marked by high vacancy rates in commercial buildings.

The pattern of relative decline of retail trade in older shopping districts may also be seen in the New Jersey portion of the Metropolitan Area (Table 7). The retailing gains in the older shopping districts have been less, in all instances, than the over-all gains in their counties.

TABLE 7.   GAIN IN RETAIL SALES 1954–1958
(per cent)

County		Largest City	
Hudson	6.7	Jersey City	3.6
Passaic	16.5	Paterson	2.3
Bergen	28.3	Hackensack	5.5
Essex	8.1	Newark	2.0
Union	28.6	Elizabeth	9.0

The rise of regional shopping centers in suburban areas has had a curious multiplier effect on automobile traffic volumes. Such centers generally have drawn upon each other's respective trading areas to an extent not anticipated by their designers. Distance is no real barrier to the patron traveling by automobile, and families in great numbers have developed triangular and even more complex routing patterns in visiting various shopping centers, generating a totally disproportionate amount of travel per dollar of purchase.

In summary, regional shopping centers in the New York Metropolitan Area have had a greater effect upon the older shopping districts in suburban counties than they have had upon New York's primary Central Business District in Manhattan. They also have had the side effect of generating travel on major routes.

CONSUMER SERVICES

Closely allied to retail trade are certain consumer services: (1) personal services, ranging from laundries and dry cleaning establishments to shoe repair and funeral services; (2) automobile repair and allied services; and (3) miscellaneous repair services. These three activities in 1958 accounted for 150,000 of the Metropolitan Area's jobs and for more than $1.6 billion in business. These services, like retail trade, have tended to grow more rapidly in the outlying area than in New York City and Manhattan, although the shifts in relative strength have been moderate (Table 8).

In the personal services group there have been but minor changes in the proportions of the activity accounted for by different parts of the Area. It is somewhat surprising that Manhattan's share is as high as 27.5 per cent of the Area total, higher than its share of retail trade. The presence of a large daytime, nonresident, population, part working force, part visitor, is a strong contributive factor and an important stabilizing influence.

The shift toward the suburban counties has been more marked in the case of automobile repair and allied services. Unexpectedly, Manhattan actually increased its share of this business in the 1948–1958 decade. Its gain may be traced to huge gains in the receipts of commercial parking lots and parking garages; Manhattan now accounts for almost 60 per cent of the Metropolitan Area's parking lot receipts and slightly over 75 per cent of its parking garage receipts.

Somewhat the same pattern of distribution features the miscellaneous repair services. While Manhattan's share of the receipts in this group of services has declined rather sharply, it still commands 27.4 per cent of Metropolitan Area receipts.

THE HOTEL INDUSTRY IN THE NEW YORK AREA

New York is the nation's leading hotel center. Its 1,000 hotels contain a total of 134,000 guest rooms, and 141 hotels have 300 or more rooms. The next ranking center, Chicago, has but 61 hotels in this size group.

In 1958, New York's hotels generated $383 million in receipts, and disbursed $140 million in payrolls to 48,000 employees. A high percentage of these re-

TABLE 8. TRENDS IN THE DISTRIBUTION OF CONSUMER SERVICES RECEIPTS
IN THE METROPOLITAN AREA
(per cent of total)

	Personal Services		Automobile & Allied Services		Miscellaneous Repair Services	
	1948	1958	1948	1958	1948	1958
Metropolitan Area	100.0	100.0	100.0	100.0	100.0	100.0
New York sector (S.M.S.A.)	78.3	77.7	78.3	75.6	79.3	76.5
New York City	69.0	64.2	68.8	61.1	65.6	60.4
Bronx	8.7	7.0	9.8	6.4	9.3	7.5
Kings	20.6	18.2	19.3	11.6	14.6	14.5
New York	29.7	27.5	31.8	34.4	32.6	27.4
Queens	9.2	10.6	7.4	8.2	8.2	10.3
Richmond	0.8	0.9	0.5	0.5	0.9	0.7
Other New York	9.3	13.5	9.5	14.5	13.7	16.1
Nassau	3.1	5.9	3.2	6.8	4.0	8.5
Rockland	0.3	0.4	0.4	0.5	0.3	0.5
Suffolk	1.0	1.9	1.8	2.4	5.2	2.2
Westchester	4.9	5.3	4.1	4.8	4.2	4.9
New Jersey sector	21.7	22.3	21.7	24.4	20.7	23.5
Jersey City S.M.S.A. (Hudson)	5.1	4.3	4.0	4.0	4.1	5.0
Newark S.M.S.A.	10.2	10.5	10.6	11.8	10.2	10.8
Essex	7.4	7.0	7.3	8.0	6.8	7.3
Morris	0.6	0.8	0.8	1.1	0.6	1.1
Union	2.2	2.7	2.5	2.7	2.8	2.4
Paterson-Clifton-Passaic S.M.S.A.	5.1	5.8	4.7	6.2	4.8	6.0
Bergen	2.4	3.2	2.4	3.7	2.7	3.5
Passaic	2.7	2.6	2.3	2.5	2.1	2.5
Middlesex	1.0	1.3	1.8	1.7	1.1	1.4
Somerset	0.3	0.4	0.6	0.7	0.5	0.3

ceipts, possibly as much as 60 per cent, represents income flowing into the Region from other parts of the nation and from other countries and, therefore, contributes to the basic income of the community.

The relative level of hotel activity in New York may be taken as a composite measure of the degree to which the area is maintaining its position as the leading business, industrial, professional and cul-tural center of the nation. Further, the degree to which hotel activity remains concentrated in Manhattan indicates the degree to which the metropolitan business functions performed for the nation are resistant to the forces of dispersion.

Forces Influencing the Hotel Business

There were actually fewer hotels in op-eration in 1958 than in 1948. While annual hotel receipts during this same period grew from $2.2 to $2.8 billion, it appears that the increase resulted from higher rates rather than from increased occupancy of rooms.

The hotel business is intimately related to transportation and travel. Most hotels operating on a year-round basis are geared to provide lodging for transient guests arriving and departing by common carrier. While it is true that more people are traveling today than ever before, and traveling more frequently, these travel gains are not reflected proportionately in hotel receipts. The shift in usage of common carrier travel from rail to air during the past ten years appears to have inhibited rather than stimulated the development of the hotel trade.

Two factors in the shift of first-class travel from rail to air have had a profound influence on postwar hotel activities. One involves a change in travel habits and the other a change in the internal routing of travelers within the metropolitan area.

More and more business trips tend to be made on short notice, as the occasion requires. The speed of air travel encourages point-to-point journeys with short sojourns at place of destination, rather than itineraries composed of a number of stops. The average stay of travelers at hotels, as a consequence, has shortened and now averages less than a week, with the greatest number of visits clustering around a three- or four-day occupancy. Many journeys by air involve a return trip the same day and completely eliminate the hotel sojourn.

Rail passenger terminals play an important role in funneling travelers into central business district hotels, but downtown subterminals for air passengers are much weaker in this regard. In most large cities, including New York, the traffic through such collecting centers is a shrinking proportion of the air passenger traffic handled at field terminals. The rise of airport hotels in recent years is a manifestation of shrinking utilization of transient hotels in central business districts oriented around rail intercity transportation. Most airport hotels have a decided advantage in that they, in most cases, can also draw heavily upon the patronage of automobile travelers.

The increased use of the private automobile in intercity travel has brought in its wake a new and distinctive type of lodging, the motel. Beginning a few decades ago with "tourist rooms" and other modest establishments, sometimes but a notch or two above camping out, motels have now developed to the point where many offer the same range and quality of services as those available in hotels. The primary distinction now between the hotel and the motel is that the latter is planned and operated so as to meet the requirements of people traveling by automobile. The greatest impact of the motel has been in those metropolitan areas where recent growth has tended to diminish the influence of the central business district. In Los Angeles, for example, the motel business now accounts for more than 20 per cent of the area's hotel receipts and probably for more than a third of the area's room receipts. In Chicago, where the dispersion from the Central Business District has been of a much smaller order, the ratio of motel to hotel receipts is less than a third of the relationship observed in Los Angeles. In the New York Area, the strength of the central focus of the metropolis has been maintained to an unusual degree and the impact of motels so far has been slight. As late as 1958, total motel receipts were still less than 3 per cent of the total hotel revenues.

Trends in the New York Area. New York is one of the few major cities that has maintained a growth rate in hotel activity equal to the national rate of growth. Its share of the nation's total hotel trade in 1958, as in 1948, was just under 14 per cent. Chicago's portion of the national trade declined. Los Angeles increased its share slightly, but not at all in proportion to its massive growth in population, trade and industry. Presumably, resort hotels in smaller places have increased their business disproportionately to the national hotel business total.

Distribution of Hotels within the Area

Manhattan has maintained its dominance of the Area's hotel business, about 85 per cent of total receipts.

Outside Manhattan, the volumes of business of hotels in the Bronx and Brooklyn have shown absolute declines, while

TABLE 9. TRENDS IN HOTEL RECEIPTS IN THE METROPOLITAN AREA

(receipts in thousands of dollars)

	1948		1954		1958	
	Receipts	Per Cent	Receipts	Per Cent	Receipts	Per Cent
Metropolitan Area	$302,934	100.0	$336,457	100.0	$386,962	100.0
New York sector (S.M.S.A.)	285,805	94.3	319,338	94.9	366,653	94.8
New York City	271,003	89.5	304,520	90.5	347,657	89.8
Bronx	1,583	0.5	1,745	0.5	1,474	0.4
Kings	11,083	3.7	10,332	3.1	9,865	2.5
New York	255,305	84.3	288,468	85.7	330,280	85.4
Queens	2,953	1.0	3,896	1.2	5,996	1.5
Richmond	79	(a)	79	(a)	42	(a)
Other New York	14,802	4.8	14,818	4.4	18,996	5.0
Nassau	4,783	1.4	5,174	1.5	6,661	1.7
Rockland	2,317	0.8	1,334	0.4	3,307	0.9
Suffolk	4,483	1.5	4,920	1.5	5,249	1.4
Westchester	3,219	1.1	3,390	1.0	3,779	1.0
New Jersey sector	17,129	5.7	17,119	5.1	20,309	5.2
Jersey City S.M.S.A. (Hudson)	1,909	0.6	2,184	0.6	2,627	0.7
Newark S.M.S.A.	11,749	3.9	12,410	3.7	14,473	3.7
Essex	7,904	2.6	8,335	2.5	9,928	2.5
Morris & Union	3,845	1.3	4,075	1.2	4,545	1.2
Paterson-Clifton-Passaic S.M.S.A.	1,475	0.5	1,093	0.3	1,683	0.4
Bergen	161	0.1	67	(a)	567	0.1
Passaic	1,314	0.4	1,026	0.3	1,116	0.3
Middlesex	1,351	0.5	785	0.3	1,019	0.3
Somerset	645	0.2	647	0.2	507	0.1

a—Less than 0.05%.

Queens exhibited a slight increase. The outlying counties in the New York portion of the Metropolitan Area, Nassau, Suffolk, Westchester and Rockland counties have shown some growth, but their impact on the Area's total hotel business has been slight.

There has been little recent change in the share of the Metropolitan Area's hotel business accounted for by the New Jersey counties.

Motels in New York

Relative to the rest of the country, motels in the New York Metropolitan Area have developed late and rather slowly. As late as 1948, the total receipts of motels were slightly under $900,000, equal to about 0.3 per cent of the Area's total hotel business. In 1958, motel receipts totaled $11 million but were less than 3 per cent of the Area's total hotel receipts and considerably below the level prevailing in other large metropolitan areas. In that year motel receipts in the Chicago and Los Angeles areas accounted for 5 per cent and 21 per cent, respectively, of the total hotel business.

The sharpest growth within the New York Area, as might be expected, has taken place in the outlying counties: Bergen, Suffolk and Westchester accounted for 59 per cent of the motel business in 1958. Lesser concentrations are found in Morris and Union counties.

Surprisingly, in 1958, Manhattan accounted for 4.5 per cent of the Area's motel business. For earlier years Manhattan's motel business did not exist. Since 1958, at least six motels have either been completed or have been advanced to the active planning stage.

Future Growth

The hotel industry depends primarily for its patronage upon travelers employ-ing common carrier passenger services, particularly those who normally use first-class travel accommodations. Prior to World War II, rail Pullman services handled the greater majority of these travelers. After World War II, the balance shifted to air and today Pullman handles the smaller and a dwindling proportion of the trade.

There has been close agreement between the level of national income and the volume of first-class travel for more than 40 years, despite the fact that during that period there have been drastic changes in the use made of different modes of transportation.

Hotel patronage, on the other hand, has not kept pace with the increase in national income. Dips in national income produce declines in hotel receipts, but a rise in national income results in only a fractional hotel gain. Under these circumstances it is possible to foresee only a nominal increase in hotel patronage during our forecast period.

The forecast prepared in connection with the New York Metropolitan Region Study emphasizes growth of business services in New York City and especially in Manhattan. This optimistic outlook is predicated on New York's continued and perhaps growing dominance in the transaction phase of the nation's industry, commerce and finance, and its high ranking in a host of related activities such as headquarters for foundations, labor organizations, trade groups and professional associations. All these are potent generators of travel, especially travel into the area requiring hotel facilities.

Much of New York's existing hotel facilities will need to be replaced or modernized during the next 20 years, for a high proportion will have become obsolete. The narrowing of profit margins in hotel operations, and the consequent need for efficiently designed structures, should hasten the process of replacement. An estimate of future activity suggests that Manhattan's capacity over the next 20 years may well be increased by 10 per cent. A greater increase would not seem to be warranted because of air transportation's persistent influence in shortening the hotel visit and in eliminating some hotel business altogether.

The question remains of where in Manhattan new hotels will be established. Some replacement within the existing hotel complex may be expected. There is a strong presumption, supported by the recent construction of two large hotels west of Fifth Avenue and north of 42nd Street, that many of the new hotels will be located on the West Side of midtown Manhattan. If past trends and current schemes are any guide, it is to be expected that new hotels will tend to group themselves around the bus and air terminals on the West Side.

If intercity short-haul rail passenger service should continue to deteriorate, a service gap which neither air nor bus transport can fill satisfactorily will widen, and may force much of the business travel from cities lying within a 300-mile radius into private automobile transport. Existing hotels are poorly arranged to accommodate it. A motor hotel complex has already begun to develop on the West Side, with built-in parking for private automobiles and prime access to the Lincoln Tunnel. The potential for future growth is of a high order.

Because of the abundance of open land available in Staten Island and the prospect of new major highway connection with the Narrows Bridge, an unusual rate of growth of motor hotels may be expected for that borough. Its location benefits from being in an area providing a convenient break in the stages of the mo-

tor journey, and will have the advantage of superior access to Long Island and New England.

The continued concentration of business headquarters and essential business services in the New York portion of the Metropolitan Area argues that no more than replacement or modernization of existing hotels will be required in the New Jersey counties. It is more likely that motor hotels, rather than hotels, will develop in this area.

THE BUSINESS AND PROFESSIONAL SERVICES

There is another category of economic activity which is important in a study directed toward estimating the transportation requirements in the future. It is the group of activities which may be termed the business and professional services. They encompass a broad range, from corporate headquarters functions through professional and consulting services of specialized natures, to advertising.

The category is important for two principal reasons. First, it looms large in the economic base of the New York Metropolitan Area, both in the amount of regional income it generates and in its contribution to regional employment. Along with financial activities, it is a clear reflection of the Area's status as the nation's economic nerve center. The economic well-being of the Metropolitan Area in the future is closely bound up with the prospective growth or decline in its strength in national economic leadership.

Second, from a strictly transportation point of view, the business services have a strong affinity for a Central Business District base. Consequently, future levels of activity will exert powerful leverage on the volume of core-directed travel. In the past these services have been and in the future will continue to be the primary market for mass passenger transportation service. The New York Metropolitan Region Study estimated that in 1956 a total of 978,000 persons were employed in this broad group of services.

Administrative or
Central Office Employment

The New York Metropolitan Region Study estimated that the regional employment in this class of economic activity was about 170,000 in 1956, but there are no firm, comprehensive data available for analysis. An important segment, however, is capable of study, for the 1958 Census of Manufactures provides data on

manufacturing industries' employment in administrative and auxiliary establishments located away from production facilities. The data give some important clues as to growth potential of central offices in the New York Area.

For the nation as a whole, employment in such establishments in 1958 was slightly under 500,000 (Table 10). Employment growth has been fairly sluggish, increasing by only 3.8 per cent over 1954. The New York Metropolitan Area contained some 125,000 or 25 per cent of the nation's jobs in this category, an impressive gain, 17 per cent, over 1954. The remainder of the nation's employment was widely scattered. Detroit accounted for 12.9 per cent

TABLE 10. ADMINISTRATIVE EMPLOYMENT IN THE MANUFACTURING INDUSTRIES
IN THE NATION AND IN 15 LEADING METROPOLITAN AREAS: 1954 AND 1958

	1954		1958		
	Employees	Per Cent of Nation	Employees	Per Cent of Nation	Per Cent Change
Nation	474,000	100.0	492,000	100.0	3.8
New York Area	106,432	22.5	124,526	25.3	17.0
New York sector	86,586	18.3	100,601	20.4	16.2
New Jersey sector	19,846	4.2	23,925	4.9	20.6
Detroit	52,209	11.0	63,493	12.9	21.6
Chicago–Gary–Hammond–E. Chicago	40,952	8.6	41,477	8.4	1.3
Pittsburgh	28,162	5.9	34,077	6.9	21.0
Philadelphia	17,130	3.6	20,608	4.2	20.3
Wilmington	15,170	3.2	17,321	3.5	14.2
Boston	a		15,341	3.1	
San Francisco–Oakland	13,071	2.8	12,962	2.6	−0.8
Los Angeles–Long Beach	7,282	1.5	12,513	2.5	71.8
St. Louis	a		11,792	2.4	
Cleveland	10,677	2.3	11,017	2.2	3.2
Albany–Schenectady–Troy	9,901	2.1	10,591	2.2	7.0
Minneapolis–St. Paul	a		8,823	1.8	
Cincinnati	2,964	0.6	6,238	1.3	110.5
Allentown–Bethlehem–Easton	3,943	0.8	5,574	1.1	41.4

aNot available.

TABLE 11. BUSINESS SERVICES EMPLOYMENT IN THE METROPOLITAN AREA
1948 AND 1958

	1948		1958	
	Employment	Per Cent	Employment	Per Cent
Metropolitan Area	74,821	100.0	152,849	100.0
New York sector (S.M.S.A.)	70,433	94.1	134,696	88.1
New York City	69,353	92.7	124,931	81.7
Bronx	1,096	1.5	1,626	1.1
Kings	2,553	3.4	4,878	3.2
New York	64,316	85.9	112,553	73.6
Queens	1,342	1.8	5,532	3.6
Richmond	46	0.1	342	0.2
Other New York	1,080	1.4	9,765	6.4
Nassau	611	0.7	5,579	3.7
Rockland	b	b	130	a
Suffolk	38	0.1	589	0.4
Westchester	431	0.6	3,467	2.3
New Jersey sector	4,388	5.9	18,153	11.9
Jersey City S.M.S.A. (Hudson)	791	1.1	2,294	1.6
Newark S.M.S.A.	2,859	3.8	10,412	6.8
Essex	2,341	3.1	7,668	5.0
Morris	118	0.2	959	0.6
Union	400	0.5	1,785	1.2
Paterson–Clifton–Passaic S.M.S.A.	609	0.8	4,572	3.0
Bergen	335	0.4	3,145	2.1
Passaic	274	0.4	1.427	0.9
Middlesex	129	0.2	825	0.5
Somerset	b	b	50	a

aLess than 0.05 per cent.
bData not available for Rockland and Somerset for the year 1948.

and Chicago for 8.4 per cent. Although the Los Angeles area showed a sharp growth rate over 1954, its 1958 share of the nation was still only 2.5 per cent. It appears that few cities can challenge New York in this sphere. In a period of modest national growth, New York's gain in four years exceeded the total employment in this field of Boston, Los Angeles, San Francisco and Cleveland. Most of this employment was located on the New York side of the Area, which accounted for 101,000 of the 125,000 Area total.

Although employment in administrative and auxiliary establishments of manufacturers is predominantly clerical, a heavy weighting by management and executive personnel raises the average annual expenditure for wages and salaries per employee to unusually high levels. In the New York Area the average annual wage for 1958 was $8,000, and in the New York portion even higher, $8,200, the highest in the nation. In New Jersey the average wage was lower. It is likely that the kinds of functions performed in New Jersey are less in administrative activities and tend to fall in the general category of regional establishments maintained by manufacturers for servicing their products.

Miscellaneous Business Services

Among the service industries in the Metropolitan Area, those geared to the business client have shown the sharpest rate of growth. They include advertising, dominantly, plus a broad array of activities including business management and consulting services, news syndicates, detective agencies, duplicating, mailing and stenographic services. During 1948–1958 the total employment in business services rose from about 75,000 to 153,-000 in the Metropolitan Area (Table 11) in contrast to the other services which showed only modest gains during this same period.

The total volume of receipts from the business services in the New York Metropolitan Area in 1958 amounted to $3.2 billion. Manhattan accounted for $2.8 billion or 87 per cent of these receipts.

During 1948–1958, employment in the business services in the New York Area more than doubled. All counties participated in the growth. Noteworthy is the threefold rise of employment in the New Jersey portion of the Area.

Many of these services are of the type which provide important "external economies" to industrial and commercial enterprises located in the Metropolitan Area. While more and more of them are becoming available in the outlying counties, in

no one locale or major sector of the Area do they approach the array of services that are available in Manhattan. More than one company in relocating its headquarters outside of Manhattan has found that the expense of providing its own services, or the inconvenience of delays in securing them from a distant center, more than outweigh lower rentals and other advantages expected in suburban locations.

The nature of most of these services is such that they tend to concentrate in Manhattan. Among them, advertising and business management and consulting services, merit further discussion.

Advertising

The nation's expenditures for advertising have expanded enormously during the past 20 years, from slightly under $2 billion in 1939 to $10.3 billion in 1957.

The New York Area is the leading center in the nation for advertising. Receipts of advertising agencies in the Metropolitan Area in 1958 amounted to more than $2 billion, which represented more than 42 per cent of the national total. The next ranking centers, Chicago and Los Angeles, with 14.7 and 5.3 per cent of the nation's advertising business, respectively, have not seriously challenged New York's commanding position.

A number of influences have contributed toward maintaining New York's dominance during this period of expansion. Increased entry by manufacturers into national marketing programs during the postwar period has been conducive to the centralization of advertising functions. The growth of media such as magazines and television which are national in coverage has been a powerful inducement for producers to expand from regional to national markets.

In 1954–1958 there was phenomenal growth for the Metropolitan Area, with advertising agency receipts rising from $1.5 billion to $2.1 billion, a gain of 25 per cent. Manhattan has accounted for nearly all of the agency business in the Area, up to 97 per cent, for a number of years. In 1958 advertising agencies in the Area expended $257 million for salaries and wages, an increase of more than $80 million over 1954. An increase of similar magnitude took place in the volume of employment, which rose from 24,778 in 1948 to 36,560 in 1958. Paralleling its overwhelming share of Area advertising business, Manhattan has accounted for 96 to 97 per cent of Area payrolls and employment, and there is no evidence to cause doubt as to its continuing dominance.

The potency of advertising as an economic force in Manhattan may be gauged by a few comparisons. Advertising's annual payroll is two and one-half times that of all automotive repair services and garages, including parking lots, parking garages and auto laundries, in the Metropolitan Area. In dollar volume of business the ratio is 7 to 1 in favor of advertising. Although hotels and motels in the Area employ more than 50,000, their total annual payroll falls $74 million shy of the wages and salaries paid to the 36,560 in advertising.

A realty company prominent in leasing space to Manhattan advertising agencies states that of the 32 large agencies in the country having billings of over $25 million annually, 31 have offices in New York City. They occupy a total of 2,131,000 square feet of office space.[1]

Advertising is of special interest in a study of the Metropolitan Area's economy, for it is not only large in its own right but, like finance, it necessitates frequent face-to-face contacts in carrying out transac-

[1]Julian J. Studley, Inc. cited in *Editor and Publisher,* July 5, 1957.

tions. The rise or decline of advertising in Manhattan can be an indicator of any changes in the strength of the Metropolitan Area's position as the nation's business headquarters.

Business Management and Consulting Services

There is another mixed bundle of activities which reach a high degree of concentration in the New York Metropolitan Area, particularly Manhattan. It includes establishments engaged in business analysis and research, efficiency engineering, fashion and package designing, industrial management, market research, personnel management, public relations, sales engineering and statistical and allied services.

The receipts of establishments in this service group amounted to almost one-quarter of a billion dollars in 1958, and employment was just under 15,000. Manhattan is the focal point of this activity and accounts for 82 per cent of the Area's receipts and payrolls. Although about 7 per cent of the Area's receipts have originated in the Newark area, there is little indication that this is the type of activity which tends to suburbanize. The only other counties with significant shares of the Area's activity are Westchester with 3 per cent and Nassau with 2.5 per cent.

The New York Metropolitan Area accounts for a high share of the nation's activity in this sphere, about a third. The outlook for this kind of economic activity depends primarily on the degree to which the New York Metropolitan Area continues to attract corporation headquarters and on the degree to which these corporations seek outside services.

The industry is highly productive; average annual wage per employee, including casuals, is about $6,200, and the volume of receipts per employee is an extraordinary $14,500.

The Financial Services

For more than a century New York has been the financial capital of the United States. There is little to suggest that it is in any danger of losing its pre-eminent status in the foreseeable future.

The New York Metropolitan Region Study has made a thorough exploration of the history and future prospects of the financial services provided here and we can do no better at this point than to present a brief account of their findings.[2]

The financial services, as treated in the New York Metropolitan Region Study are made up of five major groups, employing in 1956 a total of 311,700 persons (Table 12).

TABLE 12. Employment in
Financial Services in the New York
Metropolitan Region

(in thousands)

	Number	Per Cent Distribution
All Services	311.7	100.0
Commercial Banking	82.3	26.4
Life, Accident, Health Insurance	83.2	26.7
Property Insurance	72.6	23.3
Securities	38.1	12.2
Miscellaneous Financial Institutions	35.5	11.4

Except in the securities field, the gain of the New York Region in financial employment fell below the growth rate of the nation as a whole during the 1947 to 1956 period. As a result, the Region's share of national financial employment dropped from 18.6 per cent in 1947 to 16.1 per cent in 1956.

New York City's financial employment, while growing from 192,800 to 240,700

during 1947–1956, nevertheless declined as a share of the Region. The decline in share position from 79 to 77.2 per cent during this period was due almost entirely to geographic shifts in commercial banking employment. In all other important sectors New York City gained in relative position.

The estimates of future employment look to a growth in employment in the Region's financial services from 311,700 in 1956 to 537,100 in 1985, a truly substantial gain but a rate of increase below that projected for the nation. Is this relative decline to be taken as a sign of future weakening of New York as the nation's money market? The authors,[3] after examining a number of possibilities, dismiss all but one:

"The force with the best chance of setting off a chain reaction is economics — just as it was 125 years ago. Should the economic base of outside areas continue to develop faster than that of New York, the banks in these places would eventually become more formidable challengers. At some critical point in size, one of the new banking clusters might be in a position to establish its own trading desks, undertake more extensive investments, begin to assume greater responsibility in advising its correspondents, and generally spread its influence in the nation. The accumulation of substantial funds in this new center would attract representatives of New York securities houses. The importance of having the trader at the salesman's elbow, and the economies realized through reaching price decisions in proximity to major buying and selling interests, could lead to an increasing number of local dealers and could break down New York's trading dominance.

"But our guess is that the New York money market is too firmly entrenched to

[2]See Robbins and Terleckyj, *Money Metropolis,* Harvard University Press, 1960.

[3]*Ibid.*

be jarred loose within the next quarter-century. Though the economic importance of the New York area may decline relative to that of other areas in the aggregate, no believable projection that we have tested brings any other single locality within challenging distance of New York during the period of our forecast."

As for the future distribution of financial employment within the region, a higher rate of growth outside New York City is foreseen, bringing about a relative decline of substantial proportions in the city's share (Table 13) in all but the securities phase.

Lying behind this shift is the assumption that the consumer-oriented activities rather than the money-market participants will be responsible for the larger portion of the growth in financial employment, and like all consumer-generated

TABLE 13. NEW YORK CITY'S SHARE OF REGIONAL FINANCIAL EMPLOYMENT

1956 (actual)	77.2%
1965	71.8
1975	68.4
1985	64.9

employment will follow the path of population expansion.

Manhattan is expected to maintain its dominant position as the center of the city's financial employment. However, the proportioning of financial employment between downtown (below Chambers Street) and the area between Chambers and 60th Streets, is expected to change, with relatively greater increase in the uptown area.

CHAPTER 8

TECHNOLOGICAL DEVELOPMENTS IN TRANSPORTATION

Advances in science and technology have drastically transformed the mode of human existence in all but the most remote and undeveloped regions of the earth. Methods of transportation have not escaped their impact, and seem unlikely to do so in the future.

The wooden sailing vessel reached its zenith about a hundred years ago, crowning several thousand years of useful and productive service to mankind. By 1900 the steel-hulled steamship had successfully pre-empted its position. Today, aircraft handle more than 80 per cent of the overseas passenger traffic. Similarly, the stagecoach yielded to the railroad during the second half of the nineteenth century. Though reaching a peak of 891,000,000 passengers carried in 1945, American railroads have, in turn, had to make way for the motorbus, the airplane and the automobile. In the early 1800's the world's speed record was held by a man on horseback. In 1961, man orbited the earth at better than 17,000 miles per hour. In view of the increasing pace of change over the last century, what can we expect in the next 20 years?

Major technical innovations most often make their initial appearance in a highly imperfect state. The first heavier-than-air flight, in 1903, covered some 120 feet in 12 seconds. A later flight on the same day stretched this achievement to 852 feet, but still at an average speed under 15 miles per hour. Some ten years earlier, the New York Central had run its Empire State Express over a measured mile at 112.5 miles per hour. About 20 more years were to

pass before the airplane was to capture the speed record. In 1910, the *Scientific American* editorialized, "To affirm that the airplane is going to revolutionize the future is to be guilty of the wildest exaggeration."

Once born, a technological innovation faces a future governed by an array of economic, social and psychological forces as well as by the inherent technical development problems. The degree of refinement to which an innovation will eventually be developed will also depend on when a succeeding one appears and the extent to which that innovation fulfills a significant portion of its predecessor's function. There can be a shift in technical and economic interest to the promising newcomer, and a consequent tapering off of effort on the earlier development. To complicate matters further, there will often be several competitors for the same functional area, each in a different stage of its development cycle.

The following speculations as to technological advances in transportation during the next 20 years must be regarded as highly selective. We can expect that the accelerating rate of scientific and technical progress will create a number of innovations which cannot now be foreseen, but which will significantly alter transportation practices. The jet airliner made its appearance before the jet engine was ten years old, and another ten years brought almost universal acceptance.

In general, technological advances which consist primarily of further refinement or modification of well-established modes of transport are excluded in this discussion.

The point of view expressed herein is that of 1962.

MOTIVE POWER
AND ENERGY CONVERSION

All forms of transportation require some means of propulsion. A certain amount of mechanical work must be performed to move a pound of matter from one place to another. The rate at which this work is performed and the manner in which it must be produced depend on the speed and the form of transport. Horsepower per net ton of payload ranges from 0.2 for a six-barge tow in river transport to 800 or more for an all-cargo airplane. The energy used for these purposes must be converted from the form in which it is found in nature to the form in which it can be used for motive power. There are a number of current developments in this field.

Solar Energy

Almost all of the energy now used by man is derived indirectly from the sun. Interest in space flight has spurred increased efforts to develop efficient means of converting the radiant energy from the sun directly into electrical or mechanical energy. Although sunlight is free, the equipment required to collect and convert it into another form of energy is not. Immediately outside the earth's atmosphere the incident energy of sunlight is in the neighborhood of 130 watts per square foot. It is possible in that remote location to collect almost 2 horsepower on 10 square feet of collector surface. However, the net output from the collection and energy-conversion system will be dependent upon its over-all efficiency which, with known techniques, could range from 10 to 40 per cent.

Though high-efficiency systems may be obtained for space applications, it is unlikely that such devices will be used to provide motive power for transportation systems at or near the earth's surface. Energy from the sun is attenuated by the atmosphere to a value of about 80 watts per square foot. Even if an over-all efficiency of 100 per cent could be achieved, an output of 100 horsepower would require a collection surface about 20 feet wide by 50 feet long. Because of the intermittent availability of direct sunlight an energy storage system would also be required.

Atomic Energy

There are two known methods of extracting energy from the atomic nucleus — fission and fusion. In the first, atoms of heavy elements are split into atoms and fragments of lighter elements whose combined mass is less than that of the original atoms, and the decrease in mass results in energy release. In the second, atoms of light elements are combined into atoms of heavier elements whose mass is also less than the combined mass of the original atoms. The difference in mass again appears as energy.

In each case, the mass converted into energy is a tiny fraction of the total mass involved in the reaction. This percentage is greater for the fusion than for the fission reaction, however, and the energy released is approximately a thousand times larger. Extremely high temperatures (on the order of 20 million degrees) are presently required to initiate the fusion reaction, and it is now usually termed "thermonuclear."

Fission Energy. The fission process is accompanied by intense release of radioactivity which requires heavy shielding, complicated and cumbersome handling and control systems, and elaborate safety precautions. Moreover, uranium, the only element presently suitable for use in producing fuels which will sustain the required chain reaction, is relatively rare and expensive.

Several years ago, the Atomic Energy Commission instituted a program of cooperative effort with industry to make the cost of electricity generated from atomic fuels competitive by 1968 with that generated from fossil fuels in high-fuel-cost areas (over 35 cents per million BTU). A number of nuclear power plants are under construction, a few are in operation and others in the planning stage. It now appears, however, that the basic objective may not be met on the proposed time scale. As a result few new plants are presently being started. This situation will probably continue until the cost of such plants is brought to a lower level by further research.

We may be well into the 1970's before nuclear-fueled central-station power plants can compete effectively on a broad scale with high-cost-area fossil-fueled stations.[1] It thus seems unlikely that the cost of centrally generated electricity will be markedly reduced before 1980 through the use of fission energy. Hence, during this period, transportation systems using electric power for propulsion are likely to remain largely unaffected by the advent of atomic energy.

Fission reactors have, of course, been used with considerable success in submarines, and there has been discussion of cargo-carrying nuclear submarines operating under the polar icecap. Although studies have been made, no such submarines seem to be under development or in the serious planning stage. It is not likely that they will appear within the time period we are discussing. The ability to remain submerged for long periods yields a purely military advantage to the nuclear submarine which transcends other considerations. Viewed as a commercially competitive device, though, it is subject to the same type of economic problems discussed above, which are further aggravated by the compactness of design required. It is doubtful that cargo submarines sliding under the icecap could compete economically with cargo aircraft flying over it.

The Maritime Administration has sponsored the construction of a nuclear-powered cargo vessel, the *Savannah*. This ship was fueled in the latter part of 1961, and it is expected that it will complete its sea trials and enter semicommercial service in 1963. The Maritime Administration has plans to initiate a cooperative program with the maritime industry for a more advanced nuclear ship to become operational in 1965.

The extent to which this program is carried out will no doubt depend largely on the results obtained from the *Savannah*. The *Savannah* is not expected to be economically competitive with conventional vessels, but will serve to explore the problems and ramifications associated with nuclear cargo craft. As in the case of central-station power plants it is unlikely that economical operation sufficient to provide a significant reduction in shipping rates can be achieved by 1980.[2]

When, and if, nuclear cargo vessels become an important part of our merchant fleet some specialized port facilities may be required. An alternative presently under consideration is that of providing lighterage service to an offshore anchorage.

After ten years of effort the military

---

[1] In some other countries, where fossil fuels are much costlier than in the United States, a competitive situation may appear earlier.

[2] The *Savannah's* namesake was the first steamship to cross the Atlantic (1819). She also was not economically competitive, for the burden of power plant and fuel left little capacity for cargo. It was not until 1871 that regular scheduled transatlantic steamship service materialized.

nuclear-aircraft program was abandoned before the flight stage was reached. It appears that the prospective military advantages to be gained were not sufficient to offset the difficulties encountered. Because of the enormous development costs, no commercial craft will be developed without a military predecessor, and therefore we can safely eliminate the commercial nuclear airplane from consideration for this time period.

Fusion Energy. All of the power reactors so far considered are based on the fission process. The fusion reaction promises much higher energy release from cheaper and more abundant fuels, with greatly reduced attendant radioactivity. There is also a possibility that electrical energy can be generated directly from the reaction, without an intervening heat-cycle and its inescapable energy losses and associated machinery. The technical problems involved in developing the fusion-power reactor, however, are formidable. These arise largely from the extreme temperatures involved, which are approximately those existing in the center of the sun. Several concerted and expensive attempts have been made to achieve a developmental breakthrough in fusion reactor design, but the fundamental processes involved are not yet sufficiently understood. Although controlled thermonuclear reactions have been sustained for a fraction of a second, it appears that more basic research is needed before a workable design can be evolved.

Should feasibility be established in the near future, another five years could see prototype power reactors in operation with wider use developing in another ten. Hence a breakthrough in this area could have a salutary effect on most of the transportation applications of nuclear energy.

Radionuclides. The radioactive decay of unstable isotopes is accompanied by the release of energy by radiation. Much of this energy can be absorbed and converted into heat through sealing the decaying material in a properly designed container. The heat thus generated can then be converted into mechanical or electrical energy as appropriate. Interest in this form of power generation comes primarily from the need for a long-lived source of power in circumstances where refueling and maintenance are extremely difficult, if not impossible.

Isotope-fueled power generators have been used in the Transit navigation-satellite system and in a remote unattended weather station installed in the Arctic. Some of the radioisotopes useful for this purpose are by-products of the fission reaction, and have been considered as waste heretofore. Others have been developed by exposing stable elements to high-intensity neutron radiation. The Transit system employs Plutonium-238, obtained by the latter process, and the weather station is powered by Strontium-90, a fission product.

The energy available from such a source is continuous but diminishes in a steady, predictable manner. Plutonium-238 has a half-life of about 86 years, Strontium-90 a half-life of about 28 years. There are, of course, other isotopes available with a wide spectrum of characteristics.

For use in the noncontinuous fashion necessary to most transportation vehicles, provision would have to be made for energy storage during periods when full power is not required or for the disposal of large amounts of waste energy. Coupled with the necessary safety precautions, this characteristic probably makes impracticable such power plants in terrestrial transportation systems of commercial interest during the time period under discussion.

This technology is quite young, however (the first practical isotopic power generator, SNAP-3, was unveiled in 1959), and its future is difficult to predict.

Heat Engines

Heat engines convert heat into mechanical energy. Steam engines, steam turbines, gas engines, diesel engines, gas turbines, rocket engines and the common automobile power plant (the Otto engine) — all fall in this category. The variations in mechanical arrangement, refinement and modification of these basic types are endless, and there are rotary combustion engines, free-piston gas generators coupled to gas turbines, compound engines, and gas turbines with regenerators and intercoolers.

In general, the more efficient such devices are, the heavier and more complicated they are. Conversely, simplicity and light weight are not usually accompanied by high efficiencies. Near one end of this spectrum is the simple gas turbine, which is distinguished by low weight per horsepower, compactness and functional simplicity, but which has an efficiency that is relatively low under usual circumstances. Near the other end of the spectrum lies the Stirling air engine with perhaps the highest basic efficiency, but which tends to be heavy and complex.

Gas Turbine. Gas turbines came into commercial use in the 1930's, largely for special applications utilizing waste heat in oil refineries, or as peak-load power plants in central generating stations. It is as an aircraft power plant, however, that the gas turbine has really come into its own. In addition to the basic advantage of low weight-per-horsepower, so vital to aircraft design, the over-all efficiency of the gas turbine is helped by the cold air found at high altitudes and by the precompression of the intake air developed by the ram effect at high speeds. Moreover, its natural

mechanical configuration lends itself to low-drag aerodynamic design. It seems probable that the gas turbine will continue to serve as the primary power plant for transport aircraft throughout the next two decades.

Its turboprop, turbofan and turbojet versions tend to overlap somewhat in application. However, the turboprop is best suited to low-speed aircraft, such as all-cargo carriers, and the turbojet is more generally suitable for higher speeds. The turbofan can also be competitive in each of these areas, depending on the specific design.

A great deal of attention has been paid to the use of gas-turbine power plants for ground transportation, and experimental gas-turbine locomotives, automobiles and motor trucks have been built. The turbine's efficiency for such applications can be improved through the addition of intercoolers and regenerators, but these additions operate against its weight advantage.

The functional simplicity of the gas turbine is somewhat misleading, for a large number of precision parts must be made and assembled and many of these are formed from expensive alloys. As a result its manufacturing costs are high. It is not likely that this type of power plant will replace the diesel engine for locomotive use.

When considered as a potential automobile power plant, the gas turbine suffers a further disadvantage in that it has an inherent tendency toward lowered efficiency in small sizes. Moreover, its efficiency is generally poorer at the part-load condition where the automobile so frequently operates. Except for its relative freedom from vibration and cold weather starting problems, the gas turbine seems to offer little practical advantage as an automobile power plant. It is possible, nevertheless, that gas-turbine automobiles would receive a certain amount of consumer acceptance because of their novelty value.

The high power-to-weight ratio of the simple gas turbine is more attractive for a truck or bus power plant, as the weight and space saved represent payload gained, and it may have considerable usage in this capacity by 1980.

The compactness and light weight of the gas turbine also make it an attractive power plant for hydrofoil vessels and for ground-effect machines, to be discussed later.

Stirling Engine. The Stirling engine is a rather complicated reciprocating engine requiring two pistons per cylinder and employing a sealed-in working fluid such as air or hydrogen, which is passed back and forth through a regenerator during the working cycle.

Heat is transferred to the working fluid from an external source, and no combustion takes place inside the cylinder. It was invented by the Reverend Robert Stirling in Scotland in 1816. This was several decades before it was known that heat energy and mechanical energy could be equated, and Stirling did not understand that the work output from his engine was provided by the heat added. It was quiet in operation, however, and did not require a steam boiler, so thousands of them were built. Although the engine is based on a thermodynamic cycle of high efficiency, the early engines were so crude in design that the inherent efficiency was not realized, and they became virtually extinct by 1939.

In recent years interest has revived in this type of power plant and, with the application of modern technology, efficiencies as high as 40 per cent have been achieved. The engine is still much heavier than the conventional gasoline (Otto cycle) engine, though its efficiency is ap-

proximately twice as high. It may be that further development of the Stirling engine will result in its use in some transportation vehicles where economy of fuel consumption is considerably more important than weight or complexity. However, it seems more likely that such application may be captured by some other device, such as the fuel cell.

Rocket Engine. The rocket engine produces a direct thrust from the high-velocity expulsion of the products of combustion of a fuel and an oxidizer, both of which must be carried by the propelled vehicle. The combustion is carried out at elevated pressures and temperatures, and a high rate of energy release is obtained. The Saturn booster being developed to a thrust of 1.5 million pounds produces 33 million horsepower in a space about twice the size of a railroad locomotive.

The rocket engine is thus in a class by itself in terms of power-to-weight ratio. Moreover, its operation does not depend on the use of oxygen from the atmosphere. These characteristics ideally suit it for space vehicle and satellite applications, where it will see considerable service during the period under discussion. It is not well fitted for terrestrial and atmospheric applications, however, as it is an inefficient form of propulsion at low (aircraft) speeds, and requires the carrying of an oxidizer as well as fuel, even where atmospheric oxygen is available.

Direct Conversion of Chemical Energy into Electrical Energy: The Fuel Cell

Today most of the energy used by man is made available through the oxidation of fossil fuels (wood, coal, petroleum, gas, etc.) by chemical reaction in the combustion process. The heat generated is converted to mechanical energy by a heat engine, as discussed above. If electrical energy is desired, an electrical generator is used to convert the mechanical energy.

Means have long been available for converting chemical energy directly into electrical energy. The simplest direct conversion device is the dry-cell battery. The storage battery has a longer life but must be periodically recharged by an electrical input to restore its electrical potential. The fuel cell makes use of the same basic electrochemical principle but is designed so that the production of power can be continuous through additions of fuel and oxidant (which can be air, as in the normal combustion process).

The fuel cell offers the prospect of high efficiencies. Values as high as 80 per cent have been attained experimentally, and values approaching 100 per cent are theoretically possible. When coupled to an electric motor, the over-all efficiency of the combination promises to be three to four times as high as that of the typical gasoline engine and two to three times that of the diesel engine. When this advantage is coupled with its quietness of operation and lack of noxious exhaust products the future of the fuel cell seems attractive. There are presently a large variety of projects under way in an effort to reduce cost and size and to seek methods of utilizing readily available hydrocarbon fuels.

It seems highly likely that the fuel cell will see intensive development, which should result in practical power plants for many uses in land and sea transportation. It may even stimulate the return of the electric automobile. The combination of fuel cell and electric motor, however, is relatively high in weight per horsepower and would not appear to be suitable for applications where this is of great importance, such as in air transportation.

Direct Conversion of Heat to Electricity

Thermoelectric Generators. In 1821, a German physicist, Thomas Seebeck, discovered that an electric current will flow between two junctions of dissimilar metals if one of the junctions is hotter than the other. This phenomenon has long been used as a means of temperature measurement, in the form of the thermocouple. The possibility of generating significant amounts of electric power in this manner has risen only recently with the availability of new materials such as the lead, bismuth and germanium tellurides, which have low electrical resistance but high thermal resistance. The phenomenon is also reversible; by applying electric power, a temperature difference can be created between the two junctions, yielding a heat pump.

The thermoelectric generator is simple and reliable, but it has so far been limited in efficiency to values of 5 or 6 per cent and to heat sources no hotter than 1,100 or 1,200 degrees. It would seem to have potential applications where waste heat is available, or where silent operation, reliability or other factors outweigh efficiency considerations.

Thermionic Generators. Another means of generating electricity from heat energy is the thermionic generator. As in the case of the thermoelectric generator, the basic principle is not new. It is known as the Edison effect, for Thomas A. Edison patented a device of this sort in 1883.

The thermionic generator employs a high temperature cathode emitting electrons, which are collected on a colder anode. The temperatures employed are in the neighborhood of 3,000 to 4,000 degrees, and efficiencies in the neighborhood of 10 per cent have been obtained. These factors tend to limit the thermionic generator to relatively specialized applications, although further develop-

ment may considerably broaden its range
of usefulness.

Both thermionic and thermoelectric
generators lend themselves to use with
isotopic heat sources to provide a compact
and reliable power unit. Such units are
discussed above.

Magnetohydrodynamic Generators.
The magnetohydrodynamic generator offers yet another method of converting
heat into electricity, which can be utilized
in combination with a conventional heat-
engine cycle. In this device a flow of
ionized gases at high temperatures (over
4,000 degrees) is directed through a magnetic field. The ionized gas fills the same
role as the armature windings in an electric generator; the cutting of the magnetic
lines of force creates a flow of electric
current in the conducting gas.

After the hot gases have passed through
the magnetohydrodynamic generator,
much of the remaining heat energy can
be extracted by a standard heat-engine
cycle, such as a boiler and steam turbine
combination. In this way it appears that
over-all efficiencies in the neighborhood
of 50 to 60 per cent can be attained, which
could make this type of power generation
highly attractive for central power station
use.

TRANSPORTATION VEHICLES

Space Vehicles and Satellites

It is scarcely five years since the space
age was dramatically opened with the
launching of Sputnik I. In this brief
period, remarkable progress has been
achieved, spurred by intense rivalry between East and West and large-scale
commitment of national resources on
both sides.

Well over 50 satellites have been
launched, a deep-space probe has trans-
mitted data to earth from a distance of

22.5 million miles, there have been six
manned orbital flights, most of the far side
of the moon has been photographed, a
lunar impact has been accomplished, and
a reflecting satellite has been used for
transatlantic two-way voice transmission
and facsimile transmission of photographs
and letters.

Work in process includes an orbiting
geophysical observatory, an orbiting solar
observatory, an orbiting astronomical observatory, more manned orbital flights,
further lunar exploration culminating in
manned operations, Mars and Venus
fly-bys, and more advanced navigation,
communication and weather satellites.

These spectacular accomplishments
may seem to have little relevance to the
transportation tasks of the New York–
New Jersey Metropolitan Region, but
who can say what will be relevant by
1980? Both the automobile and the airplane appeared first as super sporting
goods items.

Some things are already reasonably
clear. Greatly improved world-wide
weather forecasting will be available and
of benefit to all forms of transportation.
Better understanding of weather processes may lead to a measure of weather
control, such as intervention in hurri-
cane formation. Communication satellites
(such as Telstar, successfully orbited in
July 1962) can greatly increase the available number of intercontinental communication channels, with improved and more
reliable transmission. These satellites
should provide high fidelity facsimile,
data and television transmission, which
may in some areas substitute for transportation of goods and people. Navigation should become more precise and
more nearly automatic through the use of
navigation satellites and more detailed
and accurate geodetic and geographic
information.

Supersonic Aircraft

The next two decades may possibly see the development and use of supersonic passenger transport, particularly for long-distance transocean traffic. Although the technical problems associated with this development are challenging, they are by no means insurmountable (supersonic military aircraft have been in use for some years), and the major obstacles are the financial and noise problems.

The development cost is beyond that which can be handled through private financing, and will have to be obtained in whole or in part from federal government sources. Moreover, the unit price may well be four or five times that of present-day jet transports. The development and use of an American supersonic transport will have to await solution of the basic financial problem, and may hence lag some years behind its introduction elsewhere. Unless supersonic passenger aircraft can be developed that can operate into and out of metropolitan airports and fly over populated areas at a tolerable noise level, it is clear that this type of aircraft will not be available in the United States.

VTOL and STOL Aircraft

Aircraft capable of vertical take-off and landing, or with greatly reduced runway requirements, may also see wider use. The helicopter is the only aircraft in this category presently in routine operation but a number of other designs have been tested which offer significant improvements in forward speed, load-carrying ability and other operating characteristics. Such aircraft, however, will probably supplement rather than supplant conventional designs and seem best fitted for short-to-medium distance trips. (See Chapter 16 for an evaluation of the use of VTOL and STOL aircraft in the New York-New Jersey metropolitan area.)

Cargo Aircraft

Constantly improving aviation technology has brought about a steady decrease in direct operating costs with each new cargo aircraft. These costs are now becoming competitive with those of surface transport and will become more competitive over the next two decades.

High terminal handling costs are thus left as the major obstacle to large-scale encroachment by aircraft on some of the conventional carriers of freight and cargo. If this barrier should be broken down within the next five or ten years, cargo transportation by air should become a significant part of the national transportation complex, particularly in overseas transport, before 1980.

Hydrofoil Vessels

There has been considerable interest lately in this country in vessels supported by foils acting to produce lift in water as an aircraft wing does in the air.

The first hydrofoil vessel was constructed in 1905 by Enrico Torlanini in Italy, and attained a speed of 45 miles per hour. A few years later, Alexander Graham Bell designed a craft of this type which established an official world's speed record of 70.85 miles per hour in 1919.

Although there has been a great deal of subsequent experimentation in the United States, the major application of the principle to commercial operation has occurred in Europe, where ships have been built up to 60 tons displacement, mostly for operation as passenger ferries. The Soviet Union initiated ferry operation with a hydrofoil vessel on the Volga River in 1958.

The 90-ton hydrofoil ship *H.S. Dennison* is now being completed by Dynamic

Developments, an affiliate of Grumman Aircraft, under sponsorship of the Maritime Administration, and sea trials were begun in 1962. In addition to exploring the technical problems of larger craft, it will be used to work out operating economies for ships of this type.

The hydrofoil vessel seems to fit in the speed spectrum between ordinary surface vessels and aircraft; i.e., from about 40 knots to 140 knots. In load-carrying ability, it is similar to large aircraft in that a considerable portion of the gross weight is available for payload and fuel. Its most likely use is on coastal, interisland and inland waterways for passenger transport and perhaps express cargo.

Since several such craft are already in scheduled service in other countries, it seems likely that the hydrofoil vessel will also be developed in this country to the point where it is in regular, though specialized, use by 1980.

Ground Effect Machines

Ground effect machines comprise a class of vehicles which are supported by a cushion of air. The cushion is generated by an engine-driven fan which pulls air into the body of the machine and discharges it downward through the bottom surface, generally in a continuous peripheral jet. Such machines are also variously called air cushion vehicles, air cars, and FASS (free air suspension system) vehicles and usually ride from one or two inches to one or two feet above the surface. Within their height limitations they are capable of traversing rough terrain, mud, water, snow, swamp and ice.

Operated as a high-speed passenger ferry, a vehicle of this type is not endangered by submerged logs or floating objects and can ride up a ramp to loading and unloading facilities. It also lends itself to other amphibious uses as well as off-the-road service over unpaved routes. As an on-road vehicle, it does not seem to offer any substantial operating advantages over wheeled vehicles but instead suffers some disadvantage, as it is less precisely controllable, inherently more noisy and generally more costly to operate. Although serious attention has been given to this field only within the last four or five years, it seems likely that the ground-effect machine will find a number of suitable applications in the transportation spectrum during the next two decades. It is unlikely, however, that it will be in competition with normal highway vehicles.

Railed Vehicles

Levacar. The Ford Levacar employs a thin film of high-pressure air a few thousandths of an inch thick between a precision rail and a supporting shoe, called a Levapad. The Levapad is thus a substitute for the wheel, and the air film provides a coefficient of friction less than that of rolling friction. However, power is required to provide the air film and the Levapad is more efficient on an over-all basis only at speeds in the neighborhood of 100 miles per hour and more.

Considerable experimental work has been done on the Levacar concept, and it appears to offer a means of intercity transport in a speed range which can compete favorably with aircraft for moderate-distance trips. Substantial capital outlays will have to be risked, however, in order to determine its true usefulness. The economic incentive to take such risks is not high, and the prospect is that they will not be taken on any large scale over the next 20 years.

Linear Electric Drive. Interest has reawakened, particularly in England, in the possible use of linear electric drive for rail vehicles. In this system a conducting strip affixed to the roadbed serves as the armature for an induction motor, the other half of which is carried on the train. Linear motors of this type have been tried as electric catapults for aircraft but have, so far, proven more costly and troublesome than other systems. Even if a successful system is developed, it does not appear likely that such a system would alter the basic characteristics of rail transport sufficiently to affect its destiny.

CONTROL AND AUTOMATION

The technology required for the automatic control and operation of transport vehicles has been available for some time. The timing and the extent of application of these techniques will depend primarily on social, economic and psychological factors.

The importance of labor costs in shipping and railroading provides a heavy incentive for automatic control. With aircraft and highway vehicles, even with the private automobile, the incentive for automation is heightened by the need to cope effectively with ever-increasing traffic densities.

In the case of aircraft, before automatic control could be adopted a great many private and public agencies and special-interest groups would have to agree on a standard traffic control system. Such an agreement has been difficult to achieve, and consequently the modernization of airways has failed to keep pace with advances in aviation generally, as has the development and use of automatic landing systems.

In the case of highway vehicles, a more fundamental problem arises. Their widespread usefulness is derived basically from the fact that they are individually controlled by individual drivers. Beyond the automatic spark advance, the automatic choke and the automatic transmission, it

is difficult to proceed without sacrificing this basic value. The most likely trend of development would appear to be one in which manual operation prevails in ordinary travel, and an automatic mode is provided for special limited-access routes of high density. Several such schemes have been proposed and experimental projects have demonstrated their possibilities. So far, such systems have required special installations in both vehicle and roadbed, and will face a substantial problem in terms of standardization and general acceptance.

By 1980 there may be considerable progress in the automation of ships and railed vehicles. Automatic landing systems should be in use at airports, and the airways should be under electronic guidance and control.

The character of the transportation task is likely to be affected also by changes in freight transport service requirements resulting from industrial and commercial application of automation and related technologies.

Automation of manufacturing and physical processing will create a need for better planning and scheduling of production, which will, in turn, create a need for close scheduling of the flow of goods to and from the production line, for closely knit integration of transportation, production, warehousing and materials handling.

Service standards can be established, reflecting, among other things, the costs of undependable schedules. Shippers will increasingly demand scheduled delivery with a high order of dependability, and transport vehicles that facilitate mechanized loading and unloading. If the common carriers cannot meet the standards demanded, shippers will be induced to expand their own private trucking operation.

TERMINAL FACILITIES

The word "terminal" tends to obscure the basic function generally performed at facilities so named. This function is that of transferring goods or people from one mode of transport to another, or from one vehicle to another of the same mode. Although a particular transportation route may actually terminate at a terminal, the people and things being transported do not.

The flow of cargo and passenger traffic through most of these nodal transfer points can be expected to continue growing in volume and complexity throughout the period under consideration, though shifting transportation patterns will force a decline at others. As the speed and efficiency of transportation are increased, the capacities of terminal facilities may tend to become the limiting factor in transportation networks. Prevention of such a situation will require the application of modern technology to the transfer function on a larger and a more advanced basis than has heretofore been necessary.

We should thus expect to see significant changes in this area. For example, containerization has been growing rapidly, forming a connective tissue among the various modes of transport. This growth seems likely to continue, and may help bring about entirely new transfer systems because of the ease with which containers lend themselves to mechanized and automated handling techniques. High-speed data processing and information-retrieval systems should come into wider use to handle the flow of paper work associated with the flow of goods and people.

POSTSCRIPT

It is impossible to predict the course of evolution of innovations which are yet to appear. However, there is a great deal of fundamental research in process which is bound to lead to a large number of such innovations during the next 20 years. Perhaps at the forefront of this work is the precise and detailed understanding of the fine structure of matter which is being accumulated at a rapid rate in biology, chemistry and physics. This knowledge and understanding should allow the creation of new materials having specific properties no material now has.

The aggressive application to electronic devices of this detailed knowledge of the structure of matter has already reduced their size and increased their speed of operation so that it may be possible by 1980 to construct electronic computers which, within practical space limitations, are of the same order of complexity as the human brain.

PART II

Transporting the Goods of Commerce and Industry

CHAPTER 9

OCEAN-BORNE GENERAL CARGO VOLUMES

For more than a century and a half, the Port of New York has been the leading port of the nation measured by volume or value of ocean-borne cargo or by the number of arrivals and departures of ship passengers. It has also led in the amount of capital invested in its cargo-handling and passenger terminal facilities and in the variety and number of such facilities.

While its primacy will be challenged in the future, as it has been in the past, it is nevertheless expected that the Port of New York will continue to maintain its position as the nation's leading port. As a major example of this continued leadership, it is estimated that ocean-borne general cargo through the port, foreign trade and domestic coastwise trade combined, will increase from an annual average of 16,070,000 long tons in the base period 1957-1959 to 22,040,000 long tons by 1980, an increase of about 37 per cent.

This estimate, and others presented in this report recognize that the volume of commerce the port will handle, the commodities that will be represented, and the number and types of terminal facilities that will be required will be determined by the conditions prevailing in future years. Some will be broad and general in effect while others will be limited to specific commodities or particular movements. Some will be beyond the control of the port. Others will be strongly influenced by port development policies and programs. The proposed World Trade Center, for example, by strengthening the region's position as the nation's primary center of foreign commerce, should exert a favorable influence on the volume of

foreign trade through the port, as will the continuing development of modern marine terminal facilities by improving the efficiency of cargo handling. An evaluation of future prospects, with all its fallibility, is indispensable to the formulation of a long-range plan for the development of the port's marine terminals.

FACTORS INFLUENCING FUTURE VOLUMES OF FOREIGN TRADE

Two different sets of factors will affect the future volume and composition of ocean-borne foreign trade cargo to be handled at the Port of New York. One set consists of those factors of national and international character which are of controlling importance in determining the magnitude and nature of the nation's total foreign trade. The port has little or no influence over the course of events in this area. The other comprises factors directly related to interport competition, which determine the ability of the port to participate in the international commerce of the nation.

Within the first set there are the general trends and cyclical movements in the national economy, the balance of international payments, the composition and direction of trade, the nation's commercial and financial policy, the strategic stockpiling program, the foreign aid and economic development programs and the state of the economies of other nations. Also, there is the prospective impact of technological developments, illustrated in recent history by the substitution of synthetic rubber and synthetic fibers produced domestically for the natural materials produced overseas. The influence of these factors on foreign trade is pervasive, spreading through the entire economy, but their effects upon the port may be specific. The port's loss of the once substantial silk import trade is an example.

The international pattern of utilization of natural resources is also important, as exemplified by the nation's increasing dependence on foreign sources of supply for iron and other steel-making ores. Conversely, the shift in the nation's position in the vegetable oil trade from that of a net importer to that of a net exporter has had a significant effect on port tonnage. Programs designed to stimulate the export of particular types of commodities, for example Public Law 480 relating to agricultural commodities, influence both the volumes and the domestic sources of supply, and hence the ports of exportation. There are also the choices by agencies of the federal government as to the ports through which foreign-aid and defense shipments should be routed.

Population growth and its regional distribution and regional differentials in economic growth further influence port volumes and commodity composition.

The second group of factors consists of those which are more directly related to the ability of the port to perform its function and to its basic strength in relation to other ports. These factors can be, and are, influenced in varying degrees by the programs and activities of those responsible for port management. They include inland rail rates; terminal rates and accessorial charges, including free time; adequacy and physical condition of marine terminal facilities; accessibility of truck and rail transportation facilities; frequency and geographic coverage of steamship services; availability and efficiency of forwarder, packaging, banking and consu-

lar services; size and strength of the hinterlands as a source of exports and as a market for imports; location of industry; configuration of the foreign commerce structure; and other factors.

SOME BASIC ASSUMPTIONS AFFECTING TOTAL NATIONAL VOLUMES

National Population and Economic Growth

A few years before the 1960 census of population was taken, the Bureau of the Census published projections of future population to 1980. Under an assumption of the lowest fertility rate the 1980 population projection became 231,000,000, under the highest, 273,000,000. Shortly thereafter the preliminary results of the 1960 census of population became available and indicated that there had been a rate of increase in the population reasonably close to an intermediate fertility rate, one that would lead to a total population of about 250,000,000 by 1980, compared to the 1960 population of approximately 179,000,000.

A number of projections of gross national product have been made by economic research agencies, governmental and institutional. All projections are keyed to projections of future population. Although there are differences in their appraisals of the future, they suggest an annual growth rate of between 3.1 and 3.5 per cent. Projected to 1980, these rates of growth would yield a gross national product of $920,000,000 to $993,000,000, in 1959 prices, or from 1.91 to 2.06 times the 1959 level.

Long-range forecasts of industrial production are less frequently prepared, but three such forecasts to 1975 are available. Using the data presented, and extending the projections forward to 1980, the indications are for a low of 296 (1947–1949 =

100) and a high of 362. An index of 325 for 1980 appears reasonable. This provides for a growth rate of approximately 3.5 per cent annually, about the same as the rate of growth for the period 1920–1959.

Regional Trends in Population and Industrial Development

The distribution of population and industrial activity throughout the regions of the country has shifted substantially during the past few decades. The New England and the Middle Atlantic States now account for smaller shares of the total national population than they did formerly. The East North Central Region share has remained relatively stable. These are the areas which are served by the Port of New York. Regions which are not directly served by the port, however, particularly the South Atlantic, the Pacific Coast and the Mountain States, have increased their shares of the nation's population.

The shifts in the distribution of manufacturing employment and of value added by manufactures have been even more pronounced. There have been losses in the New England and the Middle Atlantic States and relative stability in the East North Central States, modest increases in the West North Central States, modest increases in Southern States and sharp rises in the Pacific Coast States.

It is likely that these trends will continue and that there will be increases in the shares of manufacturing activity accounted for by regions tributary to ports other than those of the North Atlantic coastal area.

In short, for the nation as a whole, population is expected to increase from about 179,000,000 in 1960 to 250,000,000 in 1980, or almost 40 per cent. For the 22-county New York Metropolitan Region, the projected increase for the same period, based upon work done for the New York Metropolitan Region Study, is from 16,141,000 to 20,900,000, about 30 per cent. The principal area served by the port, New England, the Middle Atlantic and the East North Central Regions, the eastern half of the West North Central Region and the northern tier of the South Atlantic Region, is expected to have an increase of some 23 per cent. By contrast, the remaining regions of the country, those which are not tributary to the port, are expected to increase in population by almost 43 per cent. Particularly notable are the increases projected for the Mountain and Pacific Coast Regions, 45 and 58 per cent respectively.

Growth rates in regional economic activity may be expected to correspond closely to rates of population growth.

Trade Policy

It may be assumed that recent efforts toward reduction of trade barriers and liberalization of the conditions of international financial transactions related to trade will continue. It is likely, however, that export competition between the United States and other supplying countries will be intensified, particularly as a result of the development of an integrated Western European economic system. Additionally, it is probable that there will be further shifts in the directions and composition of export movements, with the Far Eastern, Australian and Indian Ocean areas becoming more important as export markets, and supplied increasingly from Pacific Coast ports.

On the import side, it is probable that the impact of technological developments, notably in the development of domestic substitutes for commodities formerly imported, will continue. This is also true of the development of domestic natural resources and their substitution for imports.

The former is exemplified by the progressive substitution of synthetic fibers for raw silk and wool, plastics for hides and skins, and synthetic rubber for natural rubber; the latter by the shift from a net import to a heavy net export position in vegetable oil and the increasing proportion of total wood pulp consumption accounted for by domestic production. These and other such developments will also affect the commodity composition and distribution among the regions of the country as sources of exports. Synthetic rubber, petrochemicals, synthetic nitrogen and superphosphates are now important export items.

It is also assumed that the existing divisions between the free world and the Communist bloc will continue but that there will be no major world war. Presupposed also is relatively little trade between the United States and the countries of the Communist orbit. Should restrictions currently imposed on this trade be relaxed, the result could be substantial increases in the volume of trade, but there is no way of estimating its future magnitude.

United States General Cargo
*   Imports and Exports*

Past experience indicates that except in times of war there is a close relationship between the nation's ocean-borne general cargo imports and its level of industrial production. The relationship is explainable on the ground that most of our imports are supplies for our industrial processes rather than consumer items. Over the past four decades, however, there has been a tendency for fewer units of imports to be related to particular levels of industrial production. For projection purposes, it is assumed that this trend will continue in the future and that by 1980 still fewer units of imports will be re-

quired to achieve the estimated levels of industrial production than are now needed.

To estimate the future national volume of general cargo imports, the method employed in this study has been to make estimates for each of the major components of the import composition and to add them up. In making these estimates, judgments have had to be formed as to the impact upon the particular commodity or commodity group of the national factors just discussed. Of great value in this endeavor have been a number of forecasts of future requirements prepared by United States government departments and by other agencies and students of the nation's economy, particularly forecasts by the Department of Agriculture dealing with the agricultural sector of the economy.

Two illustrations may be given. For coffee, tea and cocoa, the key factors are total population and per capita consumption. Trend data permit an estimate of future per capita consumption, which when applied to the estimate of future national population of 250,000,000 yields an estimate of future national volume of imports. For rubber, it is necessary to project future total rubber requirements and to estimate the proportions likely to be accounted for by natural rubber imports and by domestic synthetics, taking into account certain considerations of national policy toward the areas which produce natural rubber.

In order to arrive at a proper national total it has been necessary to prepare estimates not only for the commodities which are important to the Port of New York but also for those which move primarily through other ports and which have relatively little local importance. Twelve such commodities — copra, burlap, jute and bagging, logs, unmanufactured wood, cooperage materials, pulp wood, cement, salt, paints and pigments, phosphates, and potash — account for nearly 16 per cent of the total United States general cargo import volume, but the Port of New York accounts for little more than 4 per cent of the national total.

The same procedure has been employed in estimating the future national volume of exports, that of estimating export volume prospects by commodity or by commodity group.

In large measure, economic, political and military factors, when applied to foreign lands, influence the volume of our exports. Such data as are available with respect to anticipated trends and developments abroad in population, consumption patterns, resources development, agricultural, industrial and economic development, and trade policy have to be taken into account. There is also the likelihood that the United States will face increasing competition in export markets. A general supposition is that nations increase their trade as they develop economically and achieve higher standards of living. Increased trade will probably be accompanied by some shifts in the direction of trade movements and also in the composition of our exports.

As with imports, some fairly detailed projections were available for the agricultural commodity groups from the Department of Agriculture.

Again, there are commodities which loom large in the national picture but are relatively unimportant for the Port of New York. Seventeen commodities — condensed milk, rice, canned foods, naval stores, tobacco, cotton, logs, railroad ties, lumber, wood pulp, cement, clays and earths, salt, pig iron, and three processed fertilizer groups — accounted for 21.5 per cent of total United States general cargo exports in 1957–1959, but the Port of New York handled only 1.1 per cent of

their combined national volume.

Imports and exports combined, it is estimated that the national total of ocean-borne general cargo foreign commerce will be about 64,000,000 tons in 1980.

CLASSIFICATION OF COMMODITIES AND COMMODITY MOVEMENTS

Because of the great differences in the character of terminal requirements, in this report ocean-borne commodity movements are classified as either bulk or general cargo, depending upon how the commodity is handled. Bulk cargo is handled in loose, rather than in packaged, bundled or crated form; it moves over specialized, mechanically equipped handling facilities, and it requires little longshore or other dock handling. General cargo, on the other hand, is typically packaged, bundled or crated; moves over conventional piers or wharves and requires extensive longshore and other dock handling.

General cargo needs to be subdivided further into two subcategories: conventional general cargo and specialized general cargo. There has been an increasing use of specialized handling facilities designed for particular commodities — for example, bananas and newsprint — or for large containers of road-haul size, and of facilities owned and operated by processors, shippers, receivers and distributors for their exclusive use.

Estimates of general cargo volumes which are expected to be handled at the Port of New York by 1980 are, therefore, based on two levels of commodity classification:

General cargo, in foreign trade, represents the residual after tanker, grain, coal and certain mineral and foreign aid shipments are subtracted from total ocean-borne volumes in the case of exports, and

tanker and certain ore and mineral receipts are subtracted in the case of imports. In the domestic coastwise trades,
the general cargo volume is the residual
after subtracting molasses, coal, petroleum, sand, gravel and rock, sulfur, clays
and earths, coal tar products, industrial
chemicals and phosphates from the total
volumes.

General cargo, for purposes of this
study, is further categorized into those
commodities which are handled or may in
the future be handled over specialized or
private industrial piers and facilities; and
those commodities which now move and
are likely to move in the future over publicly used facilities of conventional design.

Included in category A are bananas,
sugar, vegetable oils, rubber latex, lumber, newsprint, scrap iron, tanker wine
and tanker citrus fruit juices, and containership operations.[1] Category B consists of all other commodity movements
falling within our standard definition of
general cargo.

The basic data for study and analysis of
ocean-borne cargo through the Port of
New York, as well as for the nation as a
whole, are those assembled and compiled
by the U. S. Department of Commerce
for foreign trade and those assembled and
compiled by the U. S. Army Corps of Engineers for domestic trade. In both cases
the data available cover commercial shipments only; military shipments are unre-
ported.

Consideration has been given to the
possibility that frozen foods and heavy-lift
shipments might be handled over specialized facilities in 1980. Foreseeable developments, however, do not indicate that

this is probable. It seems more likely that
the frozen food handling problem will be
resolved by technological developments
in the packaging field, and that the economics of handling heavy-lift shipments
will dictate a continuance of the use of
conventional general cargo facilities with
the aid of floating equipment.

It is likely, however, that there will be
new developments in the handling and
shipping of other commodities which may
influence the types and number of shore-
side facilities required. There are developing movements of cement and sugar in
bulk rather than in bags or barrels, and
there is the possible development of imports of beverage materials in processed
or powdered form rather than in bean
and leaf form. Imports of beverage materials in concentrated form, for example,
would result in sharp decreases in the volume imported, which would, in turn, affect the requirements for conventional facilities. A shift in the manner of shipping
sugar, most of which moves over specialized private facilities, from bagged or
barreled form to bulk movement, would
require a drastic change in the type of
facility used.

For the base period, 1957–1959, only
the volumes of bananas, sugar and newsprint movement actually handled over
specialized facilities in the Port of New
York were included in category A; all
other movements of those commodities
have been included in the conventional
category B. For 1980, however, it is assumed that the total volumes of those
commodities will be handled at the Port
of New York at specialized facilities.

NEW YORK'S GENERAL CARGO VOLUMES

Projections of ocean-borne general
cargo volumes through the Port of New
York must be based, first, on future na-

---

[1] The distinction between *container* operations and *containership* operations is fundamental and is explained in
Chapter 11. For our present purposes, it may be noted
that the former represents the use of containers as substitutes for other types of packaging and is classified as conventional general cargo: the latter, however, is concerned
with ships specifically designed to carry containers and is
classified as specialized general cargo.

TABLE 1. UNITED STATES AND PORT OF NEW YORK FOREIGN TRADE GENERAL CARGO
1950–1961

(in thousands of long tons)

| | Exports | | Imports | | Total | |
	United States	New York	United States	New York	United States	New York
1950	17,039	5,088	21,368	7,601	38,425	12,689
1951	19,983	6,260	20,710	7,139	40,693	13,399
1952	18,059	5,732	19,489	6,945	38,772	12,677
1953	15,290	4,757	21,222	7,304	36,599	11,917
1954	18,392	4,933	19,402	5,820	37,794	10,753
1955	23,882	6,389	22,303	6,372	46,185	12,761
1956	26,987	6,397	22,750	6,495	49,737	12,892
1957	29,331	6,626	22,633	6,311	51,964	12,937
1958	21,092	5,297	23,681	6,784	44,772	12,081
1959	23,343	4,988	29,669	8,104	53,012	13,092
1960	30,789	6,047	28,382	7,689	59,170	13,737
1961	33,462	5,731	27,332	7,263	60,794	12,994

tional totals and national trends and, second, on an estimation of the future strengths of the competitive factors which will affect New York's position relative to other ports serving the same producing and the same market areas.

There are at present a number of important cases relating to the elimination of differential rates that favor other ports on the Atlantic and Gulf coasts, but for the purpose of making a projection of future volumes the elimination of this port handicap has not been assumed.

It is assumed also that the trend toward truck movement in the land transportation of general cargo exports and imports, a major characteristic of the post–World War II period, will continue, though probably at a slower pace. Also, it is probable that the opening of the St. Lawrence Seaway–Great Lakes route for ocean shipping will influence the routing of some cargo movements generated in the upper midwestern area and that the Port of New

York will be adversely affected thereby.

On the other hand, the proposed World Trade Center should constitute a positive factor in the port's competitive posture.

Within this framework, separate projections have been made for each commodity or commodity group. To illustrate, by referring to the beverage materials:

The Port of New York during recent years has accounted for 53.1 per cent of the national volume of coffee, tea and cocoa imports, and the average annual volume handled in 1957–1959 was 834,-000 tons. However, the population of the trade area served by the port is expected to increase at a slower rate than that of the nation as a whole. For 1980 it is estimated that the port will account for about 50 per cent of a national total of 2,340,000 tons, or about 1,170,000 tons.

The results of these projections yield a total volume of New York's foreign trade general cargo in 1980 of 15,265,000 tons compared with the 1957–1959 average annual volume of 12,703,000 tons, an increase of 20.2 per cent. It must be noted, however, that whereas the 1957–1959 average includes scrap iron movements (a specialized general cargo) the 1980 projection does not. While the projection of *total* general cargo — foreign trade plus domestic coastwise trade — includes a volume of 500,000 tons for scrap iron, this volume cannot, at this time, be allocated between foreign trade and coastwise trade or between inbound receipts (including imports in foreign trade) and outbound shipments (including exports).[2] A portion of the scrap iron will be handled in foreign trade. To this extent both the 1980 absolute volume and the indicated percentage increase over 1957–1959 are understated. For example, if the indicated volume of 15,265,000 tons for 1980 is compared with the comparable volume for the annual average for 1957–1959 — also excluding scrap iron in foreign trade — 11,830,000 tons, the projected increase is 29 per cent.

For general cargo exports and imports separately, excluding the unallocated 500,000 tons of scrap iron, the figures are — exports, 6,985,000 tons in 1980 compared with 5,637,000 tons annually in 1957–1959, a 24 per cent increase; imports, 8,280,000 tons in 1980 against 7,066,000 tons annually in 1957–1959, a 17 per cent increase.

Specialized general cargo foreign trade, category A, again excluding the scrap iron, is expected to remain at about the present level of volume, 2,855,000 tons in 1980, as compared with 2,859,000 tons annually in 1957–1959.

For conventional foreign trade general cargo, category B, the projected volume is 12,410,000 tons, compared with 9,845,000 tons annually in 1957–1959, an increase of 26.1 per cent. Within this total, exports

²See Chapter 11.

are expected to increase from 4,488,000 tons to 6,640,000 tons, and imports from 5,357,000 tons to 5,770,000 tons. These would represent increases of 47.9 per cent for exports and 7.7 per cent for imports. One of the major reasons for the larger increases projected for exports than for imports is the depression during the base period of foreign trade in iron and steel mill and manufactured products caused by the strike in the steel industry at the time. During that period the traditional strong net export position in the trade of these commodities was temporarily reversed to a heavy net import position.

The national general cargo foreign trade tonnage figures cannot be classified as to specialized and conventional cargo movements, since information on other ports is not available. For total general cargo foreign trade, however, excluding scrap iron, the national volume is expected to increase by 35.1 per cent and volume through the Port of New York to increase by 29.0 per cent.

Domestic Trade

Post–World War II volumes of general cargo movements in the domestic trade routes are substantially below prewar levels for both the nation as a whole and for the Port of New York, particularly in the coastal and intercoastal as distinct from the offshore components of this trade. The steamship services available for this trade, particularly for conventional general cargo movements, are also far below earlier levels. At the Port of New York there are now no conventional general cargo common carriers in operation in either the coastal or intercoastal trades, although several still operate in the offshore trades.

Among the major causes for this dual contraction of shipment volumes and conventional steamship services were war-time suspension of the services in order to make ships available for overseas transportation of troops and war materiel; subsequent high cost of ship replacement; proportionately greater increases in the operating costs of the water carriers than in those of competing rail and truck carriers; contraction of the areas behind the ports which can be served by joint rail-water rates; selective rate adjustments by the railroads on certain important commodity movements; and in the case of coastal, as distinct from intercoastal and offshore, carriers, the increasing role played by direct point-to-point trucking.

In projecting future coastwise volumes, two additional factors must be taken into account. First, many commodities prominent in coastwise receipts, particularly those in the specialized category, compete with or supplement imports, as do sugar and lumber. Second, the recent expansion in containership operation promises to create tremendous changes in both the character and the volumes of coastwise movements. The substantial volumes already carried by this form of transportation probably represent, in part, diversions from motor-truck and railway transport and, in part, container shipments which would otherwise be handled as conventional general cargo. There is also some evidence that the service has generated a certain amount of entirely new traffic and in this sense has been responsible for some shifts in domestic patterns of distribution.

The outlook for containership operations at the Port of New York is presented in detail in Chapter 11. Developments already under way and entirely new ones which are anticipated should lead to substantial expansion of this type of cargo movement. Therefore, it is anticipated that there will be a substantial growth of containership movements in the domestic trades. This will, in all likelihood, be accompanied by a reduction in the already depressed levels of conventional general cargo movements, particularly in outbound shipments. Receipts from Hawaii, heavily weighted by canned and processed fruits and fruit juices, however, are likely to continue largely in their present form of conventional movements.

Containership tonnages for 1980 have been estimated at 4,000,000 tons, compared with the annual average of approximately 1,400,000 tons in 1957–1959. Conventional movements are projected to decline from 943,000 tons annually in 1957–1959 to 850,000 tons by 1980. The third component, specialized cargo not carried by containership, is estimated to increase from 1,023,000 tons to 1,425,000 tons during the same period.

Total General Cargo Movements, 1980

In 1957–1959, foreign and domestic trades combined, the Port of New York handled an average annual volume of 16,070,000 tons of general cargo. It is expected that the volume will increase to about 22,040,000 tons by 1980, equivalent to an increase of about 37 per cent.

Both inbound and outbound movements are expected to increase, the former from 9,291,000 to 12,305,000 tons, the latter from 6,778,000 to 9,235,000 tons. These estimates represent increases of 32 per cent for inbound movements (imports and coastwise receipts) and 36 per cent for outbound movements (exports and coastwise shipments), exclusive of the unallocated volume of 500,000 tons of scrap iron.

The volume of conventional general cargo movements is projected to increase from 10,788,000 tons annually in the base

TABLE 2. PORT OF NEW YORK
TOTAL GENERAL CARGO

(in thousands of long tons)

	1957–1959	1980
Total general cargo	16,070,000	22,040,000
Foreign trade	12,703,000	15,265,000[a]
Exports	5,637,000	6,985,000[a]
Conventional	4,488,000	6,640,000
Specialized	1,149,000	345,000[a]
Imports	7,066,000	8,280,000[a]
Conventional	5,357,000	5,770,000
Specialized	1,709,000	2,510,000[a]
Domestic trade	3,367,000	6,275,000[a]
Outbound	1,141,000	2,250,000[a]
Conventional	547,000	350,000
Specialized	594,000	1,900,000[a]
Inbound	2,225,000	4,025,000[a]
Conventional	396,000	500,000
Specialized	1,829,000	3,525,000[a]

[a]Excludes 500,000 tons of scrap iron, not allocated as to direction of movement. Included in the estimate of total general cargo for 1980.

period to 13,260,000 tons in 1980, an increase of 23 per cent. Specialized general cargo movements are projected at a higher rate of growth, 66 per cent, from 5,282,000 tons annually in the base period to 8,780,000 tons in 1980, including scrap iron.

In summary form, Table 2 presents the general cargo volumes handled at the Port of New York, as an average for the years 1957, 1958 and 1959, and the volumes projected for 1980.

Commodity Composition

All the projected increases in conventional general cargo are accounted for by projected increases in foreign trade. On the export side, a total of 6,640,000 tons in 1980, the largest groupings should consist of iron and steel mill products and metal manufactures and the broad range of machinery classifications. These, together with transportation equipment (automotive and railroad), are expected

TABLE 3. PORT OF NEW YORK FOREIGN TRADE CONVENTIONAL GENERAL CARGO

(in thousands of long tons)

	Exports		Imports	
	Average 1957–1959	Estimated 1980	Average 1957–1959	Estimated 1980
Animals, fish and products	482	561	420	408
Vegetable food products and beverages	490	653	1,925	1,982
Vegetable products, inedible, except fibers and woods	163	211	493	440
Vegetable fibers and manufactures	180	180	322	387
Wood and paper	137	162	490	400
Nonmetallic minerals	177	190	459	414
Metals and manufactures, except machinery	1,010	2,075	746	1,100
Machinery and vehicles	1,187	1,780	221	321
Chemicals and related products	552	703	175	193
Miscellaneous	108	125	105	125
Total	4,488	6,640	5,357	5,770

TABLE 4. PORT OF NEW YORK SPECIALIZED GENERAL CARGO

(in thousands of long tons)

	Inbound		Outbound	
	Average 1957–1959	Estimated 1980	Average 1957–1959	Estimated 1980
Bananas	308[a]	550	—	d
Sugar	1,028[a]	1,630	e	e
Vegetable oils	236	205	275	345
Rubber latex	18	15	—	d
Lumber	770	675	6	d
Newsprint	168[a]	400	e	e
Scrap iron	129	b	873	b
Citrus juices by tanker	63[c]	400	d	d
Wine by tanker	37[c]	60	d	d
Containership	813	2,100	590	1,900[f]
Total	3,538	6,035	1,744	2,245

[a]1957–1959 includes only volumes handled over specialized facilities; 1980 includes total volumes.

[b]Combined total volume of movement includes 500,000 tons of scrap iron unallocated as to direction of movement.

[c]Service instituted in 1957, citrus juices from Florida, wine from Pacific Coast. Annual average represents only 1958 and 1959 full-year operations. The citrus juice movement from Florida was temporarily suspended in late 1961 and the movement transferred to rail.

[d]None estimated.

[e]Handled or to be handled over conventional facilities.

[f]Estimate limited to coastwise movements.

to account for about 57 per cent of the total. The next largest broad grouping, about 18 per cent, should consist of farm and dairy products and their manufactures, including meats, packing house products, fruits and vegetables, wheat flour and packaged beverages. The remainder should consist of a wide range of industrial chemicals and medicinal products, textiles and manufactures, rubber products, glass and related products, and packaged petroleum.

With respect to imports, 5,770,000 tons by 1980, the largest single broad grouping, with about 40 per cent of the total, should consist of edible farm and dairy products and manufactures, notably the beverages in raw form (coffee, tea, cocoa), wine and liquors, semitropical and tropical fruits and vegetables, and meat and fish products. Crude rubber, which

has accounted for sizable volumes in recent years, is expected to decline in volume because of the progressive substitution of domestically produced synthetic rubber. Conversely, imported metals and minerals in semirefined and refined forms are expected to increase substantially as the country becomes increasingly dependent on foreign sources of supply. Iron and steel mill products, which have fluctuated rather widely in recent years, are also expected to increase over the 1957–1959 volumes. The fiber group (burlap, jute, sisal, hemp, wool and long staple cotton) is as a group expected to increase.

It must be recognized, however, that future economic and technological developments will have profound effects on import volumes. For example, the countries producing beverage materials may establish their own processing plants and our imports may be in the form of concentrates. Domestically produced synthetic fibers and plastics may cut into the importation of natural fibers and hides and skins.

By 1980 imports of bananas, sugar and newsprint will probably be received at specialized terminal facilities. Export movements of sugar and newsprint, however, will probably move over conventional general cargo facilities.

The 1980 volume of general cargo handled at specialized terminals includes an estimated 4,000,000 tons of containership cargo, as compared with the 1957–1959 annual average of 1,403,000 tons. As indicated earlier, both the actual 1957–1959 average and the 1980 estimate are limited to the domestic coastwise trade.

The 1980 estimates also include a directionally unallocated volume of 500,000 tons of scrap iron. Scrap iron movements, in recent years, have fluctuated widely in volume and have also shifted sharply between exports and imports. The record of the past yields no indication of what the 1980 volume may be, or if it will be in foreign or domestic trade, export or import, inbound or outbound. In any event, scrap iron would be handled over specialized rather than conventional facilities.

CHAPTER 10

GENERAL CARGO MARINE TERMINAL REQUIREMENTS

During the past five years, the steamship lines serving the Port of New York used, at various times, 170 to 180 conventional general cargo berths, widely distributed throughout the harbor. The number in use has varied from time to time in accordance with fluctuations in cargo volumes, company practices in ship movements and berth occupancy and utilization, terminal leasing arrangements, rehabilitation and reconstruction programs, cargo-handling rates and other related factors.

In 1957 when 171 berths were in actual use, they handled a total volume of 10,782,000 long tons of conventional general cargo to and from cargo ships and cargo-passenger ships. In addition, 422,000 tons of similar cargo were handled over passenger pier facilities, carried aboard passenger liners as express cargo. All told, 11,204,000 tons of conventional general cargo in the foreign and domestic trades moved into, out of and through the Port of New York in 1957.[1]

It is estimated that by 1980 the port will be handling 13,260,000 tons of conventional general cargo. About 550,000 tons will be handled over passenger pier facilities; the balance, 12,710,000 tons, will require about 170 berths for proper and efficient handling. In effect, approximately the same number of berths as were in use in 1957 will be sufficient to accommodate a volume of cargo which will have increased from 10,782,000 tons to 12,710,000 tons.

This estimate of future berth require-

[1] The 1957 volume is used here because of the need to relate the volumes handled to the 1957 ship movement and berth utilization surveys following.

ments is based on an analysis of recent experience in ship movements, cargo handling, berth occupancy and utilization, and the number of working days in the year, and an evaluation of probable trends concerning these factors in the period ahead.

Berth Availability, 1957

The geographic distribution of the conventional general cargo berths available for use in 1957 is shown in Table 1. It must be noted that the term "berth" refers solely to space which could be occupied by a ship while engaged in loading or discharging conventional general cargo. This excludes all berths which were in active use for other purposes, for example, as railroad carfloat stations or as specialized cargo terminals. Designation of a berth as available implies no evaluation of the adequacy of the wharf, shedded space or upland area available for cargo handling and storage. In fact, some berths, both used and unused in 1957, were at small terminals of obsolete dimensions and poorly provided with covered wharf area to accommodate cargo movements. In other cases, facilities had berthing capacities rated at more than the number of berths actually in use.

The number of berths available for conventional general cargo handling will vary from time to time. This may come about as a result of new construction, rehabilitation requiring temporary withdrawal of a berth from availability, and changes in the pattern of utilization, for example termination of carfloat operations at a facility or a shift from specialized to conventional

TABLE 1. CONVENTIONAL GENERAL
CARGO BERTHS, 1957

Location	In Use	Not in Use	Total
Manhattan, Hudson River	33	13	46
Manhattan, East River	8	6	14
Brooklyn	94	11	105
Staten Island	8	20	28
New Jersey, Hudson River	16	3	19
Port Newark	12	0	12
Total	171	53	224

general cargo use. The number of berths actually in use may be different from the number of berths contracted for by a steamship company or terminal operator. The former is determined by actual operating requirements at the time, the latter by contractual arrangements which may cover longer periods. Thus, a steamship or terminal-operating company may be under lease to occupy a terminal with more berths than are actually in use at a particular time. Conversely, there are some situations where facilities are designed for and leased on the basis of fewer berths than are actually used.

Table 1 indicates that there were substantially more berths available in 1957 than were actually in use. With 224 berths available, only 171 were in operation; 53 were vacant or unused by steamship lines. These latter included a substantial number in relatively good condition, more than half of them less than 50 years old, some with extensive shedded space for cargo handling. Among the unused berths at terminals built less than 50 years ago were five in the Chelsea area of Manhattan's Hudson River water front (Piers 45, 46 and 56), two in Jersey City (Harborside Pier D) and 18 on Staten Island.

Berth Occupancy and Utilization, 1957

Analysis of conventional general cargo tonnage through the port, and of all ship arrivals and departures for the calendar year 1957 at the 171 conventional general cargo berths then in use reveals the following significant features:

1. There were 6,697 ships that arrived and departed during the year. Ships remained at berth an average of 3.57 days, excluding Sundays, holidays and half of the Saturdays; total berth occupancy aggregated 23,908 ship-days.

2. There were 273 working days on the water front during the year and, accordingly, there were 46,683 berth-days available for occupancy at 171 berths. Dividing 23,908 by 46,683 yields a berth utilization rate of 51.2 per cent. There were, however, widely different rates of berth utilization at individual terminals. Some of those classified as "in use" were but slightly used while others were used heavily.

3. The average number of ships occupying berths on any one day was 87.5.

4. There were wide daily fluctuations in the number of ships at berth, with a weekly pattern showing highest occupancies on Thursdays and Fridays. On 60 days there were more than 100 ships at berth, compared with the daily average for the year of 87.5; the peak, on one day, was 125. At peak occupancy, 73.1 per cent of the berths were occupied, compared with the 51.2 per cent yearly average. (Fig. 1.)

5. The average volume of cargo loaded and unloaded per ship was 1,610 tons, equivalent to 451 tons per ship per day of berth occupancy. There were, however, substantial differences between single-call and double-call ships in the amount of cargo handled; the former had both larger volumes per call and higher daily handling rates.

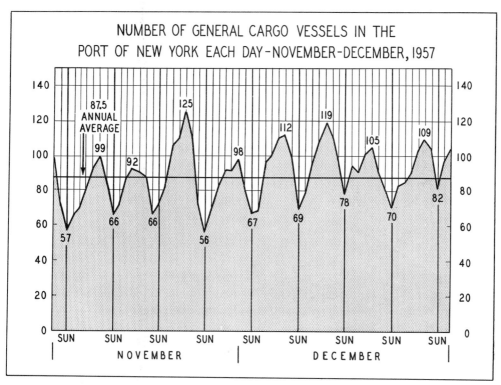

FIG. 1

6. On an annual basis, the average volume of cargo handled per berth was 63,055 tons.

To test the representativeness of the data on which the above analysis was based, similar analysis was made of data derived from another survey of the port's activity for the period October 1955–March 1956. Table 2 presents the comparative data derived from the two surveys.

Both analyses, it can be seen from Table 2, yielded much the same values for each of the factors measured; the range between the low and the high was in no case as much as 8 per cent.

Both surveys revealed wide differences in the rates of utilization of facilities located along different channels as well as differences in the rates of berth utilization at individual terminals along any particu-

TABLE 2. CONVENTIONAL GENERAL CARGO BERTH UTILIZATION IN THE PORT OF NEW YORK, OCTOBER 1955–MARCH 1956 AND CALENDAR YEAR 1957

	Oct. 1955– Mar. 1956	Jan.–Dec. 1957
Average days of berth occupancy per ship	3.78	3.57
Average berth utilization (per cent)	47.9	51.2
Berth utilization at peak number of ships in port (per cent)	67.8	73.1
Average tons of cargo per day of berth occupancy	454	451
Average tons of cargo per ship	1,718	1,610
Tons of cargo per berth per year	59,444	63,055

lar channel. In 1957, for example, the berths along the Bay Ridge–Red Hook Channel and along the Manhattan–Hudson River frontage showed average utilization of 56 and 55 per cent respectively, while those on the Buttermilk Channel and on Staten Island registered utilization ratios of only 42 per cent and 28 per cent, respectively.

Viewed as a whole, the two surveys indicate fairly consistent patterns in two of the critical factors determining berth requirements — average berth utilization and average daily cargo-handling rates. The outlooks for these, together with the rate of berth utilization at peak occupancy, the number of working days, and the total volume of cargo to be handled, are the key elements in projecting future berth requirements.

FUTURE BERTH REQUIREMENTS

If the berth utilization factor should rise in the future as a consequence of terminal consolidation, joint usage, better terminal design, or any other development, a number of berths equal to the number in use in 1957 could accommodate a greater number of ship arrivals. Further, if the rate at which cargo is loaded or discharged should rise, the anticipated increase in tonnage could be handled without increasing berthage time or, alternately, more ships could be berthed without an increase in berthing facilities.

Berth Utilization Rate

As noted, the average number of ships in port on working days in 1957 was 87.5, but there were a number of recurring peaks, the highest of which was 125 ships at berth at one time. On that peak occasion, 73.1 per cent of the port's berths were occupied. The average utilization rate, therefore, was really the product of two other ratios, one the ratio of average ship population in port to peak ship population, 70.0 per cent (87.5 ships divided by 125 ships), the other the degree of utilization experienced under peak occupancy, 73.1 per cent (125 ships divided by 171 berths).

This peaking is not unique to marine transportation. It is encountered in all fields of transportation and is particularly important in connection with terminal planning problems. For example, the Port Authority Bus Terminal has to accommodate the peak-hour demand for bus berthing space, and the airports must provide enough gate positions to accommodate peak-hour plane movements. In both examples the peaking is far more pronounced than that in marine traffic of the port.

The average-peak relationship in ocean shipping reflects such factors as sailing schedules, trade route, cargo composition, and other elements of shipping industry operations which are not susceptible to influence by a terminal development program. The degree of berth utilization, both average and peak, may be influenced to some extent, however, by the encouragement of joint usage of terminals by several shipping lines which have complementary arrival and sailing schedules. However, the recurring peaks do not include the same ships, and the peak berth occupancies in different geographic sectors of the harbor and at individual company facilities do not occur at the same time. There is, therefore, but a moderate potential for increasing the over-all port-wide berth utilization rate through changes in terminal management. Without changes in the whole pattern of sailing schedules, the theoretical upper limit for average berth utilization would be 70 per cent, which would be its value if *no* berths were vacant on the day of peak demand.

It would appear reasonable to look forward to an average berth utilization rate by 1980 of about 55 per cent in place of the 47.9 per cent in 1955–1956 and 51.2 per cent in 1957. At this rate of utilization about 80 per cent of the port's berths would be occupied on the peak day.

Cargo-Handling Rates

In estimating daily cargo-handling rates, it is to be noted that these rates are not the same as stevedoring rates, measured either per gang-hour or per day. The figure of 451 tons per day, for 1957, takes into account days when a ship was at berth but was working only one or two hatches, or may not have been loading or unloading cargo at all. It is also a port-wide average and does not reveal the differences in the loading and unloading rates of single- and double-call vessels, differences between terminals, and differences between the rates of loading and unloading. At one pier, for example, cargo unloaded per gang-hour for one particular operator consistently ran as high as 30 to 33 tons. For loading operations, however, this same operator averaged only about 16 tons per gang-hour. His over-all daily cargo-handling rate was 1,142 tons, about 2.5 times the port-wide average. Further, a terminal operator who works his ships for considerable overtime periods will probably have a higher over-all daily handling rate than an operator who does not. Projected daily cargo-handling rates may not clearly reflect, therefore, prospective improvements in stevedoring rates which may come about from more efficient cargo-handling methods.

A negative factor also influences this situation. This is the growing practice of shipping companies to make the Port of New York a double-call rather than a single-call port. There is an increasing tendency to make the port the first inbound port of call, then to proceed to the outports for both unloading and loading operations, and then to make New York the last outbound port of call. This practice results in a lower cargo-handling rate for New York cargo because of the more difficult handling problems involved in breaking out cargo on the inbound call and in stowing the top-off cargo on the outbound movement.

Nevertheless, it is believed that there will be improvements in cargo-handling which will make possible more rapid rates in the future. For example, there is a prospect of increasing palletization and of increased use of small container units to be handled over conventional facilities. It is reasonable, therefore, to anticipate a cargo tonnage rate per day of berth occupancy within a range of 525 to 575 tons by 1980. At the lower level of this range, 525 tons, it would represent an improvement in the daily cargo-handling rate of approximately 16 per cent over the two port-wide survey rates. At the upper range, 575 tons, the rate of improvement would be about 27 per cent.

Work Days Per Year

In common with industrial practices generally, the number of standard days per year worked on the water front has declined over the years. A reasonable assumption can be made that this trend will continue in the future in keeping with other industries of the nation and that the work year for the water front by 1980 will be shorter than in 1957. Caution in projecting the future is necessary here, however, because the shipping industry's operating year may not reflect reductions in the normal working time of the waterfront labor force. Just as the employees of utility companies generally work a standard 40-hour week or less, while the utility itself operates around-the-clock, seven days a week, it is possible that the water-front industry's working year may decline only moderately, regardless of which hours may be classified as straight time or overtime, or alternate shifts, or other arrangement with the labor force. It appears reasonable for the purpose of this study to assume that shipping companies may elect to reduce their present working year of 275 days to 260 days by 1980.

Berth Requirements, 1980

Grouping all the factors determining port-wide berth requirements at their estimated 1980 values — average berth utilization of 55 per cent, an average daily cargo-handling rate of 525 tons, and a working year equivalent to 260 days — a total of 170 conventional general cargo berths would be required to handle the indicated 1980 volume of 12,710,000 tons to be carried on straight cargo and combination cargo-passenger ships.

Variations in any of these estimated values would necessarily lead to different conclusions concerning the number of berths required by 1980. The several factors are interrelated as follows: Annual Tonnage = Tons per day per berth × number of working days × number of berths in use × berth utilization rate.

Assuming, therefore, that 170 berths are required in 1980, the average in-port ship population on working days will be 93.1 as compared with 87.5 in 1957. If the relationship between average ship population and peak ship population that prevailed in 1957 obtains in 1980, the peak ship population in the harbor will be 133 ships. This, in turn, will be equivalent to a port-wide utilization rate of 78.2 per cent at peak occupancy.

Table 3 presents a summary of the pertinent data on ship movements, berth utilization, cargo handling and tons per berth for 1957 and estimated for 1980.

TABLE 3. CONVENTIONAL GENERAL CARGO BERTHS, 1957 AND ESTIMATED 1980

	1957	1980
Total cargo to be handled (millions of long tons)	10.8	12.7
Average tonnage handled per day of berth occupancy (long tons)	451	525
Number of working days	273	260
Average berth utilization (per cent)	51.2	55.0
Total number of berths in use	171	170
Average number of ships in port on working days	87.5	93.1
Number of ships in port on peak day	125	133
Berth occupancy on peak day (per cent)	73.1	78.2
Tons per berth per year, average	63,055	75,000

CONVENTIONAL GENERAL CARGO TERMINAL DEVELOPMENT PROGRAM

The paragraphs which follow are concerned with an analysis of the existing situation with respect to conventional general cargo berths and the extent to which the currently available facilities will meet the port's future requirements, together with a presentation of the plans which have been announced for the construction of new berths and the factors which will need to be taken into account in planning where new berths should be constructed.

Port Situation, 1960

Under the criteria employed in this analysis a berth is considered "available" for conventional general cargo if it has shed space adjacent to it for the handling and storage of such cargo, and if it is in actual use for such purpose or is not being used for other purposes, such as a railroad carfloat station or as a specialized cargo facility. The total number of berths classified as available will vary from time to time depending on such factors as the progress of new construction, rehabilitation projects requiring temporary withdrawal, and changes in the pattern of utilization. The fact that a berth is classified "available" provides no indication of its age and implies no judgment as to the adequacy of the wharf, shed space or upland area for cargo-handling purposes. In 1957 there were 224 berths classified as available for conventional general cargo use; by October 1960, the number had increased to 236.

The number of berths in actual use also fluctuates from time to time. In 1957, the average number of berths in active use was 171; in October 1960, there were 173 berths so classified.

Some of the berths currently available for use were constructed as long ago as 1876 (Pier 42 Hudson River), while some have been constructed as recently as 1959–1962 (23rd Street, Brooklyn, and Brooklyn–Port Authority Piers 3, 6, 7, 8 and Pier 40, Hudson River). The 236 berths available for use in October 1960, in terms of their original dates of construc-

tion were as follows: prior to 1910, 60 berths; 1910–1929, 100 berths; 1930–1949, 23 berths; 1950 to date, 53 berths.

Some of the older berths have been substantially rehabilitated during the past 15 years, generally to increase operating efficiency, with improvements to sheds and headhouses but without effect on the substructure, dimensions or upland area. These include 28 berths constructed between 1910 and 1929, all of which are located in the Brooklyn sector of the harbor, and 14 berths constructed prior to 1910, all on Manhattan. A listing of all berths by date of construction by major sector of the port is given in Table 4.

Planning for the Port of New York of the future must necessarily begin with what is currently available. By 1980, many of the berths listed in Table 4 will be more than 70 years old. Included in this age bracket are some of the best-known marine terminals in the port, including the privately owned Bush Terminal in Brooklyn, most of the New York City–owned Chelsea Piers on the Hudson River and all but one of the piers on the Manhattan East River water front.

The largest age-group of berths available consists of those which were con-

TABLE 4. GENERAL CARGO BERTHS AVAILABLE AND IN USE, OCTOBER 1960 CLASSIFIED BY TIME OF CONSTRUCTION

Area	Prior to 1909		1910–1929		1930–1949		1950 to Date		Totals	
	Avail-able	In Use	Avail-able	In Use	Avail-able	In Use	Avail-able	In Use	Avail-able	In Use
Manhattan Hudson River	26	21	5	3	12	10	2	2	45	36
Manhattan East River	12	9	2	1					14	10
Brooklyn	22	14	53	42	4	4	31	31	110	91
Staten Island			32	5					32	5
New Jersey Hudson River			8	6	7	5	6	6	21	17
Port Newark							14	14	14	14
Total	60	44	100	57	23	19	53	53	236	173

structed between 1910 and 1929. While some of these have benefited by fairly extensive rehabilitation in recent years, as a group they already possess some obsolete characteristics. Included in this group are all of the piers on Staten Island, the Port Authority's Columbia Street and Erie Basin finger piers, the Sea-Land Terminal in Brooklyn, and some of the New York City-owned facilities along the South Brooklyn water front.

At the other end of the scale are facilities constructed since 1930, with many years of productive life remaining. At the end of 1960 these comprised 14 berths on the Manhattan Hudson River, 35 in Brooklyn, 13 on the New Jersey Hudson River water front and 14 at Port Newark. In 1961 six additional berths were completed and put into use in Brooklyn and two more in Port Newark. As of the beginning of 1962 there were therefore available 84 berths constructed after 1930.

To these must be added 27 berths which are currently under construction or for which firm leases have been signed. These berths will not all represent net additions to the available berth supply, however; some of them will be replacements of existing facilities.

The firmest indications at present are that in 1980 there will be 111 conventional general cargo berths less than 50 years of age — 90 of which have been constructed since 1950. They will be distributed as follows: Manhattan Hudson River, 26; Manhattan East River, 3; Brooklyn, 53; New Jersey Hudson River, 13; Newark Bay, 16. Table 5 identifies these berths.

In addition to these 111 berths, Table 5 lists 37–42 berths for which plans have been announced by The Port of New York Authority and the Department of Marine

and Aviation of the City of New York. Although these plans have been announced, no leases or other forms of firm commitment have been entered into with terminal operators, and for this reason these berths are not included in the preceding analysis of berths which will definitely be in place by 1980.

In the case of the plans announced by the City of New York, all for new berths on the Manhattan East River and on Staten Island, they are for replacements for older berths and would not, therefore, represent net additions to the available supply of berths.[2]

The berths listed as planned by the Port Authority are all to be located on Newark Bay, at Port Newark and at Elizabeth-Port Authority Piers. These would all represent new construction and net additions except for one berth at Port Newark which is already completed but is now in use as a containership terminal. The berths planned for Port Newark represent what still has to be built of the originally planned 25 berths; those at Port Elizabeth are components of a master plan which includes provision for a number of berths for other types of operations, including containerships.

The above discussion of berths which will be under 50 years of age by 1980 is limited to berths either already in place or under construction or planned for in those sectors of the port which are already developed, except for the Elizabeth-Port Authority Piers. There are also a number of potential terminal sites, not heretofore developed for marine terminals, which could be developed for conventional general cargo use. All are on the New Jersey side of the harbor. On the Upper Bay water front there are the Pavonia Avenue–Erie Railroad and Communipaw–Central Railroad of New Jersey terminal areas, and Caven Point, in Jersey City;

[2]At the time of going to press, there was underway a study of the Manhattan–Hudson River water front by Ebasco Services, Inc., for the City of New York. The results of this study had not yet been announced.

TABLE 5. BERTHS UNDER 50 YEARS OF AGE BY 1980

Location	Year Completed	Under 30 Years	Between 30 and 50 Years
In Existence, under construction, or firmly committed (Jan. 1, 1963)		90	21
Manhattan Hudson River		14	12
Pier 3	1931		2
25	1936		2
32	1931		2
34	1931		2
40	1962	2[a]	
54	1932		2
57	1953	2	
59, 60, 61	Under constr.	6[b]	
64	1939		2
76	Under constr.	2	
94	Under constr.	2	
Manhattan East River			
Belgium Line Terminal	Lease signed	3	
Brooklyn		51	2
Brooklyn–Port Authority	1956–	29[c]	
Erie Basin–Port Authority Breakwater	1955	5	
Smith Street			1
Court Street	1945		1
Continental Piers	1950	5	
Bull Line	1950	3	
23rd Street	1959	5	
39th Street	Under constr.	4	
New Jersey Hudson River		6	7
Edgewater	1930		3
Hoboken	1957	6	
Harborside, Piers D and F	1931		4
Port Newark	1960	16	
Planned	37–42		
Manhattan East River	7–9		
Port Newark	9[d]		
Elizabeth–Port Authority Piers	15		
Staten Island	6–9		

[a] Terminal will have 4 berths of which 2 are allocated to cargo movement.

[b] These piers were originally constructed in 1904–1906. The recently signed lease with United States Lines provides for such extensive rehabilitation and construction, to cost almost $16,500,000, as to reconstitute the piers as new construction, with only the substructure and outer facade of the existing sheds remaining from the original construction.

[c] As of Jan. 1, 1963, 21 berths were in operation, and 8 berths were under construction. Pier 15, constructed in 1919 will remain in place.

[d] One of these berths, complete with shed, is already in place but is now used for containership operations. These are planned to be relocated in Port Elizabeth, thus making the present berth available for conventional cargo operations.

Point Breeze at the border line of Jersey City and Bayonne; and Constable Hook in Bayonne. In the Point Breeze area, In-transit Terminals, Inc. has announced that it plans to enter into an agreement with the city of Bayonne to construct a new major marine terminal north of the existing Bayonne Naval Supply Depot. This terminal would include, according to the announcement, 18 conventional general cargo berths. As of the beginning of 1963, however, these plans had not been firmly adopted. Recommendations have also been made in the past that part or all of the Naval Supply Depot in Bayonne be converted to general cargo use.

Table 4 provides information also on the degree to which berths located in the various sectors of the harbor are actually used. The Brooklyn and Manhattan Hudson River water fronts on the New York side of the harbor, and Newark Bay and the New Jersey Hudson River sectors on the western side, have the highest ratios of berths in use to total numbers of berths available. Usage is 100 per cent at Port Newark, 82.7 per cent in Brooklyn, 80.9 per cent on the New Jersey Hudson River and 80.0 per cent on the Manhattan Hudson River. By contrast the ratios of Manhattan East River and Staten Island are 71.4 per cent and 15.6 per cent.

These data acquire further significance when viewed in light of the sector distribution of those berths which at the present time are relatively new, those constructed since 1930. All are located in the four sectors showing the highest ratios of berths in use, Manhattan Hudson River, Brooklyn, New Jersey Hudson River and Port Newark. Of 76 such berths in October 1960, 72 were being utilized. This represents a berth-in-use ratio for these newer facilities of almost 95 per cent compared with little more than 60 per cent for the older berths.

Meeting the Port's Requirements

The age a terminal will be in 1980 is only one criterion of the need for its replacement and can lead to only a first approximation of a rebuilding program. For more definitive planning, close study will have to be given to individual facilities. It will be necessary to determine each facility's physical condition and the feasibility of modernization as alternative to demolition and replacement. Additionally, it will be necessary to determine whether existing facilities should be modernized and rehabilitated within the limitations of their present physical dimensions or whether new and different design criteria should be substituted.

The Port of New York possesses the physical potential, in terms of water-front availability, for a far greater number of berths of modern design than will be required by 1980. There are already in existence substantially more berths than are currently required or will be required. There were 224 berths available in 1957, of which only 171 were in use. By October 1960, the number available and the number in use had increased to 236 and 173, respectively. While the number of berths in use has increased slightly, the over-all condition of excess capacity has not been reduced, but has rather been augmented.

For the future, one of the major planning problems will be to settle upon a sound geographic distribution of berths within the harbor, particularly of those still to be developed to meet the desired objective of 170 modern-design berths.

Ownership, jurisdiction and operation of the Port of New York's marine terminals, and responsibility for their planning, development and utilization, is shared by several public agencies and several private companies. Cooperation in planning for the reconstruction of the port's pier and dock facilities is highly desirable to assure that the total terminal plant will best meet the port's needs.

Although the general objective will be to provide conventional general cargo facilities which will incorporate the most modern design and operational characteristics, there will continue to be some berths in use which will not meet these criteria. Just as some outmoded facilities are now used by various steamship lines, it is probable that some facilities of comparable design and age will be used 20 years hence. This may, in turn, inhibit new construction up to the desired objective of 170 berths of modern design and cargo-handling characteristics. It is not possible to foresee the number of facilities which, though obsolete, will continue to be used, or the steamship lines which will use them, or the volumes of cargo they will account for. A program of construction of new facilities, or modernization of existing ones, will therefore have to be approached with an understanding of total requirements and will have to be modified according to emerging patterns of utilization of all port facilities.

If for planning purposes, however, we were to take as our 1980 objective a port in which no marine terminal will be more than 50 years old, and 170 berths as the total requirement in that year, 59 new or modernized berths would have to be provided between 1962 and 1980, over and above current construction and firmly committed programs.

Criteria for Determining Berth Location

Planning for the location of new or modernized berths will have to take into account the older berths likely to be still in use in 1980. The geographical distribution of the total 170-berth requirement may be planned approximately on the basis of existing knowledge of the following additional physical, engineering and economic factors:

1. The physical characteristics of the various sectors of the port, including protection from wind, weather and currents, channel depths and widths, locations of pierhead and bulkhead lines, availability of upland area, and accessibility for motor trucks, railroad trackage and railroad lighterage.

2. The domestic transportation — trucking, railroad lighterage, and direct rail car (wheel-to-keel) — of these shipments to and from the steamship berths.

3. The location relative to the railroad lighterage terminals, and the operational practices of the railroads in the lighterage of freight between those terminals and the steamship berths.

4. The highway network serving the port and the pattern of distribution of trucked freight to and from steamship terminals.

5. Potential uses of the water front for other purposes.

Data on the physical aspects of the several sectors of the port are available in various Port Authority reports and documents and in the publications of the U. S. Army Corps of Engineers and other public agencies. There are also considerable data concerning potential alternative uses of the water front for other than conventional general cargo terminal purposes. The following comments, therefore, are concerned with the distribution of conventional general cargo movements to and from general cargo terminals, as between trucks and railroads, as to the origins and destinations of these movements, as to some of the operational problems of the railroads and trucking companies in performing their distribution functions, and as to the importance of these factors to the geographical location of general cargo facilities.

Truck and Rail Movements to and from General Cargo Terminals

Between a third and a half of the conventional general cargo shipped through the Port of New York comes to or leaves the Port District by railroad.[3] In the language of the railroad industry, all of this freight is classified as "lighterage" cargo. Lighterage in this sense is comprised of three different components: (1) cargo which moves between railroad terminal and steamship terminal by marine equipment, that is, by lighters and carfloats operated by or for the railroads;[4] (2) cargo which moves over connecting tracks between the railroad freight stations and the steamship terminals, generally classified as "wheel-to-keel" by the Port Authority and as "apron track" delivery by the railroads; and (3) cargo which is transported between the railroad stations and the steamship terminals by truck, termed "trucking in lieu of lighterage."

When a shipment originates (or terminates) with a railroad haul, the delivering (or receiving) rail carrier is completely responsible for determining the method of terminal movement. Typically, lighters will be used for cargo which has been floored, that is, removed from the rail car at the station, and carfloats for movements

which are floated in the rail car. Similarly, the railroad will determine whether to utilize trucking in lieu of lighterage, perhaps because of light volumes or for other operational reasons, or marine equipment, even when there are rail tracks connecting directly with the steamship terminal. In this latter instance, when two or more rail carriers are involved in a direct rail movement to a steamship terminal (as for example, New York Central to Weehawken and then by connecting Erie, Jersey Central and Lehigh Valley tracks to Port Newark) the movement is termed a "backhaul" lighterage movement. This designation is of recent origin and is designed particularly to encompass movements to and from Port Newark. Except, however, for the fact that more than one carrier is involved, the operation is identical to a "wheel-to-keel" movement handled by a single carrier.

Another large segment of the total conventional general cargo tonnage moves to and from the marine terminals of the port by motor truck. Although there are no comprehensive data on these truck movements, their total can be approximated by deducting the rail tonnage from the known total of export and import tonnage. Finally, a small share of New York's general cargo originates or terminates at local tidewater industrial plants and moves to and from steamship terminals by various types of harbor craft. This volume is relatively small, however, and for purposes of the following discussion all general cargo movements are considered as moving to and from the steamship terminals by either truck or railroad lighterage.

It may be assumed that virtually all rail-handled freight has its initial domestic origin or ultimate destination outside the Port of New York District; all cargo originating or terminating within the Port District may be assumed to be truck-handled.

[3]This refers to the last carriage of exports to the piers and the first movement of imports away from the piers. With particular reference to imports, substantial volumes are moved by truck from the piers to processing plants and warehouses in the Port District and are in the present context classified as truck movements. Subsequent movements from the processing plants and warehouses, whether by railroad or truck, are classified as domestic movements. For example, most of the coffee imported through the port moves from the piers by truck to roasting and packaging plants and is therefore classified as a truck-handled import movement. Subsequently, much of the processed product is shipped to interior destinations by rail, but this is classified as a domestic movement.

[4]The only railroad which does not operate its own marine equipment and therefore contracts regularly for lighterage service is the New York, Susquehanna, and Western. For special heavy-lift movements, all the railroads use other than railroad-operated floating equipment.

While there are specific exceptions, for example, railroad movement of special heavy-lift cargo originating or terminating in the Port District, these are not of sufficient aggregate magnitude to invalidate the assumptions.

Detailed data are available on rail-handled general cargo lighterage movements for the period 1933 to date. As foreign trade accounts for more than 93 per cent of the total volume of general cargo shipped through the Port of New York, the relationships between foreign trade general cargo and railroad lighterage of general cargo may therefore be viewed as representative of the total volumes involved.

Analyses of the lighterage data, and of 1953, 1957 and 1959 conventional general cargo exports and imports, and related data reveal the following:

1. In 1953 railroad movements, including shipments trucked in lieu of lighterage, accounted for 5,628,770 tons, equivalent to 54.0 per cent of total conventional general cargo foreign trade; truck movements, therefore, accounted for 4,795,487 tons, or 46.0 per cent. For 1957 the comparable figures are 5,303,834 tons, 52.4 per cent, and 4,817,216 tons, 47.6 per cent, for rail and truck movements, respectively.[5]

2. The modest decline in the rail-handled share of conventional general cargo foreign trade between 1953 and 1957 was steeply accelerated by 1959. With a total volume in that year of 10,111,040 tons, the rail-handled portion accounted for only 3,400,863 tons, or 33.6 per cent.

3. Traditionally, the railroads have handled substantially larger volumes and also larger shares of the total volumes of conventional general cargo exports than of imports. In 1953, when total conventional general cargo exports totaled 4,705,055

[5]See Footnote [3] in this chapter.

tons, the railroads accounted for 71.1 per cent; in 1957 when the total volume was 5,333,194 tons, 70.7 per cent was rail-handled. By 1959, however, the relative shares of the railroads and trucks were more evenly balanced. With a volume in that year of 3,849,366 tons of general cargo exports, the railroads handled 2,080,903 tons, or 54.1 per cent.

4. For conventional general cargo imports, a different pattern has prevailed. The larger share has moved from the piers by truck. With a total volume of 5,719,202 tons in 1953, only 39.9 per cent was rail-handled. The pattern was accentuated in 1957 and 1959; in 1957 when the total volume was 4,787,856 tons, 32.0 per cent moved out by rail, and in 1959, when the total volume was 6,261,674 tons, 21.1 per cent was rail-handled.

5. It may be assumed that all rail-handled conventional general cargo has its domestic origin or destination outside the Port District, and that, conversely, all Port District origins and destinations are served by truck. It may not be assumed, however, that all truck-handled freight has its origin or destination within the Port District. There is a substantial portion of the truck freight that originates or terminates outside the Port District. Nevertheless, these data on the differences in the proportions of exports and imports handled by truck and rail freight would suggest that the Port District is more important as a consumption market for its imports than as a source of its exports. Fluctuations in the relative volumes of exports and imports are thus likely to be reflected in fluctuations in the relative shares of rail- and truck-handled freight delivered to or picked up at the port's marine terminals.

6. As noted previously, rail-handled volume includes a trucking-in-lieu-of-light-

erage segment. This is the volume which the railroads, for their own operational reasons, truck rather than float between their lighterage stations and the steamship terminals. For some Manhattan and Brooklyn movements, the cargo may be carfloated across the Hudson River to and from pier stations on Manhattan and trucked between them and the steamship terminals. Approximately 25 per cent of all trucking in lieu of lighterage is performed from these pier stations.

In all three years, 1953, 1957 and 1959, trucking-in-lieu-of-lighterage movements totaled approximately 750,000 tons. When these volumes are added to the direct truck movements, the over-all shares of cargo trucked to and from steamship terminals rose to 53.3 per cent in 1953, 55.0 per cent in 1957, and 73.2 per cent in 1959. Conversely, the railroad lighterage shares declined to 46.7 per cent, 45.0 per cent and 26.8 per cent for 1953, 1957 and 1959, respectively.

These data indicate that there has been a major shift in the relative shares of the railroads and trucks in the handling of conventional general cargo exports and imports. As a result, the division between railroads and trucks shifted from approximate balance in 1953 and 1957 to dominance by trucks in 1959.

Location of Railroad Lighterage Stations

In the fall of 1960 there were eleven lighterage stations in the Port of New York handling foreign trade general car-

go:[6] nine along the New Jersey Hudson River water front (six in Jersey City, two in Weehawken, one in Hoboken); the remaining two being the Harlem River terminal of the New Haven in the Bronx, and the Baltimore and Ohio terminal at St. George, Staten Island. In addition, there were three short-line connecting railroads, one in Hoboken and two in Brooklyn, which offered direct service to some steamship terminals in those areas.[7]

As indicated earlier, it is the common practice of the railroads to lighter freight – or to truck in lieu of lighterage – between their lighterage stations and steamship terminals. This is true even of those railroads having direct rail access to certain terminals: the Pennsylvania Railroad to the Harborside Terminal in Jersey City, the Baltimore and Ohio Railroad to the Staten Island piers, and the Central Railroad of New Jersey, the Lehigh Valley and Pennsylvania Railroads to Port Newark. In 1957 when the total volume of rail-handled conventional general cargo was 5,303,834 tons, only 102,385 tons was on a direct wheel-to-keel and keel-to-wheel basis.[8] The locations of the lighterage stations are thus the focal points in the rail handling of freight in the port.

The interior origins of export movements and destinations of imports are, in this context, of little importance to the railroads in their choices as to how the shipments are to be handled within the port. Whatever preferences they may have concerning the locations of the steamship terminals are related to the locations of their lighterage stations, carfloat terminals and switching facilities.

Lighterage Stations and
General Cargo Berth Locations

It is assumed, for berth location planning purposes, that there will not be any major changes in the locations of the light-

[6]There were two additional railroad properties which were operated during the preceding five years as lighterage stations, but were not in such use in October 1960. These include the National Docks of the Lehigh Valley and the 60th Street yards of the New York Central.

[7]There were a number of other short-line connecting railroads, each of which linked with one or more of the trunk-line railroads, but did not directly serve the water front. The three referred to in this text were the New York Dock Railway, the Bush Terminal Railroad Company and the Hoboken Shore Railroad.

[8]There were additional volumes of wheel-to-keel movements of specialized and bulk cargoes, notably grain, bananas, scrap iron and ores.

erage stations. While mergers, consolidations and joint operation of marine services may result in reduction in the number of lighterage stations, the general pattern of their location is not likely to be materially altered.

The lighterage and carfloat system is valuable to the railroads because it provides the means by which they can serve all sections of the harbor. The small volume of direct wheel-to-keel movement is clear evidence of this. So too is the observed practice of the railroads to lighter and to carfloat cargo to the Harborside Terminal in Jersey City, the American and Pouch Terminals in Staten Island and to Port Newark, all of which have the possibility of direct rail access. The expanse of the port area is such that the "water highway," combined with the basic concept of port unity, brings every portion of the port within an effective railroad service radius. Also, as the lighterage stations serve as consolidation and break-bulk platforms for split-car and less-than-carload movements, they are utilized for double-duty purposes.

Origins and Destinations
of Trucked Freight

Far less is known of the volumes and the origins and destinations of foreign trade conventional general cargo which is transported to and from the marine terminals by motor truck. A sample survey of truck freight moving to and from the water front in 1956, however, disclosed:

1. Twelve per cent had inland origins or destinations outside the Port District and was trucked directly to and from

[9]The fact that the truck-handled portion of conventional general cargo increased between 1953 and 1959 does not affect this conclusion. It is assumed that all locally generated freight is moved to and from steamship terminals by truck and that all rail-handled freight originates or terminates outside the Port District. The increase in the truck-handled share thus represents a shift from rail to truck of cargo generated outside the Port District.

steamship terminals. The principal inland areas served in this manner included much of New England and eastern Canada, New York and New Jersey, Pennsylvania, Ohio and Illinois.

2. An additional 28 per cent moved between points outside the Port District and the steamship terminals by way of intermediate transfer points within the Port District, over-the-road truck terminals, railroad lighterage stations and other steamship terminals.

3. All together, therefore, about 40 per cent of all cargo trucked to and from steamship terminals had origins and destinations outside the Port District.

4. The remaining 60 per cent came from or went to points within the Port District — industrial plants, warehouses or local truck terminals. This was equivalent to about 33 per cent of the total conventional general cargo handled at the Port of New York by all modes of land transportation. Thus, about 67 per cent originated or terminated outside the Port District.[9]

5. According to the survey, the areas east of the Hudson River accounted for about two-thirds of the locally generated freight and areas west of the Hudson for one-third.

6. Steamship terminals in all sectors of the harbor handled general cargo generated in all sectors, but there was a moderate tendency for those in any one sector to draw more than a proportionate share of the locally generated freight from that sector. This disproportion suggests that there is a certain amount of mutual attraction between the shipping terminal location and the point of local freight generation.

In prospect, the two lines of economic activity more closely related than any others to the generation of freight movement, manufacturing and the goods-handling phases of wholesale trade, will be relatively more prominent in areas west of the Hudson in the future.[10] To the extent that the mutual attraction referred to above between points of local freight generation and marine terminal location prevails in the future, the implication of this geographic shift is a need for the strengthening of west-of-Hudson marine terminal accommodations above their present levels.

In summary, according to the 1956 survey about two-thirds of the conventional general cargo foreign trade tonnage passing through the marine terminals of the port is generated outside the Port District.

[10]See Chapters 3, 5 and 6.

About half of this is transported to and from the Port District by rail and half by motor truck. The remaining one-third of the total is generated within the Port District, and is transported to and from the marine terminals by motor truck.

About two-thirds of this locally generated cargo comes from or is delivered to points east of the Hudson River and about one-third from or to points west of it. There is a likelihood that general cargo freight generation in areas west of the Hudson will become relatively stronger during the next two decades, which implies a need for strengthening the ability of that sector to accommodate it.

CHAPTER 11

SPECIALIZED CARGO, CONTAINERSHIPS AND BULK CARGO

The general-cargo category of ocean-borne freight includes a number of commodities, and several forms of shipment, which are handled in large part, and even entirely in some cases, at terminals especially designed for them. This subcategory of general cargo includes: bananas, sugar, vegetable oils, rubber latex, lumber, newsprint, scrap iron, wine and citrus fruit juice shipped by tanker, and containership cargo. Each of these commodities, and each form of shipment, presents a special terminal problem.

SPECIALIZED CARGO

Most of the specialized terminals are operated by companies engaged in processing or distributing the goods being transported. Frequently, the terminal accommodates only one commodity, or form of shipment. Many are integral parts of industrial plants, such as sugar refineries or vegetable oil processing facilities. The role of public agencies in planning and providing for this component of marine tonnage varies with the circumstances of each case. For some movements, for example, lumber, scrap iron and containership operations, the role is a significant one; for others, such as for sugar, vegetable oils and latex rubber, it is a very minor one.

Considerable tonnage is involved, however, and a strong rate of growth is to be expected. The average annual volume for the 1957-1959 period and the projected volumes for 1980 are presented in Table 1.

The projections for 1980 as shown in Table 1 rest upon estimates and assumptions, presented in earlier chapters, as to population, gross national product, industrial production, geographical distribution of national and regional activity, national foreign trade policy and the railroad freight rate structure, and have taken into account the probable impact of the St. Lawrence Seaway. For several commodities trade practices and trade structures have also been considered, and patterns of production and distribution.

The direction of movement of this specialized general cargo is dominantly inbound. The tonnage accounts for a large proportion of the port's total inbound general cargo tonnage. In 1959, receipts of specialized general cargo outweighed shipments by a ratio of almost two to one. By 1980 the imbalance is expected to become even greater, almost three to one. The preponderance of inbound movement is a consequence of the difference in commodity composition between inbound and outbound cargoes. Inbound cargoes include large-volume commodities, such as bananas, sugar, vegetable oils, lumber and newsprint, whereas only vegetable oils and scrap iron are large-volume outbound shipments.

In the light of recent trends it is likely that further broadening of the "specialized" category will be required in the future. There are commodities which once were handled at conventional terminals and which now utilize specialized facilities, California wine by tanker, for instance. For other commodities packaged shipment may give way to bulk shipment

TABLE 1. NEW YORK'S SPECIALIZED GENERAL CARGO MOVEMENTS
ANNUAL AVERAGE 1957–1959 AND ESTIMATED 1980
(thousands of long tons)

	Inbound		Outbound	
	Annual Average 1957–1959	Estimated 1980	Annual Average 1957–1959	Estimated 1980
Bananas	308[a]	550	—	d
Sugar	1,028[a]	1,630	e	e
Vegetable oils	236	205	275	345
Latex rubber	18	15	—	d
Lumber	770	675	6	d
Newsprint	168[a]	400	e	e
Scrap iron	129	b	873	b
Citrus juices by tanker	63[c]	400	d	d
Wine by tanker	37[c]	60	d	d
Containership	813	2,100	590	1,900
Total	3,538	6,035	1,744	2,245

[a] 1957–1959 includes only volumes handled over specialized terminals; 1980 includes total volumes.

[b] No estimate made for inbound or outbound volumes. It is estimated that inbound and outbound volumes combined will total 500,000 tons in 1980 but the total cannot be allocated as to direction.

[c] Service instituted in 1957, citrus juices from Florida, wine from Pacific Coast. Annual average represents only 1958 and 1959 full year operations. Citrus juice movement temporarily suspended in 1962.

[d] None estimated.

[e] Handled over conventional facilities.

and may require specialized terminal equipment. There is even a possibility that frozen foods and heavy-lift shipments may be handled at specialized facilities by 1980. It is more likely, however, that the frozen-food problem will be solved by technological developments in the packaging field and that heavy-lift operations will continue to rely upon floating cranes brought to conventional general cargo terminals. Further, there are commodities which were handled at both conventional and specialized terminal facilities in 1959, like bananas, sugar and newsprint. By 1980 it is probable that the total volumes of these commodities will be handled over specialized facilities.

Looking ahead to 1980, virtually all of the tonnage in this category except for containership cargo and vegetable oils will be inbound.

Such additional terminals as may be needed for sugar, vegetable oils and rubber latex are likely to be provided by private companies on private property.

There may be a need for an additional specialized banana terminal in the port which might well be jointly used by several banana importing companies.

There is now one specialized newsprint terminal in the port, owned by a metropolitan newspaper, and another is under construction, for a newsprint supplier. No additional facility requirements are foreseen for 1980.

Lumber and scrap iron are now accommodated at both public and private terminals. No additional terminal facility requirements are foreseen.

The outlook with respect to citrus fruit juices and wine transported by tankers is uncertain.

CONTAINERSHIPS

Perhaps the most significant development in freight transportation in recent years has been the trend toward integration of different modes of transport, particularly piggyback for land movement and containerships for ocean transport. In both instances, the key factor has been the use of the highway trailer as a shipping container.

In piggyback, highway and rail transport are integrated by placing the trailer, with or without its chassis, on a flatcar for rail movement and subsequent highway transport to destination; in the containership operation the trailer is placed aboard ship for ocean transport. Closely related is integration of railroad and steamship transport, with railroad cars given ocean transport on a specially designed ship.

Types of Containership Operations

Containers of less than highway-trailer size have been in use for a number of years for valuable cargo or for cargo particularly susceptible to damage. Generally, these smaller containers have not exceeded 8 or 10 feet in length. They have been handled at conventional terminals, with ship's boom and tackle. Containerships, on the other hand, carry trailer-size containers, and their cargo space is different in form from those of conventional general cargo ships.

There are variations in the size of the containers, reflecting variations in the size of highway units and the requirements of particular trade routes. Almost all, however, are of standard width and height, 8 feet by 8 feet. The lack of uniformity in length has been a matter of concern to the transport industry, and the American Standards Association has recommended that the lengths of shipping containers be standardized at 10, 20, and 40 feet.

The containership may be of the roll-on-roll-off or of the lift-on-lift-off type. The roll-on-roll-off ship requires the trailer to be towed aboard or to be carried aboard by high-capacity fork-lift trucks. In the lift-on-lift-off ship, the trailer is detached from its chassis and lifted into a bulkheaded cell by crane. The crane may be ship-borne, or may be terminal equipment. In the roll-on-roll-off ship, the holds provide for horizontal movement; in the lift-on-lift-off operation, the cells provide for vertical tiering.

Sea-Land Service, with ship-borne cranes, now provides a lift-on-lift-off service for the coastal, intercoastal and off-shore trades.

Railroad freight cars are also transported in ocean-going vessels. Seatrain Lines has provided such a service at the Port of New York since before World War II. Although still transporting rail cars, Seatrain has turned recently to the transport of highway trailers also.

Advantages of the Containership

From the ship operator's point of view the principal advantages of the containership are the reduction in the cost of cargo handling and the reduction in port time. The latter can be translated into increased annual carrying capacity for each ship, or into a reduction in the number of ships required to service a trade route.

In the case of full trailer load shipments, stowage is performed by the shipper. For smaller shipments, the steamship company (or its agents) must consolidate the shipments into container loads and must break them out again at destination: there are still fewer handlings of the cargo at the ship terminals and aboard ship.

From the point of view of the shippers and consignees, the advantages are: delivery in shorter time, delivery in better condition, and delivery at lower cost. Reduction of the number of handlings, together with faster loading and unloading, reduces the total time in transit; truck waiting time at the steamship berth is almost entirely eliminated. There is less likelihood of damage or loss from mishandling, pilferage, bad stowage, weather or contamination. For perishable cargo, temperature control is possible with sealed containers equipped with refrigeration units. Important reductions in cost also come about through simpler packaging requirements.

Maximum benefits of containerization are achieved when shipments move from shipper to consignee without breaking bulk, and when the movement of containerized goods is directionally balanced.

Against the savings in operating costs, however, there must be set the higher capital costs required, for the ships are more costly than conventional ships of

equivalent capacity and the containers and the ancillary equipment are additional.

Outlook for Containership Operations

For efficient containership operation the number of ports served must be limited to permit quick turn-around, and consequent high annual carrying capacity of the ship, and to limit the dispersal of containers. The Port of New York thereby gains a competitive advantage. As the largest market on the North Atlantic and as the strongest area of generation of outbound movements it has substantial cargo volumes available for containership movement, and it is likely to become the favored base of operation for containership service. It is the only port on the North Atlantic today providing such a

Table 2. Containership Movements at the Port of New York
1947–1960

(long tons)

	Seatrain		Sea-Land		Total		Total Tonnage
	Receipts	Shipments	Receipts	Shipments	Receipts	Shipments	
1947	178,853	147,803			178,853	147,803	326,656
1948	282,547	240,810			282,547	240,810	523,357
1949	297,479	212,410			297,479	212,410	509,889
1950	380,848	215,033			380,848	215,033	595,881
1951	349,310	214,004			349,310	214,004	563,314
1952	498,718	290,843			498,718	290,843	789,561
1953	546,660	312,602			546,660	312,602	859,262
1954	532,148	219,018			532,148	319,018	851,166
1955	605,617	347,047			605,617	347,047	952,664
1956	582,077	331,926	[a]	[a]	582,077	331,926	977,260[a]
1957	557,374	306,746	114,941	112,796	672,315	419,542	1,091,857
1958	514,722	201,037	322,784	373,754	837,506	574,791	1,412,297
1959	411,141	225,402	524,615	543,533	935,756	768,935	1,704,691
1960	453,470	249,308	518,639	557,376	972,109	806,684	1,778,793

[a]Sea-Land Service started April 26, 1956. Grand total for 1956 includes 63,257 long tons without differentiation as to receipts and shipments.

service and the only one for which further service is planned.

In assessing the outlook for containership operations at the Port of New York, however, it is necessary to consider domestic and foreign trade separately.

The components of the domestic maritime services are: (1) coastal trade, within a single, or between adjacent, coastal areas; (2) intercoastal trade, between the Atlantic and Gulf coasts and the Pacific Coast; and (3) offshore trade, such as that between the Atlantic and Gulf coasts and Puerto Rico and between the Pacific Coast and Hawaii.

Domestic service may be provided by United States flag carriers only; they are not eligible for either construction or operating subsidies. When operating in foreign trade they are eligible for both types of subsidy. In foreign trade and in offshore trade the containership operator must compete only with other water carriers; in the coastal and intercoastal service he must compete with land transportation as well.

Coastal and Intercoastal Trade

Prior to World War II coastal and intercoastal shipping carried substantial tonnage. During the late 1930's it accounted for about a third of the port's total volume of ocean-borne general cargo. Since the end of World War II, however, these services of the conventional general cargo carriers have all disappeared, except for a few carriers who specialize in the carriage of lumber from west to east and iron and steel products from east to west.

Lying behind this decline are many factors, including the competition with rail and motor truck transportation, the increased cost of terminal operations and the high costs of replacing the ships formerly in the domestic trade. Experience so far, however, suggests that the contain-

ership, because of its advantages, may bring about an important revival of coastal and intercoastal shipping. This expectation must be tempered, however, by an evaluation of the influence of new developments in land transportation, notably piggyback.

Much will depend on national transportation policy regarding the competition between the various modes of transportation, and particularly on the policy adopted by the Interstate Commerce Commission regarding transportation rates. The ability of coastal and intercoastal shipping to provide dependable, efficient and economical containership operations will be largely determined by these policies.

Assuming that national transportation policies will favor the revitalization of ocean shipping in domestic trade, the containership will be competitive with the railroads and the motor carriers for coastal and intercoastal shipments. Because of the prospective rises in population, gross national product, and industrial production, domestic intercity tonnage volumes should increase by a significant amount. It is well within the range of reasonable probability that containership volume in the Port of New York's coastal trade will increase some 50 per cent above the 1958 and 1959 level of 1,400,000 tons to, say, 2,000,000 to 2,200,000 tons by 1980.

During the period 1955 to 1958 the annual volume of intercoastal conventional general cargo, between all Pacific Coast and all North Atlantic ports, ranged between 2,500,000 tons and 1,920,000 tons. There was also an estimated volume of more than 1,500,000 tons annually of comparable cargo carried by the railroads between the Pacific Coast and New York, New Jersey and Connecticut, and an unknown volume carried across the continent by truck.

Not all of the volumes carried by ships, railroads and trucks represent potential container cargo. For example, some iron and steel mill products, which in total have amounted to more than 700,000 tons annually in westbound trade in recent years, are not considered containerizable because of their dimensions and low stowage factors. Other commodities about which there is doubt as to feasibility of containerization include iron and steel pipe and some electrical machinery and nonmetallic minerals, lead and lead-based alloys and wood pulp.

Several estimates of intercoastal containership potential have recently been developed by outside study groups. Using somewhat different assumptions as to the factors affecting this trade, these estimates of potential volume range from 1,340,000 to 2,140,000 long tons at the present time, to 4,200,000 tons by 1966 and 5,000,000 tons by 1976.[1]

If we accept the most conservative of these estimates there is a potential volume, at the present time, of 1,500,000 tons annually for containership operations between the Pacific and North Atlantic coasts. By 1980 this potential should exceed 2,000,000 tons annually. Increase in population alone should expand the containership potential because of the relative importance of consumer goods in the coast-to-coast movement, notably fruits and vegetables, other grocery products, wines and distilled spirits, edible molasses and syrups and manufactured goods. Assuming, therefore, that intercoastal containership services will be available and that these operations will be based at New York, it is estimated that the Port of New York's 1980 volume will approximate 1,500,000 tons annually.

[1]These estimates and their authors are as follows: Arthur D. Little, Inc., 1,340,000 long tons in 1960; Coverdale and Colpitts, 2,140,000 long tons in 1962; Robert R. Nathan Associates, 4,150,000—4,200,000 in 1966 and 5,000,000 long tons in 1976.

Offshore Trade

The third major component of domestic ocean-borne transportation is the offshore trade. It is exemplified by cargo movements between the Atlantic and Gulf Coast ports and Puerto Rico, and between Pacific Coast ports and Hawaii.

In serving the offshore areas the water carriers are not confronted with competition from the railroads and motor carriers. Competition in the offshore trade is between conventional shipping and containership operations, and, moreover, limited to United States flag lines.

Trade between the North Atlantic ports and Puerto Rico consists of two major components: (1) a northbound sugar movement, and (2) miscellaneous cargo moving southbound. In the period 1955 to 1958, the total annual volumes of conventional general cargo movements in the North Atlantic-Puerto Rican trade, including volumes handled at Boston, Philadelphia, Baltimore and Norfolk-Newport News as well as at New York, ranged between 650,000 and 735,000 tons. Some 80 per cent appears to be containerizable.

Assuming that containership operations to Atlantic offshore points will continue to be concentrated at the Port of New York, it is likely that by 1980 the total volume so handled will increase to some 600,000 to 650,000 tons.

Foreign Trade

The future of containership operations in foreign trade will be controlled by factors radically different from those affecting the domestic trades. There are four of major importance: (1) customs and other regulatory problems, (2) characteristics of trade route composition, (3) trucking and highway standards and systems abroad, and (4) length of ocean haul.

All imports into the United States are

subject to customs examination and appraisal, including even those shipments which are duty-free. Many commodities are subject to special regulations and quota limitations, and some are subject to special health and entomology regulations. Comparable, and sometimes more rigorous, requirements are applied by other countries. In regard to United States exports, there are quantity controls on certain commodities because of national security considerations, and special controls on trade with certain countries. There are many other administrative controls applied to foreign trade movements both here and abroad, and regulations and practices covering container movements vary from country to country.

Generally, these regulations and controls are applied at the ports of lading and unlading. The use of sealed containers complicates these procedures. Additional problems arise when duties are assessed on a weight basis and the container itself, when sent inland with its cargo, is adjudged an import item.

At New York and at San Francisco procedures are in effect under certain circumstances which permit import merchandise to move directly to importers' premises in the container. The importer may request that a customs inspector be sent to the delivery point to appraise the merchandise. There is no cost to the shipper or receiver when the point of inspection is within the local area, but when the point of inspection is outside it the cost of transportation of inspecting personnel must be paid for. Containers going to destinations outside the New York customs district must be shipped in bond; for such shipments the carrier must pay a special fee.

Approval for all such outside inspections must be obtained from the Appraiser's Office. Approval is granted readily when the cargo consists of one or only a few commodities, when the shipment is consigned to only one importer, and when no public health or pest control problem is involved. When the container carries a cargo of mixed commodities requiring the services of several inspectors, or a number of shipments to different importers who cannot agree on the point of examination, approval is seldom granted.

The volume of containerizable cargo varies widely from trade route to trade route and from country to country. Even when there is a considerable amount of containerizable cargo destined for or originating in a particular country, it may not be feasible to concentrate the movement in a few ports so as to achieve the full benefit of containership operation. As a case in point, cargo destined for or originating in Italy is now handled in Sicily, Naples, Genoa and at a number of Adriatic ports. Even if there should be enough containerizable volume in the Italy-United States trade to support containership operation, it is unlikely that any one of the Italian ports would have sufficient volume to warrant the service. This would also be true in France, where cargo is handled at Mediterranean, Atlantic and Channel ports.

There also are wide variations in the practices and standards of highway transport in foreign countries, and many of them are different from those of the United States. Thus, it is more likely that containership service could be established with those areas whose practices and standards approximate those of the United States, e.g., the West Indies and the north and east coasts of South America, than with Western Europe.

The longer trade routes, like those to Australasia, South and West Africa, and the Indian Ocean area, present weaker prospects for the development of containership service. In general, they have smaller trade volumes; when there are substantial cargo volumes, there is usually a limited number of commodities, which are either not readily containerizable or which have dispersed origins in several countries. An exception is the trade with Japan, which is both large in volume and diversified in character. Also, ships on the longer routes generally call at a number of ports, in different countries. To serve all of them by containership would sacrifice the port concentration necessary for successful containership operation. On the longer trade routes the reduction in port time is of relatively less importance, the annual carrying capacity of a ship is not increased materially nor is the number of ships required to serve a given trade route reduced.

The outlook for the establishment of containership service in foreign trade by the American flag lines is also related to ship replacement programs. A substantial proportion of the ships now in the American merchant fleet are of World War II vintage and will be due for replacement during the next few years. The replacement programs which have been announced for carriers serving the North Atlantic coastal district do not include containerships, except for three combination ships for the Grace Line. If the current schedules are adhered to it will not be until the next round of replacement, sometime in the 1970's, that containerships are likely to become of major importance.

These observations on the factors affecting containership operations in foreign trade suggest that they will develop at a slower rate than in the domestic trades. The many advantages to be gained by such operations, however, indicate that some of the current limiting factors will be overcome and that world trade will in the future be served by containerships as well as by break-bulk vessels. There is no current basis, however, for estimating the quantities likely to be involved.

Further, there is every likelihood that the use of containers on conventional general cargo vessels will increase substantially. This trend is, in fact, already in evidence. These movements, however, will be accommodated at conventional steamship terminals.

TERMINAL REQUIREMENTS FOR CONTAINERSHIP OPERATIONS

Terminal areas for containership operations must meet three basic requirements: (1) water depths capable of accommodating deep-draft vessels; (2) sufficient open land; and (3) good highway access. Preferably, the berths for a highway trailer type of operation should be of the quay type to permit a continuous forward movement of the trailers.

If the operation is to provide also for piggyback transport, the terminal areas must have rail connections that permit the containers to be transferred to and from the rail cars quickly and economically.

On the basis of the port's brief operating experience it appears that the practical and effective capacity of a containership berth for an operation like that of the Sea-Land Service is about 500,000 tons per year. The open area required to support a berth is six to twelve acres. The amount of shedded space required for consolidation and break-bulk operations depends on how much of those functions are performed in the terminal area.

The tonnage potential for containership operation in 1980 is estimated at 4,000,000 tons. If all containership berths in the port should operate at the 500,000 ton annual capacity figure, a total of eight berths would be required. But such capacity operation cannot be assumed. The number of berths needed for the entire port will be dependent upon the number of containership operators, upon how containership tonnage is divided among them, and upon the extent to which joint terminal usage will be feasible.

BULK CARGOES

Bulk cargo, as distinguished from general cargo, is handled as loose material, rather than in a packaged, bundled or crated form; it moves over specialized, mechanically equipped terminal facilities and requires little longshore labor or other dock handling. The following commodities are the most prominent:

(1) As exports: grains, including corn, barley and rye, wheat, oats, sorghum grains, soybeans and flaxseed; coal; nonmetallic minerals, including sulfur and phosphates; and tanker cargo, principally petroleum derivatives.

(2) As imports: tanker cargo, including petroleum and its refined derivatives; molasses; benzol, benzine, and other coal-tar derivatives; nonmetallic minerals; and ores of iron, manganese, chrome, aluminum, copper, lead and titanium.

(3) In domestic trade: tanker cargo, including petroleum and its derivatives, molasses, coal-tar products, and industrial chemicals; coal; sulfur; sand, gravel and rock; and phosphates.

Five categories account for most of the bulk tonnage handled at North Atlantic ports: ores, nonmetallic minerals, petroleum, export grains, and sand, gravel and rock. The last category is almost entirely an intraport movement and although the annual volume at the Port of New York approximates 10 million tons, terminal requirements are not such as to compete for prime water-front space on deep-draft channels.

The bulk ores include the important iron and steel-making ores — iron, manga-nese and chrome — and the ores of aluminum, copper, lead and titanium. The combination of tremendous wartime drains on our mines and the increasing demands of an expanding economy have made it necessary that the nation look increasingly to foreign sources of supply. In consequence, our imports have increased eight-fold since the end of the war, from 5,166,-000 tons in 1946 to almost 41,000,000 tons in 1959. The outlook is for imports of metallic ores in ever-increasing volumes, particularly the iron and steel-making ores and bauxite. By 1980, the total volume may exceed 70 million tons a year.

The role of the Port of New York in handling iron and steel-making ores has been minor, accounting for only 848,000 tons in 1959. Its future role is wholly dependent on the rail rate structure from seaboard to interior consumption centers. If the rates from New York to the interior should be equalized with those of Baltimore and Philadelphia it would be possible for the port to compete for the future ore volume to be imported through the North Atlantic ports, provided that a modern ore handling facility would be built to accommodate it. Under such circumstances, New York's potential volume would be about 6 million tons a year by 1980.

While the volumes of the other import ores are expected to increase moderately, no additional terminal facility requirements appear to be needed.

Nor is any future need foreseen for additional facilities for the movement of coal and bulk minerals—gypsum, sulfur, sodium nitrate and phosphate rock. They are generally handled at terminals which are components of industrial facilities, privately owned and operated.

The outlook for movements of petroleum and refined petroleum products brings up a different sort of problem. All of the terminal facilities in the port area, except for those at the airports, are owned by the oil companies, the refiners and distributors. It is estimated that tanker receipts of petroleum and petroleum products will increase from 52.5 million tons in 1959, to more than 81 million tons by 1980. The problems for the future have to do primarily with channel accommodations, channels deep enough and wide enough for supertankers, and land enough for the terminal facilities required by the increased petroleum product consumption.

In 1951 there were only 8 tankers in the free-world fleet which were over 30,000 deadweight tons; by 1957 there were 133, some as large as 85,000 tons. At the end of 1955, only 7.6 per cent of the total carrying capacity of the world's tankers was represented by tankers of 30,000 tons and over. By the end of 1960, this ratio had increased to 36.8 per cent. Of the tankers reported under construction or on order at the end of 1960, almost 70 per cent were ships of 40,000 tons or more.

The T-2 tanker, 16,600 tons, which was standard for many years, and which can be accommodated readily in the port's channels, has a loaded draft of 30 feet, 2 inches. By comparison a 35,500-ton tanker has a loaded draft of 35 feet, 7 inches; a 46,000-tonner, 37 feet, 10 inches; a 60,000-tonner, 41 feet, 7 inches; an 80,000-tonner, 46 feet; and a 100,000-tonner, 48 feet, 4 inches. Dredged channels must provide at least 3 to 4 feet of additional depth for keel clearance.

Because of natural deep water at the Narrows, part of the Staten Island pier area may be used in the future for tanker berthing, and linked by pipeline with the refineries and distribution facilities.

The outlook for grain movement through the Port of New York is not encouraging. During the interwar period, most of the grain exported through New York was of Canadian origin. Canadian grain no longer moves through United States North Atlantic ports, because of Canada's policy of favoring its own ports. Forced to rely upon grain of domestic origin the port is handicapped, for the locational pattern of domestic grain production does not favor the Port of New York. Neither do the trends in the grain trade, which are toward integration and concentration and toward full-shipload rather than parcel-lot movement. There are rail rate handicaps relative to the ports of Baltimore, Philadelphia and Norfolk. Handling and trimming costs are high in the port. As long as these unfavorable factors remain in effect, and in view of the present unused elevator capacity in the port, there does not seem to be any need for additional grain terminal facilities.

CHAPTER 12

CHANNEL AND WATERWAY REQUIREMENTS

The most familiar point on the sea charts of the world is probably 40 degrees 41 minutes North Latitude, 70 degrees 02 minutes West Longitude, the location of the Statue of Liberty. It is the symbol of the Port of New York, the principal gateway to the United States for cargo and passengers. The port is the journey's beginning and the journey's end for the movement of more ocean-going cargo and passengers than any other port in the United States.

Although the term "the Port of New York" is the familiarly accepted designation, it is in fact "the Port of New York–New Jersey," for its political geography includes portions of both states and numerous municipalities.

The area embraced by the port includes eight large bays — Lower New York, Upper New York, Sandy Hook, Raritan, Newark, Jamaica, Gravesend and Eastchester — each of which is larger in area and in potential for development than many American and European harbors. Flowing into and linking these bays are the Hudson, Raritan, Passaic and Hackensack rivers and the four tidal straits known as the Harlem and East rivers and the Arthur Kill and the Kill van Kull. The Hudson River, Upper New York Bay, Arthur Kill and Kill van Kull also provide the basic line of political jurisdiction: they separate the states of New York and New Jersey. The Narrows, the inner gateway to the Port of New York, connects the Upper and Lower bays. The port, thus defined, includes approximately 650 miles of frontage on navigable waterways measured along the bulkheads, 395 miles in New York and 255 miles in New Jersey. It is a naturally sheltered harbor area requiring few breakwaters, with modest tidal ranges and an equable climate throughout the year.

DEVELOPMENT RESPONSIBILITIES

Historically, prior to the adoption of federal legislation on this subject, bulkhead and pierhead lines and thus the dimensions of the open navigable channels in the waterways of the port were fixed under state authority. The construction and operation of marine terminal facilities were and still are undertaken by private interests and various municipalities and federal and state agencies.

It was not until 1888 that the United States government, through an Act of Congress, assumed control over the fixing of bulkhead and pierhead lines. The implementation of this authority was given to the Corps of Engineers of what was then the War Department, and has remained with this agency through all the subsequent administrative reorganizations of the defense establishment. Pursuant to federal law, solid fill may be used up to the designated bulkhead lines without specific permission; beyond this line only with permission. And no construction of terminal facilities may be undertaken beyond the designated pierhead lines except by specific permission of the Corps of Engineers.

The construction and maintenance of navigable waterways within the harbor

173

lines of the Port of New York, as in other ports and navigable waterways, is also the responsibility of the Corps of Engineers. Beginning with the early years of the nineteenth century, the functions of the Corps of Engineers have been progressively expanded to the point where the Corps now has certain development and regulatory responsibilities over all ports and navigable waterways of the United States which serve interstate and international commerce.[1]

The development responsibilities include the preparation of all preliminary investigations, authorized surveys and reports on proposed projects relating to development and improvement of navigable waterways, and construction and maintenance of these improvements after authorization and appropriation of funds in the normal legislative process of the federal government. The reports provide the technical basis for the authorization and appropriation of funds; the construction and maintenance functions may be carried out directly by the Corps of Engineers or may be contracted for under certain established procedures.

The regulatory responsibility is that Corps of Engineers' approval must be obtained for construction or other activities which may affect ports and navigable waterways, such as the construction of bridges, tunnels or causeways.

Access between the navigable channels and facilities constructed within the harbors and along the waterways is normally undertaken by those owning and operating the facilities. For example, the Corps of Engineers provides a channel in the Hudson River from Upper New York Bay

to a point north of 57th Street at a minimum width of 2,000 feet and a minimum depth of 45 feet. Those who own and operate marine terminal and industrial facilities along the Manhattan and New Jersey water fronts bordering this stretch of the Hudson River provide access to this channel and maintain the necessary water depths alongside their facilities. As another example, this time with reference to Port Newark, the Corps of Engineers maintains a 400-foot wide channel at a 35-foot depth running down the middle of the full channel width; and The Port of New York Authority, which operates Port Newark, maintains an additional 142.5 feet on each side of the central channel. There is thus provided a total channel with a 685-foot over-all width and a uniform 35-foot depth.

Even though the primary responsibility for construction and maintenance of harbor improvements and navigable channels is that of the Corps of Engineers, it is on the basis of the initiative of local interests, public or private, or both, that a proposal for harbor, river or channel improvements will be considered in normal congressional and Corps of Engineers' procedures. It was in this light that the Port Compact of 1921, which established The Port of New York Authority, included provisions authorizing the Port Authority to make recommendations to the legislatures of the two states and to Congress concerning the need for and justification of harbor and channel improvements in the Port of New York. Since then, the Port Authority has worked closely with local maritime, industrial and other interests and groups in initiating and urging various improvements to the harbor and the navigable channels of the port.

Each proposal must, in the first instance, meet the tests of economic bene-

---

[1]There are some specific exceptions to this statement; for example, the New York State Barge Canal. The major construction and maintenance of this canal, which is owned by the state of New York, has been undertaken by the state. However, by a 1959 amendment to the New York Constitution, the State Legislature is authorized to lease or transfer the Barge Canal to the federal government.

fits as measured by the benefit-cost ratio. In the field of general navigational projects, the benefit-cost ratio is defined as the ratio of estimated savings in the costs of transportation resulting from the completed project — and hence the public benefit — to its capital, operation and maintenance costs. The higher the ratio above parity, the greater the project is assumed economically justifiable.

If the proposal is justified in these terms, local interests are required to meet certain minimum conditions of local cooperation. While these may vary, depending on the physical and economic character of the project, they generally provide that there should be made available:

". . . without cost to the United States all lands, easements and rights-of-way required for construction and subsequent maintenance of the projects and of aids to navigation upon the request of the Chief of Engineers, including areas determined by the Chief of Engineers to be required in a general public interest for initial and subsequent disposal of spoil and necessary retaining dikes, bulkheads and embankments therefor or the costs of such retaining works."

Further, assurance must be given that the federal government will be held free from damages resulting from the construction works. These are among the minimum conditions of "local cooperation." Under certain conditions, it may also be necessary for local interests to provide, without cost to the federal government, such alterations as may be required in sewer, water supply and other utility facilities.

CURRENT PRIMARY CHANNELS SITUATION

The first harbor improvement project carried out by the Corps of Engineers in the Port of New York consisted of dredging and removing rock obstructions at Hell Gate in the East River in 1853. For the next 15 years or so, little additional work was undertaken, but since then the federal government has undertaken improvement of the harbor and its navigable waterways on a more or less continuous basis. As of 1960, the federal government, operating through the Corps of Engineers, provided and maintained a total of 290 miles of navigable channels in the Port District.

The provision of navigable channels in the Port of New York as in other seaboard ports is, in the first instance, related to the requirements for water-borne movement of cargo and persons. This is in accord with the basic functions of the port to serve as the transshipment center and transfer point between ocean and land transportation. Often, however, the requirements for navigable channels derive from the needs of industrial facilities along the waterways. The availability of navigable channels in the port has exerted an influence on the establishment of industrial facilities in the port area, and in this manner on its employment, income and general level of economic activity.

The location of many of the port's industrial activities can be traced to the availability of water transport: refining and distribution of petroleum products, chemical products manufacturing, sugar refining, coffee roasting, paint and vegetable oil manufacture and processing, copper and lead refining, jute and cordage manufacture, freezing and cold storage of various food products, and a host of other basic manufacturing and distribution operations. As the port has developed over the years, it has contributed to the growth of the industrial, manufacturing and distribution activities of the metropolitan New York–New Jersey area; reciprocally, as the area has gained stature as an industrial, manufacturing and distribution center, it has contributed greatly to the waterborne volumes of the port.

The present configuration of the port's marine terminal facilities for the handling of ocean-going cargo and passenger ships is the result of more than two centuries of continuing change and development. Essentially, it has the following form:

1. Almost all of the port's passenger ship trade is accommodated at terminals along the Hudson River, particularly on the Manhattan side south of 57th Street.

2. There are six major concentrations of terminal facilities for the handling of conventional general cargo. These are (a) along the Brooklyn water front, including the Bay Ridge, Red Hook, Buttermilk, Gowanus and East River channels; (b) on Manhattan along the East River; (c) along the Hudson River on the Manhattan side; (d) along the Hudson River on the New Jersey side; (e) at Port Newark on Newark Bay; and (f) on Staten Island on Upper New York Bay. The extent of actual utilization of these areas, as distinct from the availability of facilities in them, varies widely. Chapter 10 presents, in detail, data on their present utilization and also the projected plans for future use. Development of the Elizabeth-Port Authority Piers, directly to the south of existing Port Newark, will provide additional facilities for both conventional and specialized general cargo.

3. Terminals for handling specialized general cargo and bulk cargoes, the latter

²It has been announced that the operations at the Raritan Arsenal are shortly to be terminated. Operations at the Caven Point Terminal of the Department of the Army in Jersey City were terminated in 1959.

³Some of the terminals and yards are now operated in conjunction with deep-sea marine terminal facilities, e.g., Claremont Terminal of the Lehigh Railroad, the Edgewater Yard of the Susquehanna Railroad, and the Weehawken Yard of the New York Central Railroad.

generally operated in conjunction with industrial and manufacturing plants, are located primarily on the Arthur Kill and Kill van Kull on both the Staten Island and New Jersey sides; on the western side of Newark Bay; along the lower reaches of the Raritan, Hackensack and Passaic rivers; and on the New Jersey side of the Anchorage and Hudson River channels. Lesser concentrations are located along portions of the Brooklyn and East River water fronts.

4. The federal government operates several establishments requiring deep-sea access. These include the Navy Yard and the Army Supply Base in Brooklyn, the Bayonne Navy Supply Base, the Earle Ammunition Depot and the Raritan Arsenal in New Jersey.² Additionally, there are a number of large, privately operated shipbuilding and ship-repair yards in Brooklyn along the Bay Ridge and Gowanus channels, in Hoboken along the Hudson River and on the north shore of Staten Island on the Kill van Kull.

5. All of the trunk-line railroads serving the port have their major freight-handling terminals and yards on the New Jersey side of the Hudson River, except for the New Haven Railroad in the Bronx and the New York Central's 60th Street terminal. The fact that many of these terminals and yards are situated on deep-water frontage has had profound influence on the geography of port development. Among other things, they occupy land and water frontage which might otherwise be available for the development of marine terminal facilities and industrial plants.³ It is possible that prospective railroad mergers and consolidation of operations will in time make some of their present sites in the port available for such use.

The railroad geography of the port will also influence the location of any future

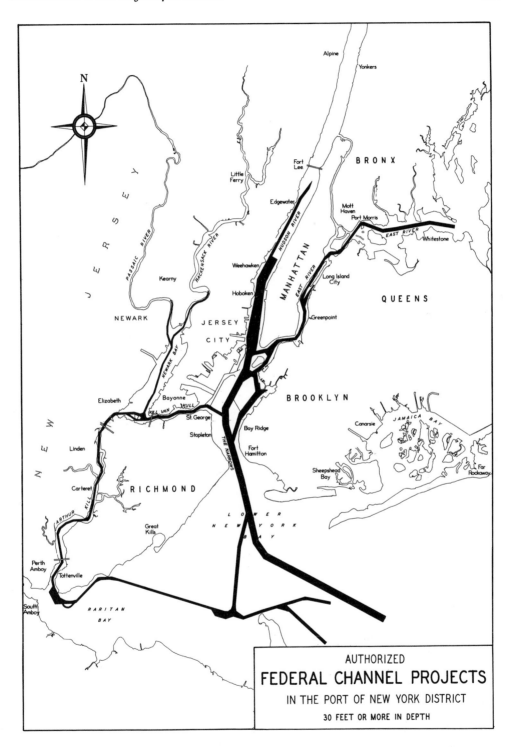

Fig. I

major ore-handling facility. Of necessity, an ore-handling facility would have to be linked directly to or be a component part of one or more of the existing railroad terminal areas.

As the volumes of commerce and industrial and manufacturing activity have increased over the years, ocean-going vessels have increased in length and in draft. The port's waterways and channels have also been developed and improved to accommodate larger vessels. The principal entrance channels — Ambrose, Narrows and Anchorage — provide a clear run from the ocean to the heart of the port in Upper New York Bay. They are maintained at minimum widths of 2,000 feet and depths of 45 feet below mean low water. All of the port's primary channels branch out from the Upper Bay except Newark Bay and the Raritan River; the former is linked to the Upper Bay by the Kill van Kull, the latter to the Ambrose Entrance Channel by the Arthur Kill and the Bayside and Gedney channels.

The Hudson River, flowing down into the Upper Bay from the north, provides a basic 40-foot-deep channel across its full width between the pierhead lines and 45- and 48-foot depths in the center of this basic channel. These greater depths are designed specifically to accommodate the great passenger superliners, all of which berth along this waterway.

The other primary channels are the Bay Ridge, Red Hook, Buttermilk and Gowanus channels in Brooklyn, the East River, the Arthur Kill, the Kill van Kull and Newark Bay. All these channels are used extensively by dry cargo ships and by tankers. All are now generally maintained at minimum depths of 35 feet, with some at 40 feet. This is deep enough to provide complete safety in the operation of all of the cargo ships now in general use except the supertankers which are

coming into increasing use in the petroleum trade. This is the basis for a recommendation concerning the channels most frequently used by oil tankers which is spelled out later in this chapter.

Table 1 presents details of the dimensions of all of the port's channels which are used by ocean-going cargo and passenger ships.

Secondary Channels

In addition to these primary channels, there are many secondary channels in the Port District with depths varying from 8 to 15 feet. These channels are used chiefly for local transfer and distribution of coal, petroleum and chemical products, lumber, sand, gravel and rock, cement and other building materials, vegetable oils, and other raw materials and processed commodities. They also make possible barge movements of imports and exports and coastwise receipts and shipments between the deep-sea terminals located on the primary channels and industrial and manufacturing establishments located along the secondary channels. These secondary channels are thus an important adjunct to the channel complex of the Port District. They constitute an essential element of the local transportation network and provide the metropolitan region with a basic and economical means of cargo and commodity distribution.

The principal secondary channels with depths ranging generally between 8 and 15 feet are the following: New Jersey Pierhead Line Channel, Passaic River (upper reaches), Hackensack River (upper reaches), Eastchester Creek, Westchester Creek, Bronx River, Harlem River, Jamaica Bay, Raritan River (upper reaches), Newtown Creek (upper reaches) and Flushing Creek.

TABLE 1. PORT OF NEW YORK: FEDERAL CHANNEL PROJECTS USED BY
OCEAN-GOING CARGO AND PASSENGER SHIPS

Channel	Authorized Depth Below Mean Low Water (feet)	Project Width (feet)	Approximate Project Length (miles)
Entrance Channels			
Ambrose	45	2,000	10.2
Narrows	45–100[a]	2,000+	3.4
Anchorage	45	2,000	5.7
Anchorage Area	30– 40	[b]	[b]
Bayside-Gedney	35	800	3.7
South[c]	35	800	3.4
Main Ship	30	1,000	5.3
Anchorage Area	38	[b]	[b]
Brooklyn			
Bay Ridge	40	1,200	3.0
Red Hook	40	1,200–1,750	1.0
Buttermilk	40	1,000	2.3
Gowanus Creek	30	200– 500	0.8
East River			
Main	40	1,000	2.5
	35	900	2.3
	35	550	5.5
	35	1,000	5.5
Branch	30	500– 900	1.5
Newtown Creek	20– 23	75– 130	2.6
Hudson River			
Main	40[d]	Full Width	6.0
	45[d]	2,000	4.25
	48[d]	2,000	1.75
Weehawken-Edgewater	30	750	5.0
New York–New Jersey			
Arthur Kill	35	600	15.5
	35	500	7.0
	35	500– 600	3.5
Kill van Kull	35	800	4.8
Anchorage Area	38	[b]	[b]
Newark Bay			
Main	35	550	1.5
	35	400	1.5
	34	400	1.7
Branch	35	600	0.5
Port Newark	35	400	1.1
Port Elizabeth	[e]	[e]	[e]
Hackensack River	32	400	1.1
	32	300	2.8
Passaic River	30	300	2.6
Raritan River			
Main	25	300	5.7
South	25	300	0.7

[a]Natural deep water.

[b]Varies.

[c]Under construction, to replace all of Gedney and part of Bayside channels.

[d]Full channel width runs 6.0 miles between pierhead lines. Lower portion of 4.25 miles includes 2,000 feet of full width maintained at 45 feet depth and upper portion of 1.75 miles at 48 feet.

[e]The Port Elizabeth Channel, recently completed by The Port of New York Authority is 1.7 miles long, 600 feet wide at the outshore end and 800 feet wide at the inshore end and of uniform 35-foot depth. Congress authorized the federalization of the center 400 feet of this channel in 1962, subject to approval by the Secretary of the Army and the President.

The port's future requirements for navigable channels and other harbor improvements will be conditioned by three interrelated factors. These are (1) the adequacy of its entrance and primary channels to accommodate the ships which will be in general use by 1980, (2) the geographic distribution of common-carrier marine terminal facilities and (3) the requirements of water-borne industrial cargo movements. Analysis and evaluation of these factors point to the following conclusions:

1. The width and depth of the port's present entrance and primary channels are considered adequate for all passenger ships of the future and for all major types of cargo ships with one, possibly two, exceptions. The one definite exception is the supertanker, which is being used increasingly by the petroleum industry. It will be necessary to deepen and widen, where possible, those channels along which are located the major petroleum industry installations, particularly the Arthur Kill, the Kill van Kull and Newark Bay. The possible additional exception relates to ocean-going ore carriers. The need to provide for the larger ore carriers will depend, first, on the prospect for the equalization of New York freight rates with those of Baltimore and Philadelphia and, second, on the specific site which would be chosen for construction of an ore-handling facility.

2. There is not likely to be need for any significant additions to the mileage of entrance and primary channels. The new South Entrance Channel, now under construction by the Corps of Engineers, will eliminate the dangerous intersection where the Bayside-Gedney Channel, with its heavy tanker traffic, now crosses the shallow-draft Swash-South Channel used by scows taking refuse out to sea for disposal. Also, it is expected that the new Port Elizabeth Channel, recently constructed by The Port of New York Authority, with a channel of 35-foot depth, will come under the jurisdiction of the Corps of Engineers when approved by the Secretary of the Army and the President.

3. In the light of probable increases in the port's cargo volumes and of further industrial development on Newark Bay, along the Passaic and Hackensack rivers and in the Meadows, it will be necessary to improve the existing channels in these waterways by widening, easing bends and by deepening the two river channels.

4. It will be necessary to convert the Jamaica Bay Channel from a secondary to a primary channel in order to accommodate ocean-going tankers. The consumption requirements of the area served by the oil terminals in this area will be large enough to justify a primary channel by the savings in the costs of transportation.

5. The remaining primary ship channel requirements are in the field of realignment, widening and straightening of existing channels. This is particularly true of the newer sections of the port, notably in the Newark Bay–Passaic River–Hackensack River area. There will also be need to improve and increase the number of the port's anchorage areas.

6. Some of the port's secondary channels along which are located major concentrations of industrial facilities will need to be improved by provision of additional depth, turning basins, widening and other such improvements. These include, but are not limited to, the upper reaches of the Raritan, Passaic and Hackensack rivers and Newtown and Flushing creeks.

Trends in Ship Construction

Looking ahead to 1980, the merchant fleets that will be in use then will consist primarily of ships constructed since the end of World War II. Many, in fact, will have been constructed after 1960. In the United States, current statutes provide for the replacement of the vessels of subsidized passenger and cargo ship operators after 25 years. While law and commercial practice vary from country to country, efforts to increase efficiency of operation and to reduce costs will lead generally to replacement of obsolescent vessels. There will also be substantial net additions to existing fleets, particularly ships for the transport of bulk cargoes and containerships, to take advantage of newer techniques of cargo handling.

In the present context of navigable channels and other harbor improvements, the immediate concern is with the physical dimensions of the ships that will be in use rather than with their cargo-carrying capacities, means of propulsion or other characteristics. While these characteristics are important in decisions concerning vessel size and in calculations of benefit-cost ratios, the actual channel and other harbor improvement requirements are keyed to the physical dimensions of the ships — draft, length and beam. The draft determines the channel depths; the length and beam, the channel widths, angles of bends, turning basins, etc. Draft and channel depth are not synonymous, for a vessel laden down to the 35-foot mark requires a minimum of 3 to 4 feet of additional keel clearance for safety of operations.

Passenger Ships

The largest passenger liners now in use are the *France* and the two "Queens." The *France*, with an over-all length of 1,034 feet, is now the longest commercial vessel afloat, exceeding the 1,031 feet of the *Queen Elizabeth*. The only other passenger ship with a length of more than 1,000 feet is the *Queen Mary* at 1,019 feet. All three have beams in excess of 100 feet, 119 feet for each of the "Queens" and 109 feet for the *France*. However, whereas the *France* draws 34 feet, the "Queens" both draw approximately 39 feet 5 inches. All other passenger liners, including the major United States flagships — *United States, America, Constitution* and *Independence* — measure less than 1,000 feet in length, less than 100 feet in beam and less than 35 feet in draft. The *Liberte* which has a beam of 102 feet was recently withdrawn from service.

The proposed replacements for the *Queen Mary* and the *America*, should they be constructed, will both be smaller than the *France*. This is also true of the ships which have either been announced or are now actually under construction for the Italian Line, Home Line and Zim Israel Line. All of these are considerably smaller than the *France* or the "Queens."

It has already been noted that all regularly scheduled passenger liners are accommodated at berths along the Hudson River channel. It is likely that this will also be the pattern of the future. No channel problems, therefore, are evisaged on this score.

General Cargo Ships

Most conventional general cargo ships now in use are under 500 feet in length and have beams and drafts of less than 70 feet and 30 feet respectively. This is as true of American flag vessels as it is of foreign ships. Only a few, generally of American registry, go beyond these dimensions, and even these do not go beyond 570 feet by 80 feet by 31 feet.

The C-2, C-3 and C-4 classes represent the larger ships now in general use. Representative dimensions of these ships and some others recently constructed are shown in Table 2. Such evidence as is available of recent trends in the construction of conventional cargo ships indicates that the general dimensions shown in this

tankers and the port's channels. The picture that emerges is that the channels along which all of the port's refineries and

TABLE 2. CURRENT CARGO SHIP DIMENSIONS

Ship	Operator	Length	Beam	Maximum Draft
C-2 *(Robin Locksley)*	Robin Lines	479' 8"	66' 5"	28' 11"
C-3 *(Mormacmail)*	Moore-McCormack	492' 0"	69' 6"	29' 5"
C-3 *(Mormacpride)*	" "	483' 3"	68' 0"	31' 4"
C-4-S-60a[b]	" "	550' 9"	75' 0"	31' 0"
C-4 Mariner *(President Jackson)*	American President	563' 8"	76' 4"	29' 10"
C-4 Mariner *(President Lincoln)*	" "	563' 7½"	76' 0"	29' 10"
C-4-S-57a[a]	United States	560' 6"	75' 0"	28' 6"
Bolivia Maru	"K" Line	469' 3"	60' 6"	26' 10"
Yamataka Maru	Yamashita	484' 2"	64' 7"	30' 10"
City of Auckland	Ellerman	507' 6"	67' 0"	28' 0"

[a]In construction.
[b]Planned.

table are not likely to be exceeded in any important degree in the foreseeable future.

Most of the specialized cargo ships now in use were originally conventional ships which have been modified for their specialized operations. There are only two exceptions, those designed specifically to carry containers and the special tankers used to transport wine and citrus fruit juices. The latter present no problems, since they are well within the physical dimensions of conventional ships. The containerships, however, may run up to 700 feet in length; their draft nevertheless would still be under 31 feet. They will not require, therefore, channels of greater dimensions than the existing ones.

Tankers

In Chapter 11 there is a discussion of the recent trends in tanker construction for the petroleum industry and the relationships between the increasing size of

all but one of its major storage and distribution terminals are located are not capable of accommodating the larger tankers. These channels, ranging generally from 30 to 35 feet in depth, are deep enough only for tankers of less than about 35,000 dead weight tons — and then only at high tide — whereas most of the new tanker capacity which has come into use during the past few years, or which is now under construction, exceeds 40,000 tons. A tanker of approximately 40,000 tons requires 40 feet for safety of operations; a 46,000-tonner, about 41 feet; a 52,000-tonner, 43 feet; and a 60,000-tonner about 45 feet.

Inability to accommodate these large tankers could lead to an economic penalty in the cost of marketing petroleum products in the metropolitan area. It is estimated that tanker deliveries of crude oil and refined petroleum products to the port's tidewater installations will increase from 52.5 million tons in 1959 to approximately 81 million tons by 1980.

All but one of the port's six refineries and 19 of its 35 major storage and distribution terminals are located along the Arthur Kill and the Kill van Kull. In 1959, these two channels accounted for 13.4 million tons of the port's total water-borne receipts of crude oil and 25.3 million tons of its refined petroleum receipts, 97.8 and 65.2 per cent respectively.

These channels, as indicated earlier, have prevailing depths of 35 feet while the maximum widths in the Arthur Kill and Kill van Kull are 600 and 800 feet respectively. The minimum widths and, therefore, the controlling dimensions with respect to deep-sea movements are 500 feet in each channel. If they were to be deepened to 45 feet and broadened wherever possible to 900 feet, they would be able to handle tankers up to about 60,000 tons.

Bulk Ore Ships

It has been pointed out earlier that the establishment of a high-capacity ore-handling facility in the Port of New York is not feasible unless the railroad freight rate structure from seaboard to inland consumption centers is amended to provide for equalized rates for New York with those of Baltimore and Philadelphia. Assuming, however, that the rates are to be equalized and that it is decided to construct such a facility, one of the major considerations in the determination of the specific site for it will be the depth in the channel along which the facility would be located. The importance of this consideration lies in the fact that there is a strong trend towards the construction and utilization of ocean-going ore carriers of more than 40,000 tons dead weight, with lengths approaching 800 feet and with loaded drafts approaching 39 feet. Carriers of this size require minimum channel depths in the 42-43-foot range.

At the present time, only the major entrance channels into the Port of New York and the Hudson River channel provide such depths. Were an ore-handling facility to be located along either the Anchorage Entrance Channel or the Hudson River Channel, no channel depth problems would be encountered other than those of providing for access from the main channel to the specific site of the facility. As noted earlier, this would be the responsibility of those who would construct and operate the facility. Should it, however, be determined to locate a facility along any of the other channels of the port, this would limit the full use of the newer ore carriers.

New Developments in Ship Design

Until now, we have been concerned with ocean-going ships which are already in use or whose trends of construction and utilization are evident. It is necessary now to turn to several new types of vessels which are still in the early stages of development and to assess their possible impact on the port's future channel requirements and harbor improvements. These are the nuclear-propelled ship, the hydrofoil ship and the submarine tanker.

The *N. S. Savannah*, the first nuclear-propelled surface vessel designed for commercial operations, began its sea trials early in 1962. Whether or not these tests indicate commercial feasibility in comparison with conventional oil- and diesel-powered vessels, it is more than likely that additional prototype vessels will be constructed during the next 10 or 15 years.

It is believed that to the extent that such ships are designed for conventional general cargo operations — as is the *N. S. Savannah* — they will not affect the port's channel requirements. The length of the ship, however, 596 feet, may have an effect on the length of the berth which it will require, since conventional general cargo berths are now generally planned at 600 feet.

Although nuclear-propelled vessels may not present any major channel problems, special precautions will have to be taken with respect to refueling and the disposal of spent nuclear cores. It may even be necessary to provide for special servicing establishments for such operations. Apart from these safety considerations, however, the berthing and the handling of cargo carried by nuclear-propelled ships should present no new problems.

The hydrofoil ship, too, presents no special waterway requirements. When under way at full speed, the ship is supported by submerged foils which provide lift to bring above water level the hull which is normally under water. It is the draft of the ship when not under way or when moving at slow speed, therefore, which is of importance in determining its channel requirements.

Submarine tankers are in a less advanced state of development than hydrofoil ships, but it is possible that they may ultimately be developed to dimensions comparable to those of large naval submarines. But submarine tankers have to surface when in port to load and discharge cargo and no special channel requirements are foreseen.

In summary, it is believed that the port's future condition will be such as to enable it to accommodate all of the various types of ships that may be in use except for the supertankers and possibly some of the newer ore carriers.

Location of
General Cargo Terminals

It has been noted that there are now six major concentrations of terminal facilities in the port for handling conventional gen-

eral cargo, and that the channels on which these six concentrations are located have sufficient depth and width to accommodate both present and future cargo ships. If it could be assumed that the future pattern of location of the port's conventional general cargo terminals would be in the same general areas, no new channel problems would arise. With one exception, the prospect for 1980 is that these same six sectors of the port will account for the conventional general cargo terminal operations. The exception is the Elizabeth-Port Authority Piers now under development, for which 15 conventional general cargo berths are planned. A number of additional berths are planned for handling specialized general cargo; no bulk cargo facilities are planned for the new terminal area.

As part of the development program for the Elizabeth-Port Authority Piers, a 35-foot-deep channel branching out from the main Newark Bay Channel, varying in width from 600 to 800 feet, has been constructed. This channel is of sufficient dimensions to accommodate all of the cargo ships, conventional and specialized, which are likely to use it.

Even if future marine terminal development programs bring about a somewhat different distribution of marine activities among the various sectors of the port, no new channel requirements are foreseen for the accommodation of general cargo vessels in common-carrier service. All of the areas still available for development, including Communipaw, Pavonia Avenue and Caven Point in Jersey City, Point Breeze and Constable Hook in Bayonne, and a number of additional sites north of Jersey City on the New Jersey shore, are located along the existing primary channels of the port, and all these channels are fully capable of accommodating both present and future cargo ships.

CHANNEL REQUIREMENTS FOR INDUSTRIAL CARGO MOVEMENTS

There has been a close relationship between the development and improvement of the port's channels and the location of industrial facilities along them. The availability of improved navigable channels in the port has been directly responsible for the specific site location of many of the port's major industrial and manufacturing complexes; reciprocally, the requirements for water-borne movement of the input components of production for these industries and for the water-borne shipment of their output influenced the development and improvement of the channels. These relationships are as valid today as they were in the past, and will be equally so in the future.

In recent years, there has been considerable emphasis on the establishment of one-story manufacturing plants on extensive tracts of land in outlying portions of the Metropolitan Region, away from the densely developed inner core. This has been particularly true of "light manufacturing" industries. This trend will undoubtedly continue into the future.

Parallel with this development has been the establishment of new industrial facilities along both the primary and secondary channels of the port, a continuation of the long-term historical trend. In recent years, these have included new petroleum industry installations and facilities for production, packaging and distribution of chemical products, building materials, vegetable oils, floor coverings, paper board and other paper products. There is no doubt that this pattern of industrial location will also continue into the future and that there will be further additions to the industrial development along the port's channels and waterways. Generally, the companies choosing such locations will be those engaged in "heavy industry," requiring substantial volumes of raw materials and other components of production, or those engaged in large volume distribution, or both. For such operations, immediate availability of water transportation offers substantial economies in transportation and distribution.

Future industrial development along the port's channels and waterways is expected to include some sites not yet developed, as well as redevelopment of some other areas. It is possible, for example, that prospective railroad mergers and consolidations may make a number of prime water-front sites available for future industrial use.

There is no simple formula for evaluating the comparative desirability, costs and utility of development of new sites or of redevelopment. The merits, and demerits, of each case will necessarily need to be appraised by the companies and agencies involved, in terms of the specific circumstances and planning considerations. These will include, in addition to direct access to deep water, such factors as highway and rail connection, sources of raw materials and patterns of distribution, land costs, development or redevelopment costs, tax structures, zoning regulations, and the many other considerations that enter into industrial location.

Among the water-front areas likely to become available for either development or redevelopment are various sites along Newark Bay, the Passaic, Hackensack and Raritan rivers, the Kill van Kull and the Arthur Kill, the New Jersey side of the Hudson River and Upper New York Bay, the Kearny Peninsula, and the Meadowlands, parts of the Brooklyn-Queens water front and the southern Bronx, and along some of the port's secondary channels. As industrial developments along these waterways take place and as the volumes of water-borne movements generated by them increase, it will be necessary to improve these channels to provide for more economical movement and distribution of cargo. It is already evident that it will become necessary to deepen the primary channels in the Passaic, Hackensack and Raritan rivers to 35 feet and to deepen the secondary channel in the Hackensack River from 12 to 15 feet. Where possible, these channels should also be widened, bends eased and turning basins provided.

Newtown and Flushing creeks, which currently have maximum prevailing depths of 23 feet and 12 feet, respectively, are also in need of deepening. Similarly, some of the port's other secondary channels, including the Harlem River, Bronx River and Westchester and Eastchester creeks should, where possible, generally be deepened to provide for depths up to 15 feet. The improvement would add considerably to their utilization and would improve the desirability of the abutting areas for industrial development and, in some cases, redevelopment.

In the planning, development and improvement of these channels, it will be necessary to take account of the physical and air space requirements of land and air transportation. Low-level fixed bridges over navigable waterways, for example, important as they may be for highway transportation, impose severe limitations on the dimensions of watercraft using the waterways. Similarly, runway, beacon light, glide path and other navigational requirements for aviation may affect waterway utilization. Other instances could be cited of conflicts between the needs of different modes of transportation.

The conflicts involved are frequently highly complex in nature. There are high-level fixed bridge structures, such as those over the East River, the George Washing-

ton Bridge and the new Verrazano Bridge which will span the Narrows, which provide sufficient clearance for the largest ship afloat. Other bridges, such as that of the Central Railroad of New Jersey over Newark Bay, and some over the secondary channels, are equipped with lifts or swing devices to make ship passage possible, but there are occasional delays imposed on land transportation and certain hazards to marine transportation. Still others, low-level and fixed in position, impose absolute limitations on the heights of superstructure, stack or mast of the craft using the channel.

The conflicts between channel traffic and aviation requirements are more limited in frequency, but more complex in character. At Port Newark, for example, the occupancy by steamships of certain berths otherwise available would conflict with clearance requirements for the approaches to Newark Airport; at LaGuardia Airport, ship traffic in portions of the Rikers Island Channel is in conflict with the extension of runways and the placement of approach lights.

TRIBUTARY INLAND WATERWAYS

In addition to the navigable channels in the Port District proper, the Port of New York has always had a special interest in and a measure of dependence on the tributary waterways that provide access to the Port District from the north and west. Historically, the commerce on these waterways has been of direct importance to the commerce of the port. It was the Erie Canal, which linked the lands beyond the Alleghenies with the Port of New York, and which made possible the port's ascendancy as the leading port of the nation.

During much of the nineteenth century, inland and coastal waterways played a dominant role in the development of the nation's domestic traffic. Then, with the coming of age of the railroads and then of automobile and truck transportation, waterway traffic was adversely affected, more in some areas than in others. On waterway after waterway, passenger traffic was progressively reduced to the point of virtual disappearance and cargo movements experienced drastic changes. Short-haul movements shifted first to the railroads and then to the truck. Small-volume shipments were replaced by large-volume movements, and conventional general cargo by specialized and bulk cargoes.

Only recently have some of the major inland waterways of the nation begun again to play a major role in transporting the goods of commerce. In the Mississippi, Ohio, Tennessee and Cumberland river areas, for example, many companies have established manufacturing plants which are dependent on large-volume water transportation of either their raw materials or their finished products or both. The waterways have been improved to handle the increasing volume of shipments.

In the area served by the Port of New York, there have been mixed results. The Morris Canal, linking Jersey City and Phillipsburg, New Jersey, and the Delaware and Raritan Canal, connecting the Delaware River at Bordentown, New Jersey, with the Raritan River at New Brunswick, have both fallen into virtual disuse. The New Jersey Inland Waterway, the most northerly segment of the Atlantic Intracoastal Waterway and terminating at the Manasquan River, is now used primarily by pleasure craft.

The Erie Canal, incorporated into the New York State Barge Canal system, attained its peak traffic volume in 1872 when almost 7 million tons were carried. In more recent years, the volume has seldom exceeded 4 million tons annually. Outmoded in its dimensions, the canal has not been able to attract any substantial number of new industrial plants.

On the Hudson River the Barge Canal is first encountered at Troy, about 8 miles north of the Port of Albany. From this junction point with tidal navigation, the Canal branches off, north to the Canadian border and west to Lake Ontario and Lake Erie. The northern arm, known as the Champlain Canal, runs up the Hudson River from Troy into Lake Champlain and thence to the Canadian border. From this point northward, the navigable channels, running through the Richelieu River and the Chambly Canal, are under the control and jurisdiction of the Canadian government to the junction point with the St. Lawrence River at Sorel.

The western arm runs from the Hudson River to Tonawanda and Buffalo on Lake Erie, a distance of 338 miles. At a point near Syracuse, about halfway along, there is a 24-mile spur, the Oswego Canal, linking it with Lake Ontario at Oswego.

The Barge Canal system, in its present dimensions, is the result of plans developed at the beginning of the century. Over much of its length, the controlling depth is only 12 feet and clearance under fixed bridges is as low as 15 feet. Maximum lock dimensions are 300 feet in length and 45 feet in width. These dimensions impose severe limitations on the cargo-carrying capacity of the watercraft which can use it. In simplest terms, the Barge Canal is dimensionally obsolete.

Although the Barge Canal is owned and operated by the state of New York, the federal government has at various times authorized and appropriated funds for its improvement. For example, in 1935, funds were authorized to improve the Troy to Oswego section of the canal at a cost of $27 million by increasing the controlling depth to 14 feet between locks, 13 feet in the locks and over the lock sills, and by raising all overhead structures to a minimum vertical clearance of 20 feet. The appropriation of funds for these improvements, however, has been slow, and, although $25 million has been spent, at today's price level some $11 million more would be required for completion.

Modernization of the Barge Canal by deepening, widening, and enlargement of the locks should lead to further economic development in the Hudson and Mohawk river valleys and in the Champlain Basin. It would also yield additional cargo movements through the Port of New York, which has always been the natural gateway for the commerce of these areas. In view of the magnitude of the expenditure necessary to improve the canal, consideration has been given to integrating it into the national inland waterway system by transferring the Barge Canal to the federal government. A New York State constitutional amendment, approved in 1959, makes this possible without necessitating transfer of actual title. To become effective, the amendment will have to be implemented by appropriate legislation satisfactory to both the state and the federal governments.

The northern arm of the Barge Canal links with the Richelieu River and Chambly Canal in Canada to provide through water movement to the St. Lawrence River. The controlling dimensions on this route are those of the Chambly Canal locks, a depth of 6½ feet and widths of 36 feet at bottom and 60 feet at the surface.

For many years, there have been discussions on both sides of the border concerning the desirability of providing for minimum channels on this route of 12- or 15-foot depth with commensurate width. There is already a substantial volume of traffic moving between the St. Lawrence and various points in New York State over this waterway, some moving to and from the Port of New York, and it has been estimated that a considerably greater volume would result should the waterway be improved. However, since the area needing enlargement is located in Canada, whatever plans are undertaken to improve the waterway will necessarily be those of the Canadian government. It will be highly important that these Canadian plans be coordinated with such plans as will be developed in the United States to improve the Champlain Canal sector of the New York State Barge Canal.

CHAPTER 13

RAILROAD FREIGHT AND TERMINAL NEEDS

In this chapter the freight volumes currently handled by the railroads that serve the Port of New York will be examined as to the magnitudes of their various segments. In the light of past trends, projections will be made of future volumes of railroad freight into, out of and through the Port District.

Since 1933 the Port Authority has compiled comprehensive railroad freight tonnage statistics obtained from the freight-station records of the major railroads that have served the Port of New York. Tonnage data are also available for certain earlier years for Manhattan stations south of 59th Street, and for some waterfront stations in Brooklyn and the Bronx.

In summarizing these data, two primary categories have been established: (1) tonnages that moved through the New York–New Jersey Port District and (2) those that have moved into and out of it.

Shipments within the first category, through the port, have been further classified into two major groups: (a) tonnages interchanged between pairs of railroads across the harbor and (b) tonnages largely transshipped between railroads and steamships throughout the New York harbor.

Within the second category, into and out of the port, shipment tonnages have been classified according to the commodity groups that have been identifiable by the data: (a) coal and coke; (b) perishables, consisting of fresh fruits and vegetables, dairy products, live and dressed poultry, livestock and dressed meats; (c) less-than-carload merchandise;

and (d) carload merchandise, which includes all other commodities.

In summarizing the data, certain principles have been followed which depart somewhat from customary railroad terminology. What is termed interchange freight represents only those freight volumes that were interchanged between railroads across the harbor waters of the port and which were bound for points beyond the Port District. Consequently, it excludes (1) freight interchanged between other railroads, and the Long Island Rail Road tonnage, which is considered to be "local" freight; (2) that interchanged with the Hoboken Shore Railroad, which is considered to be either "lighterage" or "local" freight, depending upon whether it was destined for shipside or local delivery; and (3) other rail freight which is interchanged between railroads within the port, but which originated or came to rest at railroad freight stations within the Port District and hence is also considered "local" freight.

Freight volumes transshipped within the port between railroads and steamships in domestic and foreign trade have been computed from what has been recorded by the railroads as *lighterage tonnages*, which, according to railroad usage means the tonnages handled through the offices of their *lighterage agents*. "Lighterage," as referred to in the discussion which follows, consists not only of all lightered freight, in railroad-owned, privately owned, or railroad-chartered lighters, but also the rail-vessel transshipments that are (a) floated in railroad cars to shipside in lieu of lighterage, (b) trucked in lieu of lighterage, or (c) handled "wheel-to-keel." In addition, lighterage volumes include freight lightered between railroad lighterage piers and local water-front plants. This portion of railroad lighterage freight is, in reality, local freight picked up by and delivered by lighters. For most of the railroads, this freight cannot readily be segregated from other lightered freight, and it has been necessary to estimate it, using whatever data have been available.

What is termed herein as local freight, into and out of the port, thus represents all freight not included in through freight; that is, freight that is not interchanged between railroads across the harbor waters nor interchanged as rail-vessel transshipments. Local freight, therefore, includes all Long Island Rail Road freight and thus freight to and from Nassau and Suffolk counties on Long Island, areas not technically within the boundaries of the Port District.

RAILROAD FREIGHT VOLUMES INTO, OUT OF AND THROUGH THE PORT DISTRICT IN 1960

In 1960, the railroads that served the Port of New York handled a total of 58.0 million tons of freight into, out of and through the Port of New York (Table 1).

As a commercial and industrial area, a total of 46.8 million tons of freight was handled into and out of the Port District for consumption, processing, manufacturing, warehousing and distribution. As a gateway for interchange between railroads, largely between the South and New England, the railroads moved through the port about 5.7 million tons of freight. In transshipment between the railroads and vessels in the port, the railroads moved into and out of the port about 5.5 million tons of freight.

TABLE 1. RAILROAD FREIGHT VOLUMES THAT MOVED INTO, OUT OF AND THROUGH THE PORT OF NEW YORK, 1960

(Short Tons)

Into, out of and through the port	57,965,000
Into and out of the port for consumption, manufacture, distribution and storage (local freight)	46,768,000
Through the port:	
Rail-rail interchange across the harbor	5,701,000
Rail-vessel transshipments, between railroads and vessels in domestic and foreign trade	5,496,000

Components of Local Freight

Let us now examine the major components of the local freight for which statistics are available (Table 2).

TABLE 2. COMPONENTS OF LOCAL FREIGHT, 1960

(Short Tons)

Local freight into and out of the port	46,768,000
Coal and coke	13,978,000
Perishable foodstuffs	2,301,000
All other freight ("merchandise")	30,489,000

The 14 million tons of anthracite and bituminous coal and coke which entered the port in 1960 were received at eight tidewater terminals, all but one in New Jersey and at numerous team tracks and sidings distributed over the entire Port District.

About 70 per cent of the coal receipts into the Port District arrived at tidewater terminals; 30 per cent were received at team tracks and sidings throughout the port. About 80 per cent of all receipts were bituminous coal, most of which was received at tidewater terminals.

Perishable Freight

Perishable freight tonnages (Table 3) consist primarily of fresh fruits and vegetables, and secondarily of livestock and dressed meats, which altogether account for nearly 95 per cent of the total; the remainder consists of milk and dairy products.

TABLE 3. RAIL-HANDLED PERISHABLE FOODSTUFFS, 1960

(Short Tons)

All perishables	2,301,000
Fresh fruits and vegetables	1,257,000
Dressed meats	535,000
Livestock	372,000
Dairy products	70,000
Milk	67,000

Carload and Less-than-Carload Merchandise Volumes

Almost all of the railroad merchandise freight moved as carload freight. However, about 1.7 million tons were handled by forwarding companies and shipped as carload freight. About 80 per cent of the forwarding company freight was handled to and from Manhattan. These companies consolidated into carload lots package freight which in earlier years moved by rail as less-than-carload freight.

Merchandise Freight Handled in the New York and New Jersey Sections

Of the 29.4 million tons of carload (CL) and less-than-carload (LCL) freight that railroads handled in 1960[1], about 18.3 million tons moved through freight stations in New Jersey; about 11.1 million tons through freight stations on the New York side of the port.

On the New Jersey side of the port, Hudson County generated more mer-

[1]Exclusive of the freight lightered to and from waterfront plants. Local origin and destination data are not available for this freight component. For 1960 it represented an estimated 1,051,000 tons.

chandise freight in 1960 than any other county, 5.3 million tons, about 30 per cent of the total freight on the New Jersey side.

TABLE 4. CL AND LCL MERCHANDISE FREIGHT TONNAGES HANDLED IN NEW JERSEY COUNTIES, 1960

(Short Tons)

Bergen	1,473,000
Passaic	1,000,000
Hudson	5,334,000
Essex	3,662,000
Union	2,832,000
Middlesex	3,956,000
Monmouth	78,000
New Jersey side of port	18,335,000

Of the 11.1 million tons handled on the New York side of the port, freight stations on Manhattan handled about 29 per cent in 1960, those in Brooklyn about 19 per cent and those in the Bronx about 17 per cent.

TABLE 5. CL AND LCL MERCHANDISE FREIGHT TONNAGES HANDLED IN NEW YORK COUNTIES, 1960

(Short Tons)

New York	3,231,000
Bronx	1,840,000
Westchester	1,100,000
Kings	2,084,000
Queens[a]	1,182,000
Nassau & Suffolk (without the Port District)	1,069,000
Staten Island	597,000
New York side of port	11,103,000

[a]Includes part of Nassau within Port District.

Marine-Handled Merchandise Freight

Freight stations of the New Jersey railroads on the New York side of the port are served only by carfloats. They are either pier stations, largely on the Manhattan water front, or team track stations, immediately back of the water front, supplemented by float bridges.

Until recently some of the stations of the New York railroads were also served by carfloats. To and from Brooklyn, Queens and Long Island freight stations, practically all freight must be carfloated. However, a substantial portion has been accounted for by Brooklyn freight stations which have been operated by the railroads or by the four contract terminals, Bush, New York Dock, Jay Street, and Brooklyn Eastern District. The remainder of the railroad freight has been handled through the on-track stations of the Long Island Rail Road.

More than half of the freight to and from the New York side of the port was carfloated in 1960.

TABLE 6. MERCHANDISE FREIGHT
CARFLOATED TO AND FROM THE NEW YORK
SIDE OF THE PORT DISTRICT, 1960

(Short Tons)

Manhattan	1,331,000
Brooklyn, Queens & Long Island	4,334,000
Bronx	173,000
Total	5,838,000

Freight Interchanged between Railroads Across the Harbor

In 1960, there were 5.7 million tons of freight that moved through the port as a railroad gateway, as interchange freight between the New Jersey and the New York railroads, carfloated across the harbor. More than half was interchange tonnage between the Pennsylvania Railroad and the New Haven Railroad, moving largely between the South and West and New England. The remainder was interchanged between the other New Jersey railroads and the New Haven and New York Central Railroads through its Weehawken Yard and its 60th Street Yard.

The Pennsylvania Railroad–New Haven Railroad interchange was via the Bay Ridge Division of the Long Island Rail Road–New York Connecting Railroad–Hell Gate Bridge Route. Freight interchanged between the other New Jersey railroads and the New Haven Railroad was carfloated up the East River to the New Haven's Oak Point Yard float bridges in the Bronx.

TABLE 7. RAIL-RAIL INTERCHANGE
BETWEEN NJ RR's AND
NHRR AND NYCRR, 1960

(Short Tons)

Between New Haven Railroad and	
Pennsylvania Railroad	3,477,000
Other New Jersey Railroads	1,422,000
Between New York Central Railroad and New Jersey railroads	802,000
Total rail-rail interchange	5,701,000

Freight Transshipped Between Rails and Vessels

In 1960, the railroads handled about 6.5 million tons of lighterage freight (Table 8). Of this total, about 1.1 million tons represented freight lightered to and from local water-front plants, which is, in reality, local freight. Rail-handled general cargo for transshipment to and from vessels moving in foreign trade amounted to about 4.1 million tons or about 63 per cent of total lighterage.

TABLE 8. LIGHTERAGE FREIGHT, 1960
(Short Tons)

Total Lighterage	6,547,000
To and from local water-front locations	1,051,000
Rail-vessel transshipments	
Domestic trade	787,000
Grain (exports)	265,000
Ore (imports)	328,000
General cargo exports	2,860,000
General cargo imports	1,256,000

The general cargo transshipped between railroads and vessels in foreign trade amounted to about 27 per cent of the port's 15.4 million short tons of total foreign general cargo, as reported by the Department of Commerce.[2] The 2.9 million tons of rail-handled exports represented about 42 per cent of the 6.8 million short tons of general cargo exports; the 1.3 million tons of rail-handled imports represented less than 15 per cent of the 8.6 million short tons of general cargo imports through the port (Table 9).

The railroads trucked in lieu of lighterage about 704,000 tons, 404,000 tons of exports and 300,000 tons of imports.

Only about 2.5 million tons, or 36 per cent of all general cargo exports, and only about 1 million tons, or 11 per cent of all general cargo imports, were handled by the railroads with marine equipment. Although there are no definitive data on the subject, it must be supposed that trucks delivered most of the remaining 64 per cent of the exports to the piers, and picked up from them the remaining 89 per cent of the imports. The high proportion of import freight handled by motor trucks for inland transport is consistent with the observation that most imports through the port are destined for processing, storage or distribution establishments either within the Port District or within economical truck haul distances.

Projections of Segments of Port District Rail Freight

Forecasts and Projections

A distinction must be made between a projection and a forecast; a forecast is absolute while a projection is conditional. Projections rest upon a set of assumptions,

---

[2]Railroad tonnages reported by the railroads and foreign trade tonnages reported by the U. S. Department of Commerce are not strictly comparable, a matter discussed in a later section of this chapter.

TABLE 9. Rail-Handled and Total General Cargo Foreign Commerce, 1960

General cargo in foreign commerce (short tons):	
Exports	6,773,000
Imports	8,612,000
Rail-vessel transshipments through the Port of New York (short tons):	
Exports	2,860,000
Imports	1,256,000
Rail-handled transshipments as per cent of total through the Port of New York:	
Exports and imports	26.8
Exports	42.2
Imports	14.6

either implicit or explicit. More often than not, in projections the implicit assumption is made that the determining conditions which have prevailed in the past will, for the most part, continue into the future. This is the assumption made in many instances in the present discussion. For example, with reference to the projected volumes of iron ore movement, it has been assumed that the freight rate structure will be in the future what it now is. If the future should bring about an equalization of New York's inland rail rate with that of Philadelphia and Baltimore, the volume of iron ore moving through the port might be far higher than the volume projected here.

The assumption of the continuation of present influences may appear tenuous. There is little alternative, however, when there is no way of predicting future events and future decisions that may be of controlling importance, and when the causal relationships between the determining factors and the values being projected may not be known quantitatively.

In the projections which follow, future declines are prominent. In most instances they are continuations of declining trends in the past. They are not straight-line continuations, however, but constant-percentage declines. For example, if a value of 100 has declined by 20 per cent over the past ten years to a value of 80, it is assumed that over the next ten years there will be another 20 per cent decline, from 80 to 64, or a numerical decline of 16.

In a number of instances informed judgment as to the prospective future of the region has led to modification of the statistical projection.

Projections of Interchange Freight

Freight interchange between railroads across the harbor has always been by carfloats. Since 1950 these volumes have been shrinking steadily and it is likely that they will continue to decline in the future.

Table 10 shows the volumes likely to be interchanged between railroads during the next 20 years, on the assumption that the influences bringing about the decline during the past decade will continue into the future.

The bankruptcy of the New Haven in July 1961, however, introduces an important new factor into the situation. About 85 per cent of the rail freight interchanged by carfloats has been made between the New Haven Railroad and the New Jersey railroads, about 63 per cent with the Pennsylvania Railroad. The New Haven Railroad performs the floating operations between the Pennsylvania Railroad's Greenville Yards in Jersey City and Bay Ridge, Brooklyn, whence it moves the interchange freight, via the New York Connecting Railroad, the Long Island Rail Road and the Hell Gate Bridge to its Oak Point Yard in the Bronx. If the New Haven should discontinue its carfloating operation, 85 per cent of the carfloat inter-

change in the harbor would disappear. Freight movements between the South and West and New England might then be routed via Maybrook, New York, to which the Pennsylvania Railroad now has trackage rights over the Lehigh and Hudson.

Projections of Lighterage Freight

Railroad lighterage freight in the Port of New York, it has been explained earlier, consists of several segments, namely: (a) freight lightered to and from local water-front plants; (b) freight transshipped to and from vessels in domestic trade; (c) bulk cargoes (grain and ore) transshipped to and from foreign-trade vessels; and (d) general cargo transshipped to and from vessels in foreign trade. The tonnages accounted for by these segments have followed different trends in the past and will probably continue to do so in the future.

Freight lightered to and from local water-front plants has maintained a fairly constant volume, but the movement to the port from the interior has followed a slightly upward trend, while the movement out of the port has been much smaller in volume and has been shrinking.

The rail-vessel transshipment volume in domestic trade has fluctuated widely but has shown no established trend. This segment of the lighterage volume is likely to follow somewhat the same fluctuating characteristics in the future.

Rail-handled foreign trade has been declining consistently in the past decade, some 5 or 6 per cent a year. It is likely that rail-handled foreign trade will continue to decline in the future at approximately these rates of decline.

Table 11 shows the various segments of railroad lighterage in the Port of New York for selected years in the past and projected into the future to 1980.

TABLE 10. RECORDED AND PROJECTED ANNUAL RAILROAD FREIGHT TONNAGE
INTERCHANGE BETWEEN RAILROADS ACROSS THE HARBOR, 1939-1980

		Interchange Between			
	New Haven Railroad			NYC RR	NH & NYC RR's
	and PRR	and Other NJ RR's	and All NJ RR's	and All NJ RR's	and all NJ RR's
		(in thousands of short tons)			
Recorded					
1939	3,943	2,024	5,967	1,023	6,990
1949	4,939	2,228	7,167	973	8,140
1950	5,205	2,347	7,552	1,072	8,624
1951	5,274	2,258	7,532	1,042	8,574
1952	5,241	2,089	7,330	1,126	8,456
1953	5,255	1,990	7,245	1,052	8,297
1954	4,453	1,749	6,202	1,011	7,213
1955	4,901	1,896	6,797	988	7,785
1956	4,844	1,704	6,548	981	7,529
1957	4,255	1,614	5,869	965	6,834
1958	3,814	1,402	5,216	783	5,999
1959	3,958	1,399	5,357	912	6,269
1960	3,477	1,422	4,899	802	5,701
Projected					
1970	2,450	800	3,250	750	4,000
1980	1,600	450	2,050	600	2,650

Rail-handled exports fell from a level of 70 per cent of total reported exports through the port in 1952–1953 to about 42 per cent in 1959–1960. Similarly, rail-handled imports fell from a level of about 25 per cent of total reported imports in 1955–1956 to about 15 per cent in 1959–1960 (Table 12).

The percentages shown in Table 12 were computed from two statistical series which are not strictly comparable. Railroad tonnages are those recorded and made available by the railroads. Total foreign-trade tonnages are those reported by the U. S. Department of Commerce. Rail figures represent all shipments by rail. Commerce figures, based upon export and import documents, cover commercial shipments, primarily. Consequently, rail-handled exports include military cargoes, if any, moved through the Port of New York, but the volume represented is not included in the foreign-trade volume as reported by the Department of Commerce. To an unknown extent, therefore, the proportion of foreign-trade handled by rail is overstated.

Also, all foreign-aid shipments are included in reported total of rail-handled general cargo. The Department of Commerce, however, reports no commodity detail for those shipments and it is not possible to tell how much has been general cargo and how much bulk cargo. It

TABLE 11. RECORDED AND PROJECTED ANNUAL RAILROAD LIGHTERAGE FREIGHT VOLUMES
TO AND FROM LOCAL WATER-FRONT PLANTS AND VESSELS
IN DOMESTIC AND FOREIGN TRADE, 1939–1980

			Rail-Vessel Interchange In Foreign Trade				
			Bulk Cargo		General Cargo		
	To & From Water-front Plants	In Domestic Trade	Grain Exports	Ore Imports	Exports	Imports	Total Lighterage
			(in thousands of short tons)				

Recorded

1939	855	—	651	219	4,179	2,139	8,043
1949	1,248	571	1,015	310	5,624	2,213	10,981
1950	1,267	667	518	329	3,907	2,737	9,425
1951	1,671	631	630	495	4,620	2,813	10,860
1952	1,593	884	254	549	4,542	2,799	10,621
1953	1,330	962	711	673	3,748	2,542	9,966
1954	1,294	953	386	481	3,499	1,726	8,339
1955	1,424	1,067	602	497	4,135	1,804	9,529
1956	1,322	1,024	704	526	4,349	1,873	9,798
1957	1,115	968	293	445	4,222	1,718	8,761
1958	1,343	802	398	398	2,936	1,295	7,172
1959	1,228	714	207	333	2,331	1,376	6,189
1960	1,051	787	265	328	2,860	1,256	6,547

Projected

1965	1,100	800	150	250	2,225	950	5,475
1970	1,050	800	100	150	1,700	725	4,525
1975	1,050	800	50	100	1,300	550	3,850
1980	1,050	800	0	50	1,000	400	3,300

is assumed that they have been largely bulk cargoes and are therefore excluded from the port's foreign-trade general cargo exports. In 1959, total foreign-aid shipments amounted to only 123,000 short tons. If all foreign-aid shipments were assumed to have been general cargo and were to be included in the total of general cargo exports, the percentage of rail-handled general cargo exports would drop from 41.7 per cent to about 40.8 per cent. In 1952, there was a maximum of about 680,000 short tons of foreign-aid ship-

ments. A similarly extreme correction would reduce the rail-handled portion of general cargo exports to 64.5 per cent from the 70.8 per cent computed on the assumption that they were all bulks.

Foreign-trade general cargo not handled by rail presumably is handled by motor truck. The truck movement may be between the piers and points within the metropolitan region or points outside it.

In the case of imports, minor percentages are shown to be rail-handled. This

TABLE 12. GENERAL CARGO FOREIGN TRADE HANDLED BY THE RAILROADS

	Exports			Imports		
	Total	Rail-Handled	Per Cent Rail-Handled	Total	Rail-Handled	Per Cent Rail-Handled
	(in thousands of short tons)			(in thousands of short tons)		
Recorded						
1935	5,079	2,748	54.1	7,780	2,233	28.7
1940	10,017	6,951	69.4	7,559	2,317	30.7
1950	5,699	3,907	68.6	8,513	2,737	32.1
1951	7,012	4,620	65.9	7,995	2,813	35.2
1952	6,420	4,542	70.8	7,778	2,799	36.0
1953	5,328	3,748	70.4	8,181	2,542	31.1
1954	5,525	3,499	63.3	6,518	1,726	26.5
1955	7,156	4,135	57.8	7,136	1,804	25.3
1956	7,165	4,349	60.5	7,274	1,873	25.6
1957	7,422	4,222	58.5	7,068	1,718	24.3
1958	5,933	2,936	49.5	7,598	1,295	17.0
1959	5,586	2,331	41.7	9,076	1,376	15.2
1960	6,773	2,860	42.2	8,612	1,256	14.6
Projected						
1965		2,225			950	
1970		1,700			725	
1975		1,300			550	
1980		1,000			400	

is understandable, for much of the import tonnage consists of items such as coffee beans, which are processed in the metropolitan region and thereafter enter the domestic distribution economy. That portion which subsequently moves by rail into the interior is considered domestic freight originating in the Port District.

The projection of rail freight volumes assumes that the forces that have brought about a decline in the proportion of the total foreign-trade general cargo volume handled by rail will continue.

Projections of Rail Receipts of Coal

Rail receipts of anthracite coal have been shrinking continuously since the thirties. These shrinkages have resulted from the gradual displacement of anthracite coal by fuel oil and natural gas for home heating purposes, and by fuel oil, natural gas and bituminous coal for the generation of electric power. This displacement of anthracite coal is virtually certain to continue into the future; and further shrinkages in rail receipts are anticipated. By 1980, there is likely to be little, if any, anthracite coal received by rail in this region.

To the extent that bituminous coal will continue to be used for production of power, the railroads will continue to participate in its haulage. In the future, if atomic energy should become competitive with coal, the demand for bituminous coal would increase at first, but eventually it would drop precipitously. From the present outlook, it is likely that the long-term trend of rail receipts of bituminous coal in the Port of New York will continue downward.

Table 13 shows the rail receipts of anthracite and bituminous coal and coke at the Port of New York for selected years recorded in the past and projected into the future, to 1980.

Projections of Rail Receipts of Perishables

Rail receipts of perishables have been shrinking continually since the end of World War II largely because of diversions to over-the-road trucks and, to a small extent, to vessels. For example, in the 21-year period, 1939–1960, all rail-borne perishable foodstuffs, as a group, shrank by about 46 per cent. The changes in the components of the group varied widely and individual changes were even more striking. Thus, in 1960, no live poultry was being handled by railroads; all was hauled by trucks. At an earlier time, back in 1924, all live poultry receipts were hauled in by rail. In 1960 only 67,000 tons of milk and milk products were brought in by rail, compared with 894,000 tons in 1939 – a decline of 92.5 per cent. In 1924, practically all of the milk, cream and condensed milk receipts were by rail, by the early morning milk trains. Rail receipts of dairy products – butter, eggs, cheese and dressed poultry – also have been approaching the vanishing point in recent years. Rail receipts of fresh fruits and vegetables have shrunk by 27 per cent since 1939, continuing the decline that followed the peak year of 1927.

As far as the future of rail receipts of perishables is concerned, the question is to what extent over-the-road trucks have reached the economic limit of their pene-

tration of the more distant areas – such as Florida, California, Oregon, Washington, Texas and Arizona – which produce foods for the New York Region market. Also, there is the local question as to how the impending moves of the wholesale fresh fruit and vegetable, and butter, eggs and cheese markets from the West Side of Manhattan to Bronx sites may affect the position of the railroads in competition with over-the-road trucks in the haulage of perishables.

In any event, rail receipts of perishables are likely to continue to decline in the future. More and more of the perishables will gradually be received in truckload lots, although possibly via railroad piggyback. Table 14 shows rail receipts of perishables at the Port of New York for selected years in the past and in the future to 1980.

Merchandise Freight

Movements of railroad merchandise freight through freight stations on both the New Jersey and the New York sides of the port have followed downward trends in the past several years. Short of changed circumstances that are not now foreseeable, shrinkages in rail tonnages are likely to continue into the future, at varying rates in the different counties.

Assuming that shrinkages in rail freight volumes continue according to the experience of the past several years, the future annual volumes of merchandise which the railroads will be handling in each of the 14 counties will probably be approximately as shown in Tables 16 and 17. Manhattan will probably decline in its rail freight generation but will account for a larger proportion of the total. In other words, its rate of decline will be slower than that of the other counties.

On the New York side of the port, substantial tonnages of rail freight have been

TABLE 13. RECORDED AND PROJECTED ANNUAL RAIL RECEIPTS OF
ANTHRACITE AND BITUMINOUS COAL AND COKE, 1939-1980

	Anthracite	Bituminous	Coke	Coal and Coke
		(in thousands of short tons)		
Recorded				
1939	16,883	8,987	666	26,536
1949	9,385	10,426	981	20,792
1950	9,079	11,716	1,280	22,075
1951	8,122	13,080	1,229	22,431
1952	7,281	12,406	1,174	20,861
1953	5,490	11,090	873	17,453
1954	4,786	10,490	517	15,793
1955	4,228	11,117	731	16,076
1956	3,974	13,411	763	18,148
1957	3,035	12,661	560	16,256
1958	2,595	11,361	380	14,336
1959	2,590	10,459	332	13,381
1960	1,851	11,493	634	13,978
Projected				
1965	800	12,000	200	13,000
1970	300	11,500	100	11,900
1975	0	10,500	0	10,500
1980	0	9,000	0	9,000

marine handled in carfloats and have moved through pier stations or float bridge and team-track facilities on or near the water fronts. Also, the Long Island Rail Road's tonnages, even though handled at on-track stations, have had to be carfloated to and from the other railroads that serve the port. Annual rail tonnages carfloated across the harbor waters, that have moved through pier and float bridge stations and through the on-track stations of the Long Island Rail Road, have shown particularly strong declines in the past decade. In contrast, rail tonnages that have been trucked directly between railroad break-bulk stations and store doors on Manhattan have shown consistent expansions.

Table 15 shows the recorded and projected annual rail freight volumes that have moved to and from New York on-track stations and those served by carfloat and by truck.

THE PORT DISTRICT AS A RAILROAD TERMINAL AREA

"Our port problem is primarily a railroad problem," was the unequivocal judgment of the New York–New Jersey Port and Harbor Development Commission in its report published in December 1920. Further, the report stated, "A complete reorganization of the railroad terminal system is the most fundamental physical need of the Port of New York."

TABLE 14. RECORDED AND PROJECTED ANNUAL RAIL RECEIPTS
OF PERISHABLES, 1939–1980

	Milk	Dairy Prods.	Live Poultry	Dressed Meats	Live-stock	Fresh Fruits and Vegetables	All Perishables
			(in thousands of short tons)				
Recorded							
1939	894	477	23	536	578	1,724	4,232
1949	570	203	0	838	428	1,896	3,935
1950	458	155	0	821	444	1,708	3,586
1951	390	160	0	755	467	1,752	3,524
1952	309	154	0	751	491	1,763	3,468
1953	193	164	0	698	529	1,673	3,257
1954	164	131	0	727	557	1,649	3,228
1955	164	120	0	714	584	1,620	3,202
1956	150	141	0	707	594	1,612	3,204
1957	105	119	0	613	486	1,587	2,910
1958	74	95	0	552	420	1,452	2,593
1959	66	81	0	574	412	1,394	2,527
1960	67	70	0	535	372	1,257	2,301
Projected							
1965	20	30		450	360	1,150	2,010
1970	0	20		370	330	970	1,690
1975	0	10		300	295	825	1,430
1980	0	0		250	265	705	1,220

Manhattan Freight

Major emphasis was given by the commission to the problem of providing railroad freight service to Manhattan. Their report stated:

"The most pressing element of the entire port problem is that of railroad service to and from Manhattan. Manhattan is the district of greatest congestion, of most firmly established enterprises and customs, of greatest difficulty and expense in bringing about remodeling of facilities, because of high real estate values, restrictive quarters and physical isolation from other parts of the Port District. Only in Manhattan does the question arise whether it is feasible to bring in the standard cars of all railroads, or whether a substitute system must be found."

The commission recommended an elaborate system of freight distribution by an underground automatic electric railroad, to bring freight from a joint terminal of the New Jersey railroads in the New Jersey Meadows to a number of distributing terminals in Manhattan. The automatic electric railroad for Manhattan freight was never constructed as the motor truck in the 1920's began to take over the func-

TABLE 15. RECORDED AND PROJECTED MERCHANDISE FREIGHT MOVEMENTS
TO AND FROM THE NEW YORK SIDE OF THE PORT BY CARFLOAT,
BY TRUCK AND VIA ON-TRACK STATIONS

	Carfloated To and From		Trucked to and from Manhattan		On-Track New York Stations	All New York Stations
	Pier Stations (Man.)	Float Bridge Stations (Man., Bronx and B'klyn)	Inland Stations	Store Door		
			(in thousands of short tons)			
Recorded						
1939	1,935	3,755	60	20	5,728	11,498
1949	1,407	3,607	123	290	8,245	13,672
1950	1,424	3,691	104	274	8,722	14,215
1951	1,520	3,951	103	323	9,070	14,967
1952	1,422	3,772	105	287	8,613	14,199
1953	1,322	3,601	89	291	9,793	15,096
1954	1,302	3,368	87	281	8,783	13,821
1955	1,413	3,584	77	298	9,281	14,653
1956	1,404	3,306	71	539	9,348	14,668
1957	1,328	2,946	58	550	8,550	13,432
1958	1,050	2,490	50	555	7,739	11,884
1959	878	2,454	46	637	7,970	11,985
1960	777	2,221	53	688	7,364	11,103
Projected						
1965	660	1,710	10	805	7,045	10,230
1970	520	1,305	0	945	6,425	9,195
1975	400	995	0	1,085	5,925	8,405
1980	300	785	0	1,225	5,505	7,815

tion of local pick-up and distribution of railroad freight.

The commission found the pier stations, which then accommodated the largest proportion of the merchandise freight generated by Manhattan, to be inherently inefficient. The water-front congestion they created caused great delay in truck deliveries and, moreover, the commission was of the view that the water-front space could be much better utilized for steamship terminals. It was assumed, however, that the float bridges and their adjoining inland team-track stations would continue to be utilized for the "bulky" shipments.

Trucking itself was given considerable attention, within the context of local cartage. It, too, was found to be unduly costly, largely because of water-front congestion. The trucks studied at that time were primarily horse-drawn.[3]

Railroad freight service to Manhattan

[3]The more prominent trucking concerns were delineated as those having full-time veterinarians in their employ.

TABLE 16. RECORDED AND PROJECTED ANNUAL MOVEMENTS OF MERCHANDISE FREIGHT
INTO AND OUT OF 7 NEW JERSEY COUNTIES, 1939–1980[a]

	Bergen	Passaic	Hudson	Essex	Union	Middlesex	Monmouth	7 NJ Counties
			(in thousands of short tons)					
Recorded								
1939	1,116	748	4,027	3,853	2,512	2,281	82	14,619
1949	1,636	1,207	5,214	4,661	2,765	3,747	109	19,339
1950	1,976	1,389	6,195	4,959	3,607	4,581	127	22,834
1951	1,982	1,458	5,725	5,489	3,482	4,377	114	22,627
1952	1,857	1,432	5,308	5,155	3,021	4,116	86	20,975
1953	1,989	1,461	5,633	5,009	3,181	4,585	135	21,993
1954	2,212	1,434	5,432	4,717	3,098	4,629	107	21,629
1955	2,095	1,510	6,106	5,039	3,887	4,995	87	23,719
1956	1,787	1,454	6,796	5,273	3,441	4,597	86	23,434
1957	1,604	1,299	6,104	4,288	2,912	4,263	71	20,541
1958	1,382	1,032	5,083	3,644	2,432	3,646	70	17,289
1959	1,466	1,091	5,356	3,688	2,749	3,797	84	18,231
1960	1,473	1,000	5,334	3,662	2,832	3,956	78	18,335
Projected								
1965	1,210	1,115	4,950	3,085	2,300	4,100	70	16,830
1970	1,015	1,015	4,640	2,510	1,975	4,000	50	15,205
1975	850	920	4,350	2,045	1,700	3,890	45	13,800
1980	715	835	4,080	1,665	1,470	3,800	40	12,605

[a]Exclusive of freight lightered to and from water-front plants.

is still a problem, but the problem takes a rather different form. The outstanding problem in connection with the pier stations today appears to be the level of costs incurred by the railroads in providing the necessary marine service, and the resultant charges to the consignee for unloading rail cars.

Rail-Vessel Interchange

The commission also studied the problem of interchanging freight between the railroads and steamships in the harbor, which was entirely by lighter. It found no occasion to be critical of lighterage as such but looked forward to consolidation of the railroads' marine operations.

The railroads in the harbor still make intensive use of the lighterage system. To quote the 1920 report:

"Whatever improvements may be made in the way of better designed piers, modern machinery on them or rail access to them, it can be taken for granted that the sheltered waters of the harbor will remain a natural means of intercommunication between different parts of the port, and the demand for the lighter in its many forms will continue."

The shipping practices employed by

TABLE 17. RECORDED AND PROJECTED ANNUAL MOVEMENTS OF MERCHANDISE FREIGHT
INTO AND OUT OF 7 NEW YORK COUNTIES, 1939–1980[a]

	New York	Bronx	Westchester	Kings	Queens	Nassau Suffolk	Richmond	7 NY Counties
			(in thousands of short tons)					
Recorded								
1939	3,641	1,262	445	3,356	1,685	542	568	11,499
1949	3,632	1,715	1,056	3,465	1,988	1,031	784	13,671
1950	3,682	1,845	1,164	3,568	2,050	1,110	796	14,215
1951	3,758	1,797	1,097	3,975	2,051	1,347	942	14,967
1952	3,582	1,934	1,033	3,663	1,774	1,302	912	14,200
1953	3,716	2,317	1,259	3,481	1,722	1,715	886	15,096
1954	3,527	2,152	1,219	3,251	1,616	1,316	740	13,821
1955	3,594	2,124	1,411	3,534	1,652	1,513	824	14,652
1956	3,874	1,983	1,439	3,258	1,751	1,559	804	14,668
1957	3,671	1,860	1,253	2,871	1,564	1,461	752	13,432
1958	3,187	1,683	1,249	2,378	1,440	1,244	702	11,883
1959	3,156	1,774	1,230	2,332	1,447	1,361	685	11,985
1960	3,231	1,840	1,100	2,084	1,182	1,069	597	11,103
Projected								
1965	2,835	1,410	1,220	1,575	1,215	1,415	560	10,230
1970	2,650	1,190	1,200	1,185	1,050	1,460	460	9,195
1975	2,525	1,015	1,180	885	910	1,510	380	8,405
1980	2,435	880	1,160	690	785	1,550	315	7,815

[a]Exclusive of freight lightered to and from water-front plants.

exporters are also conducive to the utilization of the lighterage system. The common practice is for a shipper of export freight to consign his shipment to "New York Lighterage," in care of a foreign freight forwarder, rather than to a specific steamship terminal. The forwarder endeavors to book space on the ship having the earliest departure for the shipment's destination. He gives final shipping instructions to the railroad's lighterage agent while the shipment is in transit and, at times, after the rail car has arrived in the Port District. The export car in this instance is switched from the railroad's receiving yard to its water-front lighter-age yard. Even when the steamship berth is equipped with rail tracks, the railroad, in most instances, chooses to deliver the freight by lighter. Moreover, a large proportion of the export cars contain consignments for several different overseas destinations and call for deliveries to several steamship berths. The lighter in this instance serves as a sorting and consolidating device as well as a means of transporting freight.

New problems have arisen during the intervening years in connection with the interchange of freight between the railroads and the cargo ships in the port. When the commission made its study, virtually 100 per cent of steamship freight generated outside the Port District was handled by the railroads. Today a substantial portion of that freight is transported by the motor carriers. Also, the railroads now make extensive use of trucking in lieu of lighterage, and the proportion of the total so transported has been increasing steadily.

As with the Manhattan pier stations, the outstanding railroad problem in connection with lighterage appears to be the costs of providing the marine service.

The New York terminal area is unique in so many ways that cost comparisons with other terminal areas are extremely difficult. It is not unlikely that many of the basic features of this area which make it a profitable area for the railroads to serve lead to certain cost elements which might be considered to be relatively high.

For instance, the very size of the area, over a thousand square miles and including some 400 separate freight stations together with innumerable private sidings, is a measure of its total freight generating strength. On the other hand, it is entirely probable that this very size is an important factor in making terminal costs here higher than they are in areas of smaller geographic extent. It is to be expected that a railroad company will incur higher costs in distributing freight within a radius of 15 or 20 miles of its principal classification area than in distributing freight within only a mile or two of such a yard.

The export and import tonnages generated by port activities are of great importance to the railroads, but the marine terminals are numerous, with some 173 conventional general cargo berths in use, having locations extending from midtown Manhattan to Staten Island and from Newark Bay to the Brooklyn Army Base.

The Port of New York has been favored by nature with a wide expanse of sheltered waters and an extensive shore line, much of it well suited for marine terminal or industrial development. However, there is a complex configuration of the various land masses and provision must be made for harbor-crossing traffic.

In all likelihood, a deeper study of this topic would yield the conclusion that such cost elements as are considered high are in fact the costs incurred in serving a profitable area, costs which may not be incurred in less profitable regions.

Marine Operations

Today there is even more reason than there was in 1920 for improving the economy of marine operations through consolidation of equipment and facilities. A recent study by the railroads in cooperation with the Port Authority indicated that substantial amounts could be saved through the consolidation of the operation of marine equipment alone. The savings might be larger if consolidation was extended, as the commission contemplated, to the railroad marine terminals themselves.

Terminal Operation Versus Road-Haul Operation

The genius of the railroad lies in its road-haul operations. By virtue of the low friction of a steel wheel rolling on a steel rail, the railroad is capable of transporting long trains, carrying large shipments, over long distances, at high speed and at low cost. This very virtue in road-haul operations, the flanged wheel on the steel track, however, introduces a rigidity which is a handicap in terminal operations.

After the road train has been received in the railroad's breakup yard, a number of time-consuming and costly switching operations must take place before a particular car or a particular shipment can be delivered to a point where it is available to the consignee. The order of cars must be changed, and they must be sorted and reconsolidated into shorter trains for delivery to secondary special yards or to a consignee's private siding.

As a result, loaded rail cars spend most of their time in terminal areas rather than on the road. The American Railway Engineering Association conducted a survey of freight car time in transit in 1955 and concluded that "most of the time a car is in railroad hands is spent in terminals waiting to be moved; only 17.1 per cent of the total time a car is loaded is spent in road time."[4] The results of the survey were compared with a similar study made by the Federal Coordinator of Transportation in 1933, and the findings of the two surveys are presented in Table 18.

TABLE 18. DISTRIBUTION OF LOADED CAR TIME WHILE CAR IS IN RAILROAD HANDS

	Averages	
	From AREA Data 1955	From FCT Report 1933
Time in terminals	63 hrs.	53 hrs.
Time in trains	14	23
Miscellaneous delays	5	Not Shown
Total time in railroad hands	82 hrs.	76 hrs.

It is apparent that terminal time increased over the intervening 22 years while time in transit decreased. In fact, the increase in the time spent in terminal areas exceeded the reduction in road time. It is plain that the technological advances which have yielded greater road speed have been more than offset by the increase

[4]American Railway Engineering Association 1956, Vol. 57, pp. 321–324.

in time spent in terminals. Technologically, railroad terminal operation has lagged far behind its road operations.

The Motor Truck and Piggyback

The advent of the motor truck has been the most potent force in shaping the course of recent freight transport history. When the report of the New York–New Jersey Port and Harbor Development Commission was issued in 1920, trucking was viewed as a local cartage operation providing transport between the railroad freight station and the shipper or consignee. The motor truck now has become an important common carrier of intercity freight and, as such, has presented strong competition to the railroads. Perhaps even more important, it has encouraged a resurgence of private transportation which has deprived the railroads of much lucrative freight business.

The motor truck has major virtues in the operations in which the railroads are handicapped. It possesses great flexibility in transporting smaller shipments for shorter distances over a widespread network of regional streets and highways. It is not handicapped by the need to operate in trains; each unit is capable of individual dispatching; time spent in terminals can be minimized.

Since the issuance of the commission's report in 1920 there has come about the opportunity of combining the line-haul advantages of the railroads with the terminal flexibilities of the motor truck in such a manner as to utilize the inherent advantages of both.

Within recent years considerable progress has been made in coordinating railroad and motor truck transportation, through the so-called piggyback operation. Although this coordination has been technologically possible for a long time, it is only recently that acceptable rate structures have been developed which make it operationally feasible.

The railroads have been experimenting with five different piggyback rate plans, although not all roads have subscribed to all five plans. Briefly, they are:

Plan 1. The railroad carries on its flatcars the trailers of common-carrier trucking companies, at appropriate rates. The trucking company solicits the business and bills the shipper.

Plan 2. The railroad performs the entire service, including furnishing the trailers, pickup and delivery, loading the trailers onto the flatcars and taking them off. In this instance, the shipment is to be considered railroad freight transported in a particular fashion.

Plan 3. The shipper provides his own trailer and is responsible for pickup and delivery, while the railroad furnishes the flatcar, places the trailer on and takes it off the car, and provides the intercity movement.

Plan 4. The shipper furnishes the flatcar and provides the trailer and performs the pickup and delivery while the railroad provides only line-haul transportation.

Plan 5. The railroad and the common-carrier trucking company offer joint rail-truck rates. The territory of each carrier is thereby extended into that served by the other. The railroad and the trucking company divide the rate.

Plans 3 and 4 were designed primarily to attract the traffic of private shippers who have their own truck trailer fleets. Freight forwarders were among the first to take advantage of the new service. It is too early to tell whether these plans will be effective in the railroads' recapturing any significant volume of the traffic of private carriers.

The volume of freight moving by piggyback has grown substantially in recent years, particularly under Plans 1, 2 and 3. Since 1957 the District's piggyback tonnage has increased at an average rate of some 20 per cent a year. By 1961 it accounted for 3.1 million tons of the District's rail freight tonnage.

The railroads in the Port District have established a number of piggyback yards, which are the points of truck and railroad interchange. At these points the trailers are taken off the railroads' flatcars and attached to tractor units for delivery to the consignee or to the forwarder's terminal.

This operation contains a special promise for railroad freight service for Manhattan. A preponderant proportion of Manhattan's railroad freight is already handled by freight forwarders, and the prospect is that a growing proportion of it will be transported by the piggyback operation. Such development is likely to reduce gradually the amount of Manhattan's tonnage moved across the harbor by carfloat and thereby the role of the pier stations should decline.

The implication of this development is that there will be a need for a number of inland stations at which the forwarders can consolidate package shipments into trailer loads and, conversely, sort inbound piggyback freight for final delivery to consignees.

There is even the possibility that the piggyback operation may be utilized for some of the freight now moving in carload lots. It has been estimated, for example, that even for carload freight, piggyback transportation may be more economical than box-car shipment, except where a plant with a rail siding handles several boxcars a day. If experience should confirm this estimate, there are the possibilities that the railroads may recapture freight business which has been diverted to over-the-road common-carrier trucking companies and even reclaim some of the freight now moving by private transport.

SUMMARY

The New York-New Jersey metropolitan region depends heavily on railroad transportation, for its food and its fuel, and for the support of its industrial and commercial activities. In 1960 the railroads transported into, out of, and through the Port of New York District 58 million tons of freight.

From domestic points they brought into the District 2.3 million tons of perishable foodstuffs and 14 million tons of coal. General merchandise into and out of the District, embracing a vast array of commodities, reflecting the consumption requirements and the production accomplishments of the region, aggregated 30.5 million tons.

Some 5.7 million tons of freight passed through the port as a railroad gateway between areas to the south and west and those to the north and east. In ocean-borne foreign trade through the port, the railroads participated to the extent of 4.7 million tons. They accounted for 42 per cent of the port's general cargo exports, and about 15 per cent of its general cargo imports. Rail-vessel interchange in coastal, intercoastal and offshore trades aggregated another 0.8 million tons.

Although its magnitude is still great, the District's rail freight tonnage has been declining for the past ten years. Further declines, although at a reduced pace, are projected for the next two decades in virtually all the component segments of freight movement.

Some of the downwards trends of the past, and their projection into the future, can be attributed to technological change, like the replacement of anthracite coal and coke by fuel oil and natural gas for domestic heating. Still others can be ascribed to the growth in the competitive strength of motor truck transportation.

On the other hand, there have been significant increases in the integrated use of railroad and motor truck transportation. The railroads have increased their use of the motor truck in lieu of lightering freight to and from ships in the harbor and in lieu of carfloating local freight to and from Manhattan pier stations. Freight shipped and received by piggyback has shown healthy growth. It is possible that the railroads, by developing the potentialities of piggyback, may recapture some of the business they have lost in the past to the motor carriers. Implied is a future need for further development of piggyback yards and for inland sorting and consolidation stations for package freight, particularly in Manhattan. A decline in the role of the pier stations also appears a likely consequence.

CHAPTER 14

MOTOR FREIGHT AND TERMINAL NEEDS

Among the major modes of inland transportation, freight hauled by motor vehicle has exhibited the sharpest rate of growth over the past 20 years. The estimated national volume of domestic intercity freight traffic carried by all forms of transportation grew from 544 billion ton-miles in 1939 to 1,206 billion ton-miles in 1958. Motor vehicle freight climbed from 10 per cent of this traffic to nearly 21 per cent during this time. Revenues of Class I and II motor common carriers, between 1939 and 1957, increased almost eightfold. (Motor carriers are classified by the Interstate Commerce Commission by type of service and by commodity carried. Common and contract carriers are grouped as follows: Class I, those carriers with gross operating revenues exceeding $1,000,000; Class II, those between $200,000 and $1,000,000; Class III, those below $200,000.)

With the rapid expansion of motor freight transport has come diversification into a variety of highly specialized forms with differing terminal requirements. The motor truck terminal is the metropolitan seat of the motor carriers' over-all operation for freight handling and control, the corporate headquarters, and the site for storage and maintenance of equipment. The terminal is the nerve center of the trucking operation, at least for the common carriers of general freight.

For private carriage, subject to I.C.C. jurisdiction only with respect to safety requirements movement is between the factory, warehouse or other depot of the shipper, and the platform of the con-signee. Nevertheless, a number of shipper associations of private carriers maintain terminal facilities in Manhattan, principally on the piers along the Hudson River.

Contract carriers, like the private carriers, have little need for terminals of their own, since they normally operate from the shipper's platform directly to that of the consignee. Some of the specialized haulers, such as movers of household goods, require warehouse space and operate terminals for goods to be delayed in transit. Others, such as bulk movers of many liquid products, have no need for terminals. The movements of carriers of agricultural commodities (which are exempt from I.C.C. regulation) are seasonal and irregular, and because their traffic is normally in truckload lots, they rarely maintain terminal facilities in the New York area.

Local cartage, also exempt from I.C.C. regulation, covers a wide range of transportation activity, from the systematic pickup and delivery of package freight for shipper or a carrier, to the heavy hauling of bulk materials. Pickup and delivery arrangements are highly diverse, sometimes involving warehousing and a receiving station for consolidation of shipments for one or more intercity carriers.

Technically not a motor carrier, the freight forwarder also maintains terminals for the consolidation of small shipments into carload rail traffic. In New York there are 79 domestic freight forwarders, and 53 of them have terminals located along Manhattan's Hudson River water front.

Twenty-eight are located on piers, sub-leased from the railroads.

The organizational relations among the carriers also influence truck terminal needs. Among line-haul common carriers, for example, interline freight is significant. This is particularly true in a gateway city such as New York, which is the end of the journey for many intercity carriers. It is even more prominent in Chicago, an outstanding transportation interchange point. The relative importance of the interchange function is reflected in the physical arrangement of the terminal, for the amount of interline exchange has implications in the volume of interregional freight and in the number of vehicles to be accommodated at the terminals. As another illustration, a local cartageman may perform pickup and delivery service for several road carriers, and thus become a consolidator of less-than-truckload freight and operate his own terminal.

The Common-Carrier Motor Freight Terminal

The Class I and II intercity carriers of general freight are the major subject of this chapter. General freight accounted for 8.5 per cent of all Class I and II intercity motor freight in 1958. In spite of their small share of total United States tonnage, they are of key significance in terms of their terminal requirements.

In the New York Metropolitan Area there are 299 Class I and II intercity[1] motor common carriers of general freight. They operated 373 terminals in 1960. During the summer of that year the Port Authority conducted an extensive survey of the terminal operations of these carriers. The survey comprised, first, a field reconnaissance of all 373 terminals. This

[1] "Intercity" here is taken to mean the long-haul territory outside the 19-county short-haul, or metropolitan territory.

yielded a broad range of facts regarding terminal size, type and setting. Second, a study was made in greater depth of 107 terminals considered to be a representative group. Of these, 98 were full-scale terminals and 9 were receiving stations. In addition, a small number of interviews were held concerning specialized terminals, private union terminals, and truck stops.

Full-scale terminals (hereinafter referred to simply as terminals) are distinguished from receiving stations in that they handle over-the-road freight both inbound and outbound. Receiving stations are restricted to picking up and receiving outbound freight shipments. The shipments are concentrated into trailerload lots for transfer to the carriers' main terminals, there to be classified for line-haul movement.

During the first half of 1960, it is estimated that Class I and II intercity motor common carriers of general freight brought 1,023,000 tons per month into the Port District, while they carried 941,000 tons outbound. If these are normal monthly figures, the total for 1960 should have been about 12,000,000 tons inbound, and about 11,000,000 tons outbound. This would account for about one-seventh of all United States motor common carrier tonnage. New York's share of intercity freight handled in the Northeast (Middle Atlantic and New England Regions) is roughly 60 per cent.

The terminals of these carriers provide employment for about 18,000 persons, not including road drivers and salesmen. In these terminals, aggregating about 3.3 million square feet of floor space, approximately one million tons of freight are handled across the platforms each month through 5,178 truck doors or bays. The distribution of terminals by type terminal and size of carrier is given in Table 1.

TABLE 1. CLASS I AND CLASS II INTERCITY CARRIERS AND THEIR LOCAL TERMINALS
IN THE NEW YORK METROPOLITAN AREA

	Class I Large[a]	Class I Other	Class II	Total
Intercity carriers	100	88	111	299
Long distance[b]	54	8	14	76
Local terminals (single carrier)	155	113	105	373
Full-scale terminals	136	104	100	340
New Jersey	95	57	48	200
New York	41	47	52	140
Receiving stations	19	9	5	33
Joint terminals[c]	2	2	1	5
Carriers with no local terminal	0	3	5	8

[a]Carriers whose annual earnings in 1959 exceeded $2,500,000.
[b]Carriers reaching territories beyond the New England or Middle Atlantic Regions.
[c]Buildings subdivided for individual use by more than one carrier.

Breaking bulk or the transfer of freight from truck to truck is the prime function of the motor terminal, but it is by no means the only activity carried on in the terminals in the New York Area. In an estimated 274 cases, the New York Area terminal is the regional, if not the system-wide, headquarters of the carrier, since it is the meeting point for the two entirely distinct operations: (1) local pickup and delivery and (2) line-haul transport.

Since pickup and delivery service generally utilizes a different type of equipment than that used in line-haul operations, most LTL (less-than-truck-load-lot) freight is transferred from truck to truck at the terminal. The significance to the operation of the terminal of this separation of local from intercity service is that usually all line-haul vehicles, even when carrying truckload shipments, call at the terminal when arriving at or before leaving the metropolitan area. This is primarily for the purpose of changing drivers, although it also gives the carrier an opportunity to check and record the bills of lading.

Since World War II the operation of motor terminals has become increasingly expensive. The American Trucking Association reports that terminal costs for Class I and II carriers have increased from $1.17 per ton of intercity freight in 1945 to $3.31 in 1957. Terminal cost in the Middle Atlantic Region in 1957, however, was among the lowest Region cost levels, $2.83 per ton of intercity freight.

Terminal Size

Over the past 30 years larger and larger terminals have been built. Many carriers have moved from converted sheds, warehouses or garages to modern single-story, well-appointed office and freight-handling facilities ranging up to 50,000 square feet of gross floor space and providing more than 100 truck bays. New terminals are often set back from the road, handsomely landscaped and surrounded with ample paved space for truck maneuvering and storage. While terminal size has paralleled the growth of carriers, factors other than total tonnage volume often limit the maximum size of the terminal, and most terminals are of moderate size, as noted in Table 2. Greater operating efficiency often can be achieved in larger terminals, since the installation of more highly mechanized equipment is made feasible, but the carrier can often offer better service by establishing several terminals in different parts of the area. However, above a certain freight volume, requiring somewhere between 50 and 100 doors, the carrier is likely to operate several terminals. The larger carriers frequently segregate the handling of inbound from outbound line-haul freight, which may involve separate terminals, in different areas.

TABLE 2. NUMBER OF TERMINALS IN THE
METROPOLITAN AREA BY SIZE

(includes receiving stations)

Terminals	Number of Truck Bays Per Terminal
7	None[a]
161	1– 10
112	11– 20
63	21– 40
20	41– 60
7	61– 80
1	81–100
2	Over 100

[a]These do not have raised platforms fronting the outside of the buildings. They are provided with doors (like garages) through which trucks enter the building.

Where traffic justifies it, carriers find that they can achieve substantial savings and improve over-all service by dividing the metropolitan area into two or more subareas, to be served by separate terminals. It is not uncommon for the larger carriers to maintain terminals both in New Jersey and in New York City.

Generation of Motor Freight in the Region

The estimated volume per month during the first half of 1960 for Class I and II line-haul motor common carriers of

general freight moving to and from the New York Metropolitan Area is roughly 2 million tons, slightly more than half inbound. The geographic distribution of local origins and destination corresponds broadly with the distribution of commercial and industrial activity. The correlation between manufacturing employment and motor freight generation, as shown in Table 3, is striking.

East of the Hudson, each county receives more motor freight than it originates, while west of the river, each county,

TABLE 3. PERCENTAGE DISTRIBUTION OF
EMPLOYEES IN MANUFACTURING (1956)
AND MOTOR FREIGHT GENERATED (1960)
BY AREAL UNIT

	Manu-facturing Employees (1956)	Motor Freight Tonnage (1960)
Manhattan CBD	31.3	23
Upper Manhattan and Bronx	3.9	6
Brooklyn	13.9	15
Queens	7.5	8
Other Long Island[a]	5.6	3
Westchester	3.1	2
Stamford–Norwalk, Conn.	.2[b]	d
Hudson	8.1	7
Essex	8.2	13
Staten Island	.5	d
Bergen	5.4	8
Rockland	.7	d
Passaic	4.7	7
Other northern New Jersey[c]	6.9	9

Sources: Manufacturing data are derived from Edgar M. Hoover and Raymond Vernon, *Anatomy of a Metropolis* (Cambridge: Harvard University Press, 1959), p. 260. Motor freight data from Truck Terminal Survey, *op. cit.*

[a]Includes Nassau and Suffolk counties, New York.

[b]Approximate.

[c]Includes Middlesex, Monmouth, Somerset, and Morris counties, New Jersey.

[d]Less than 1 per cent.

Note: Due to rounding, sum of components may not equal 100 per cent.

with the exception of Passaic, originates substantially more tonnage than it terminates. The small volume of freight to and from Rockland County is nearly balanced.

About half of all motor freight to and from the Metropolitan Area is in less-than-truckload lots and is transshipped over terminal platforms. Truckload

in the regional aggregate between inbound and outbound movement.

An important portion of intercity truck freight moves to and from the water front for transshipment in ocean-borne trade. The volume of such movement by Class I and II intercity common carriers of general freight, based on sample tabulation, is in the vicinity of 3,000,000 tons a year,

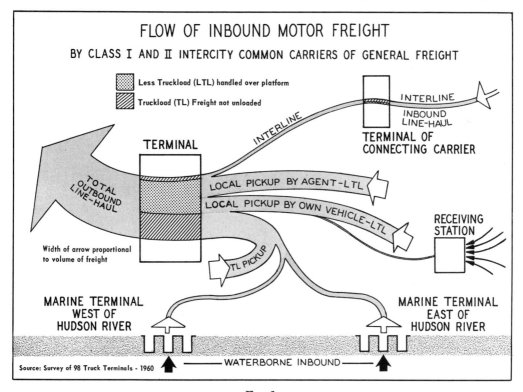

FLOW OF INBOUND MOTOR FREIGHT
BY CLASS I AND II INTERCITY COMMON CARRIERS OF GENERAL FREIGHT

Less Truckload (LTL) handled over platform

Truckload (TL) Freight not unloaded

INTERLINE

INBOUND LINE-HAUL

TERMINAL

INTERLINE

TERMINAL OF CONNECTING CARRIER

TOTAL OUTBOUND LINE-HAUL

LOCAL PICKUP BY AGENT-LTL

LOCAL PICKUP BY OWN VEHICLE-LTL

RECEIVING STATION

Width of arrow proportional to volume of freight

TL PICKUP

MARINE TERMINAL WEST OF HUDSON RIVER

MARINE TERMINAL EAST OF HUDSON RIVER

Source: Survey of 98 Truck Terminals - 1960

WATERBORNE INBOUND

Fig. 1

freight, as has been noted earlier, generally moves to the terminal, but is not unloaded there.

The volumes indicated in Figures 1 and 2 are composites of all metropolitan terminals and are not to be considered representative of any particular terminal. While individual carriers strive toward an inbound-outbound balance, they do not succeed to nearly the extent shown here. Nevertheless, there is an over-all balance

of which some 56 per cent moves inbound by truck and outbound by water (Figs. 1 and 2).

The highest proportion of freight handled by the larger intercity motor carriers moves to and from the region's manufacturing plants and manufacturers' and wholesalers' warehouses.

So important are the manufacturer's plant and the distributor's warehouse to the motor common carrier, both as ship-

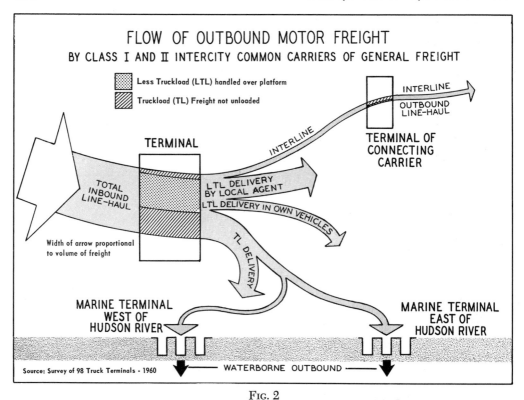

FLOW OF OUTBOUND MOTOR FREIGHT
BY CLASS I AND II INTERCITY COMMON CARRIERS OF GENERAL FREIGHT

FIG. 2

TABLE 4. INTERCITY MOTOR FREIGHT VOLUMES BY TYPE OF ESTABLISHMENT
AT LOCAL ORIGIN AND DESTINATION

	All Terminals		Manhattan Terminals	
Volume	Inbound	Outbound	Inbound	Outbound
Estimated monthly total	953,000 tons	874,000 tons	134,000 tons	114,000 tons
Per cent of total				
Marine terminal	15	13	12	13
Public warehouse	8	9	3	5
Manufacturing plant or distribution center	65	71	70	80
Retail establishment	11	7	14	1
Other	1	1	1	1

Note: Due to rounding, sum of components may not equal 100 per cent.

pers and receivers of freight, that they constitute the carrier's primary market and exert a strong influence upon the location of terminals. The garment factories and other manufacturing and distributing activities in Manhattan make up the largest single concentration of freight generation in the Metropolitan Area. There the density of freight generation, measured in tons generated per square mile, reaches its metropolitan peak. Over one-fifth (21.4 per cent) of all intercity motor freight carried by the class of carrier under study

moves to or from Manhattan's Central Business District.

The concentration of points of origin

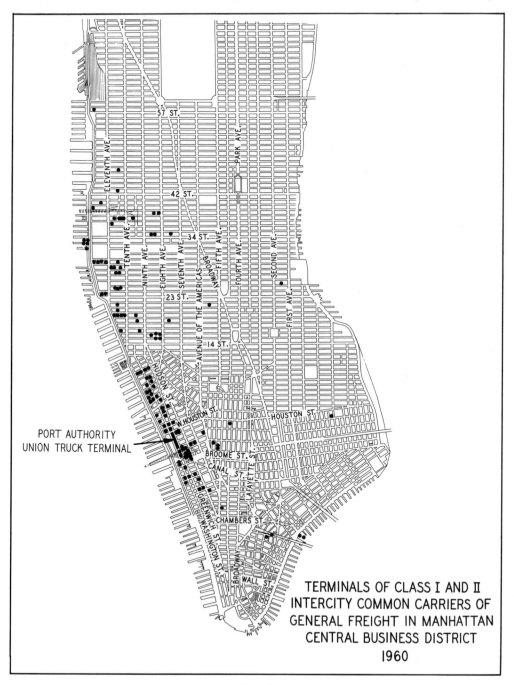

PORT AUTHORITY
UNION TRUCK TERMINAL

TERMINALS OF CLASS I AND II
INTERCITY COMMON CARRIERS OF
GENERAL FREIGHT IN MANHATTAN
CENTRAL BUSINESS DISTRICT
1960

FIG. 3

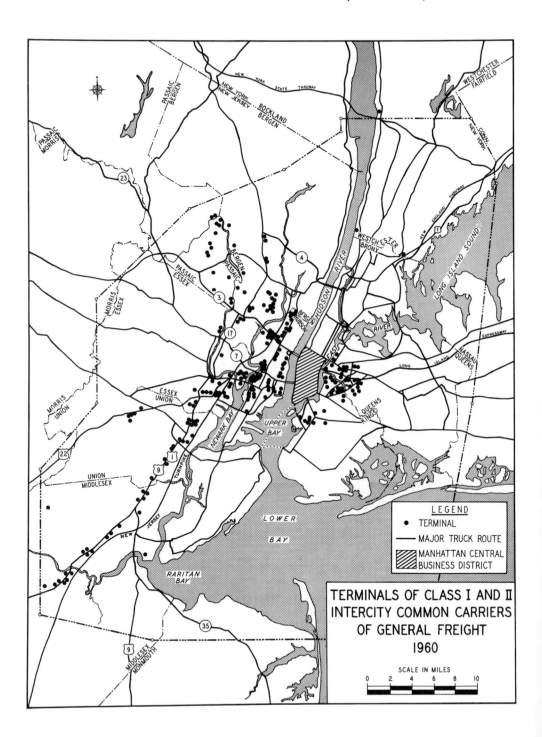

LEGEND
● TERMINAL
— MAJOR TRUCK ROUTE
▨ MANHATTAN CENTRAL BUSINESS DISTRICT

TERMINALS OF CLASS I AND II
INTERCITY COMMON CARRIERS
OF GENERAL FREIGHT
1960

SCALE IN MILES
0 2 4 6 8 10

Fig. 4

and destination in Manhattan is even greater, relative to the metropolitan total, than the density of freight volumes. The survey data show that of the three and one-half million local calls made by these carriers or their agents in the Metropolitan Area during a normal month, about a third (32 per cent) are to points in the Manhattan Central Business District. The implication is that the average size of shipment is smaller in Manhattan than elsewhere in the region (Table 5).

TABLE 5. ESTIMATED AVERAGE SIZE
OF SHIPMENT TO AND FROM
SELECTED LOCAL AREAS

(pounds)

	In-bound	Out-bound	Average
Metropolitan Area	1,111	967	1,037
Manhattan CBD	747	728	739
Rest of Metropolitan Area	1,291	1,045	1,157

TRUCK TERMINAL LOCATION

Before World War II intercity motor freight terminals were centered largely in Manhattan on the West Side, south of 60th Street, and in Brooklyn, Jersey City, Paterson-Passaic, and Newark. Only a few scattered terminals were located away from heavy urban development. Since the war the dominant tendency has been an outward movement from the densely developed areas to less built-up lands near the major highways. This may be seen in the 1960 pattern of terminal distribution shown in Figures 3 and 4. While this pattern is different from prewar days, there is still a great concentration of terminals in Manhattan, even more compact than formerly, on the West Side — between the two Hudson River tunnels within about one-quarter mile of the water front.

On Long Island there are two clusters, one north and one south of downtown Brooklyn. The smaller cluster, near the Gowanus Canal, is composed of older and smaller terminals; the terminals around Newtown Creek, particularly in the communities of Greenpoint, Long Island City and Maspeth, have been developed in the postwar period.

In New Jersey there are several large and growing groups of major motor freight terminals. The largest concentration rims the Hackensack Meadows, with terminals prominent in Secaucus, Carlstadt east of Berry's Creek, and Moonachie. The eastern margins of the Meadows are lined with terminals, particularly in North Bergen, Jersey City and Kearny. Many of these are situated on route U. S. 1, which follows the contour along the western flank of the Palisades Ridge.

Newark, like Manhattan, is the seat of another heavy concentration of terminals. Southwest of Newark is a long string of terminals following U. S. 1 as far south as New Brunswick. The terminals established in the newly developed districts, notably Newtown Creek, U. S. 1 South, and the Hackensack Meadows, tend to be much larger than their predecessors in older districts.

The Hackensack Meadows District accounts for 43 per cent of the total number of truck bays in the area, although it accounts for only 27 per cent of the terminals. Since freight-handling capacity is closely related to the number of truck bays, the Hackensack Meadows must be considered the vital center of motor-freight handling in the New York area today (Table 6).

Manhattan south of 60th Street is still the densest single freight-generating area of the region. The new motor truck terminals have sought locations outside the central core, however, because of the subur-

TABLE 6. AVERAGE NUMBER OF TRUCK BAYS AND FLOOR SPACE PER TERMINAL
(full-scale terminals only)

District	Class I		Class II		Combined	
	Bays	Square Feet Floor Space	Bays	Square Feet Floor Space	Bays	Square Feet Floor Space
Manhattan						
So. of 60th St.	12.4[a]	8,031[a]	4.1	3,917	7.5	6,221
Gowanus	14.0	9,109	8.5	3,409	11.5	7,058
Newtown Creek	22.2	10,234	8.6	5,152	18.6	8,584
Hackensack Meadows	32.0	13,465	12.1	5,812	27.4	11,675
Hudson County East	16.0	9,363	11.3	6,199	14.5	7,862
Newark Vicinity	15.7[a]	12,491[a]	17.0	18,125	16.7	10,343
Paterson–Passaic						
Vicinity	16.8	12,914	15.0	14,523	14.1	11,963
Upland Bergen County	16.0	11,337	7.7	1,179	11.0	10,259
Kenilworth Vicinity	17.6	7,225	13.0	4,200	16.8	6,721
Route 1 South	18.7	8,578	14.4	6,466	20.6	8,204
All Districts	21.2	10,898	8.8	6,057	17.1	9,006

[a]Includes Port Authority Union Terminals.

banization of industry and goods distribution. Also, as carriers have grown in the amount of tonnage handled, their terminal space needs have grown correspondingly. There has been greater need for efficiency in cargo handling, a need which can be met by spreading out, both within the building and outside it, to provide more parking, waiting and maneuvering space for vehicles. The carriers, like manufacturing firms, are faced with the problem of acquiring the kind and amount of space they require at a cost they can reasonably afford. Hence, the tendency has been to locate out of, but not far from, the Manhattan core.

The two main criteria for terminal location are shown in sharp relief and, to some extent, in conflict: (1) the need to be in the midst of one's customers (to minimize pickup and delivery costs), and (2) the need for rapid access to the main highways (to minimize line-haul costs). Of the major bases for the selection of a

site, highway accessibility is by far the most important. A terminal needs to be within easy reach of the Hudson River tunnels, particularly the Holland Tunnel — if the terminal is situated in Manhattan — and near major highways, especially U. S. 1, if the terminal is in New Jersey.

Most terminals serve the entire metropolitan area, but there is a tendency for most of their business to come from the section in which they are located. This specialization is prominent at the outlying terminals. For example, terminals in the southwestern part of the metropolitan area, for the most part, handle little freight moving to and from points east or north of Manhattan. Part of the reason for this is the cost of local pickup and delivery to distant parts of the metropolitan area and the territorial limits of the jurisdiction of the local drivers' labor organizations.

A number of the largest carriers have established more than one terminal. The

TABLE 7. EQUIPMENT AT TRUCK TERMINAL
(full terminals only)

	Total	Class I Large	Class I Other	Class II
Number of Terminals Reporting	98	49	22	27
Equipment	Per Cent of Terminals			
Facilities for truck repair	59.2	71.4	54.8	40.7
Sleeping quarters for road drivers	16.3	24.5	13.6	3.7
Forklifts	63.3	91.6	54.8	33.4
Jacks	50.0	79.0	45.4	44.3
Dragline conveyor	8.1	17.5	4.5	3.6
Automatic dragline control	3.0	5.7	4.5	0
Power-operated dock-lift	4.1	8.9	0	3.6
Pneumatic tube bill conveyor	4.1	8.9	0	3.6
Truck-to-terminal radio	22.4	46.7	18.3	7.3
Electronic billing system	13.3	35.2	0	3.6
Closed-circuit television	1.0	2.9	0	0
Plug-in dock telephone	3.0	5.7	4.5	0
Heavy crane	2.0	2.9	4.5	0

McLean Trucking Company, for example, has four terminals; Spector Freight System two; and Associated Transport four, in addition to two receiving stations. Yale Transport is an example of a carrier which has divided the metropolitan area into three roughly equal parts by establishing large terminals in Maspeth, North Bergen and Manhattan.

Terminal and Road Equipment

Over the past 30 years terminals have also been made more efficient in the physical handling of freight. Medium-size terminals generally are now equipped with forklift trucks, while the very largest usually have dragline systems and other types of installed equipment. The smallest terminals have few labor-saving devices, except perhaps for the small freight jack. The facilities are listed in Table 7.

With regard to road equipment in the

line-haul (or over-the-road) movement, carriers utilize tractor-semitrailer combinations[2] almost without exception. Such trailers are now 30 feet or more in length, ranging up to 40 feet.

Road equipment, like terminal facilities, also shows change. The use of tandem trailers, lightweight trailers, pairs of 20-foot "Strick-tainers," and better tractor design are all moves toward greater efficiency and increases in tonnage per driver mile. Line-haul equipment is becoming specialized as it evolves in the direction of ever-larger vehicles. It is becoming less and less like local pickup and delivery equipment.

Local pickup and delivery service, whether by the line-haul carrier, its local cartage agent, or the shipper or consignee, is an operation distinct from the line-haul movement and, except for truckload freight, is frequently handled in a different type of vehicle. The two-axle truck, the van of which is usually 14 feet in

[2]Hereinafter referred to simply as trailers. Where true trailers (those which support their full weight while being towed) are intended, they will be called full-scale trailers.

length, is frequently used, although line-haul carriers may use the over-the-road trailer. Some carriers make use in local pickup and delivery of a short (typically 20-foot) trailer, referred to as a "city-type" trailer.

Local pickup and delivery service in the New York metropolitan area is further differentiated territorially. Manhattan south of 60th Street is unlike the rest of the metropolis from a trucking point of view, in terms of the density of freight generation, the average size of shipment and the nature of street traffic. This difference is reflected in the road equipment. The 14-foot two-axle truck accounts for about 63 per cent of all calls made to points in Manhattan south of 60th Street. Most of the remaining calls are made in tractor-trailers exceeding 30 feet in length. Much of the freight handled by these larger units is in truckload lots.

The dominance of the two-axle truck in local pickup and delivery service, especially in Manhattan, is important in terminal design and operation. Not only does the Manhattan terminal handle more shipments per truck, but it also serves a larger proportion of local trucks than do terminals located elsewhere in the metropolitan area.

Manhattan terminals are not so well provided with basic handling equipment as terminals located elsewhere. Only 20 per cent of them are equipped with fork-lifts, compared with 79 per cent of non-Manhattan terminals. This results in slower rates of stripping and loading of vehicles. In addition, the use of smaller trucks to serve Manhattan terminals and limitations on maneuvering space lead to higher terminal operating costs in this area.

[3] Each of whose earnings in 1960 exceeded $2,500,000.
[4] Of the four carriers not maintaining a terminal in New Jersey, three serve territories directly north or northeast of New York City.

The Schedule of Terminal Operations

The two broad types of trucking to and from terminals differ also in the time of day during which they operate. Pickup and delivery is almost completely a daytime function, while line-haul movement is mostly an overnight operation. The distribution of arrivals and departures by time of day is given in Table 8. As may be seen, there is a heavy concentration of arrivals in the morning, and a peaking of departures in the late afternoon and evening. There is never a complete lull in terminal activity, and 57 per cent of all terminals remain open at all times.

TABLE 8. ARRIVALS AND DEPARTURES OF LINE-HAUL VEHICLES AT NEW YORK METROPOLITAN TERMINALS

(per cent)

	Departures (outbound)	Arrivals (inbound)
Total	100.0	100.0
4 P.M.–8 P.M.	29.0	3.6
8 P.M.–midnight	44.5	9.1
Midnight–4 A.M.	13.4	31.4
4 A.M.–8 A.M.	4.7	41.8
8 A.M.–noon	3.0	10.1
Noon–4 P.M.	5.4	4.0

THE RECEIVING STATION

The problem of serving the Manhattan shippers and receivers of motor freight has been met, in part, by the receiving station, used by the larger carriers serving all parts of the metropolitan area. Of the 100 largest New York carriers,[3] 96 have at least one large terminal in New Jersey,[4] 67 maintain freight stations in New York City (Manhattan, Brooklyn or Queens) and 50 have freight stations in Manhattan. Even though these carriers may have established their headquarters terminals in New Jersey, most of them have retained either a full-scale terminal or a receiving station on the New York side of the region. Several of the larger maintain sales offices in Manhattan, and a number utilize small Manhattan union terminals.

Twenty-six of these larger carriers maintain their own receiving stations in Manhattan where outbound freight is received from the shipper and consolidated into truckloads for transshipment to the major terminal. Several have more than one such station in Manhattan, one carrier maintaining five. In all, there are 47 receiving stations in Manhattan, and 8 in nearby areas of New Jersey. In addition, there are a few small private union terminals, and there are public receiving docks at all full-scale terminals.

The receiving stations of Manhattan vary widely in their facilities and degree of suitability to their function. Some have new sheds, or covered platforms, set back from the street to provide off-street loading and maneuvering space (although not adequate off-street parking space). From these relatively high standards, receiving stations tend to grade off to converted warehouses, piers or garages, sometimes with sidewalk platform docks. Most Manhattan terminals are located along Washington and Greenwich Streets, mixed with warehousing, wholesaling, produce marketing and other freight-handling and loft-located enterprises. The receiving stations typically are small, averaging about 4,000 square feet of floor space for stations of Class I carriers and about 1,000 square feet for those of Class II carriers.

Although they do not appear too important in terms of freight handled, by eliminating unprofitable local pickup operations they make a valuable economic contribution to the parent carrier, not to be measured by the amount of tonnage handled. Receiving stations furnished about 12,000 tons of outbound freight per month to their respective main terminals in 1960, representing nearly 7 per cent of their parent carriers' locally-originated outbound tonnage. For carriers not having full-scale terminals in Manhattan or nearby Brooklyn or Queens, the receiving station performs a highly useful function.

The receiving station as a solution to the problem of serving the central core of a metropolis is unique to the New York area. It is used only by those carriers (with one exception) whose major terminal operations are in New Jersey. Manhattan shippers are generally reluctant to carry their outbound goods across the Hudson River to New Jersey truck terminals, and the receiving station is a compromise solution for the shipper-carrier problems created by the removal of main terminal operations from the New York Central Business District.

The Outlook

It may be said with confidence that motor common carriage to and from New York in the years that lie ahead will increase above its present level, but it is extremely difficult to establish any projected level for 1980. Taking both national and local factors into account, however, it is reasonable to suppose that the annual volume should be in the neighborhood of 36 million tons, about equally divided between inbound and outbound movements.

With regard to national factors, if we assume a continuation of the present relation between total domestic freight ton-mileage and gross national product,[5] and an annual growth rate of the latter between 3.1 and 3.5 per cent, then it follows that by 1975 domestic ton-mileage will almost double, and by 1980 nearly triple its 1958 level.

---

[5]The ratio of GNP, in constant 1954 dollars, to total domestic tonnage during the post–World War II years has averaged $3.317 per ton-mile. It has fluctuated little and exhibited no significant trends upward or downward.

Motor transport is likely to grow at a faster rate than total domestic tonnage and capture a growing share of an expanding market. Such factors as the suburbanization of light industry and retail trade, the trend toward wide distribution in the form of small shipments, the demand on the part of industry and the distributive trades for closer scheduling and consequently greater dependability in transport time — all favor the truck.

But there are a number of factors which will probably limit the growth of the motor carrier's share of the total domestic transport market. There appear to be limits to the possible extent of truck diversion of rail freight. These are limits imposed by commodity differences and by service requirements, and by the ability of the railroads to retain much of their long-haul freight. Other limiting factors are the development of containerization in coastwise shipping and the rise of trailer-on-flatcar rail freight. These factors argue for a gradual tapering-off of motor transport's rate of growth.

Furthermore, the share of motor freight commanded by common carriers has been declining. Between 1945 and 1958 the intercity ton-mileage of Class I, II and III carriers (ICC-regulated carriers) grew from 27.3 to 85 billion, a growth of more than 200 per cent. At the same time the nonregulated motor carriers registered a gain of from 39.7 to 175 billion ton-miles, an over-all growth of almost 350 per cent. As a result, the share of intercity motor-freight ton-miles accounted for by regulated carriers dropped from 41 per cent in 1945 to 33 per cent in 1958.[6]

There are other important forces at play. If, as a consequence of mergers and consolidations, unification of motor common carriage materializes on a major

scale, the number of intercity motor common carriers may be reduced in the next decade to 20 or 30. This will mean (a) larger volumes, allowing more accurate scheduling; (b) lower transit times, since traffic between given points can be concentrated into fewer vehicles, thus reducing time spent in terminals; (c) greater convenience to the shipper, since shipments to varied destinations will be picked up in consolidated lots, thus lowering the number of vehicles calling at his shipping dock each day; and (d) simplification of billing procedures. Carriers' unit-costs consequently can be held down through the efficiencies of larger scale operation, lessened duplication of trips and greater utilization of equipment.

During the past 20 years there has been a tendency for manufacturers to supply goods directly to retailers through their "sales branches," displacing a portion of traditional merchant wholesaling. This development implies smaller shipments and a proliferation of points of origin and destination. But the decentralization of manufacturing increases the difficulty for both the for-hire and the private carrier of securing return freight. Thus while some firms, over the short run, may be driven to private carriage because of the lack of adequate for-hire carriage in the vicinity of their plants, such private carriage is likely to be a predominantly one-way operation and therefore costly. Thus, the effect of strengthening common carriage by unification may be that common carriage will become competitively stronger in the future, and eventually be able to stabilize, if not increase, its share of the intercity motor freight market.

At what point such stabilization could occur is difficult to judge. Freight volumes of the regulated carriers in 1975 should total between 144 and 169 billion ton-miles, and in 1980 should stand be-

[6]American Trucking Association, Inc., *American Trucking Trends: 1959* (Washington, November, 1959), p. 5.

tween 192 and 254 billion ton-miles. This assumes that the share of intercity motor ton-mileage transported by regulated carriers (i.e., Class I, II and III common and contract carriers) stabilizes in 1975 at about 28 per cent and then rises to 30 per cent.

Regulated contract carriage is small — during postwar years it accounted for about 9 per cent of ICC-regulated motor carriage. Moreover, it is intermediate in character between common and private carriage. It will probably divert some tonnage from both, but still remain a minor form of motor transport and it is estimated that common carriers will continue to account for at least 90 per cent of the freight volumes handled by the regulated carriers.

Motor Freight Volumes in the New York Metropolitan Area

Class I and II motor common carriers of general freight, as distinguished from carriers of special commodities such as liquids, household goods, and automobiles, are the major users of motor terminals. Nationally, general freight represented 8.45 per cent of all intercity motor freight carried by Class I and II motor carriers in 1958, and about 3.3 per cent of all intercity motor ton-mileage. In terms of tons handled, this category of truck transportation constitutes a small, but nonetheless significant, segment of the nation's — and New York's — trucking picture. It is the principal type of carrier making extensive use of motor terminals as distinct from warehouses or the docks of shippers and consignees.

Future tonnage levels of this group of motor carriers depend upon the over-all growth of the industry as outlined above, the general economic growth of the northeast portion of the nation, and the development of the New York metropolitan area itself.

It was forecast in the New York Metropolitan Region Study that the population of the New York Metropolitan Region[7] will approximate 18.4 million in 1970 and 20.9 million in 1980.[8] Total regional employment, according to this forecast, will stand at 7.3 million in 1970 and 8.3 million in 1980.

Manufacturing employment in the New York Metropolitan Region is expected to rise but not at a rate as rapid as that of the nation. Since manufacturing plants and distribution centers account for the generation of two-thirds of the motor freight (of the type under consideration) generated in the New York area, it is likely that future volumes of motor freight will vary directly with changes in their levels of activity, as measured by volume of production rather than by employment.

We are reduced, therefore, to the use of rather broad generalizations in the projection of motor freight volumes. The extent of uncertainty regarding future levels of intercity motor common carriage is deepened by the differential growth of private and common carriage. It is assumed that these rates will vary in New York service as in that of the nation.

The level of intercity motor common-carrier freight will depend upon the following: (1) manufacturing employment in the New York Metropolitan Area is likely to grow from its 1956 level by about 20 per cent by 1970 and by 26 per cent by 1980; (2) the total volume of freight generated (i.e., the demand for transportation) will grow at a much faster rate — if its historic relation to gross national product persists, it may roughly double by 1975 and triple by 1980.

[7]Consisting of 22 counties encircling New York City as defined in the New York Metropolitan Region Study.

[8]The figures given here are the revisions made by members of the Metropolitan Region Study Staff and the staff of the Regional Plan Association.

But the New York Metropolitan Area is expected to grow in economic activity more slowly than the nation as a whole, so that the growth in the level of all transportation demand in the New York Area will be substantially less than that of the nation as a whole.

Moreover, motor common carriage here, as in the nation, will probably grow more slowly during the next few years. Thereafter it should pick up in rate of growth as a result of corporate unification and technological advance in materials-handling and improved terminal efficiency.

The most that can be said at this juncture concerning the growth of intercity motor common carriage to the New York Area is that it will be positive but moderate; the total will probably not exceed 30 million tons annually by 1980.

The West Side of Manhattan

Although the Manhattan Central Business District is expected to show some further decline as a freight generator as a result of the continuing exodus of manufacturing industry and the goods-handling function of wholesaling, it promises to remain the most important freight generator in the area.

Equally important is the problem of arranging truck service in such a way that future truck traffic in the city does not contribute further to street congestion. What is basically needed are two elements: First, it is increasingly necessary to Manhattan terminals that space for off-street loading, maneuvering, waiting and parking be made available. Second, it is necessary that access to major arteries serving Manhattan be improved.

In Chicago a number of truck terminal districts have been established by a municipal zoning ordinance which prohibits other land uses within them. The districts are located near heavy concentrations of freight generation and have easy accessibility to the major expressways. The districts are relatively small, normally about 10 acres. The result has been a grouping of motor freight terminals and a reduction in traffic congestion. The applicability of this policy to Manhattan's truck terminal problems is worthy of detailed study and analysis.

The Garment District

The most severe problems of truck congestion are in Manhattan's Garment District. The garment industry is vital to the economy of the region and is an important freight generator as well, so that the trucking situation is of serious concern. Tractor-trailers are excluded by traffic regulation from the streets between 34th and 42nd Streets, between Fifth and Ninth Avenues, but the curbs are lined with two-axle trucks, many parked for periods far in excess of the time required for loading and unloading.

Much of the situation stems from the nature of the industry. Freight flows are sporadic and cannot be anticipated very far in advance. The truck driver often has to wait for freight, and he may not know ahead of time how much is to be moved. A multitude of relatively small establishments, in narrow-frontage buildings having limited elevator facilities and no facility for horizontal movement except the street or sidewalk, combine to present an almost insoluble transportation problem. Limited street capacity leads to much cruising for a parking place, to holding a place as a "claim," and to parking for long periods so as to function as a mobile terminal for the accumulation and transshipment of freight.

The Garment District must be recognized as an industrial district, indeed as a highly special and complex kind of industrial plant. That it should be traversed by city streets is fortuitous, and those streets might more properly be considered as industrial access than as thoroughfares. Much of the "transportation" problem is rooted in the incongruity of a major manufacturing complex situated in the heart of a central business district, athwart routes of general metropolitan movement. The industry's location is related to its marketing structure and is highly resistant to change. Its problems are aggravated by its occupancy of buildings which, by modern standards, are obsolete, with inadequate facilities for vertical goods handling and no horizontal communication between establishments except at the street level despite the many close interlinkages.

There is a pressing need for some sort of facilitation of truck access to and from the Garment District. The problem is not new. Some of the more prominent proposals have been: a ban on automobiles and taxis in parts of the district; parking meters; "surplus" trailer terminals for use when deliveries are not being made; deliveries and pickups to begin at 7 A.M. instead of 9 A.M.; one-side-of-the-street parking during specified periods; construction of a privately built and operated truck terminal; and development of parking areas and terminals along railroad rights-of-way.

The most recent truck terminal proposal was put forward by T. T. Wiley, then Commissioner of Traffic of the City of New York, in late February 1961. This proposal envisions construction of a small truck terminal between 36th and 37th Streets, west of Seventh Avenue. If such a terminal should prove successful, it is proposed that an additional terminal of similar size and layout be constructed west of Eighth Avenue.

[9] See "Proposal for Development of the Municipally Owned Waterfront and Piers of New York City," 1948 pp. 63-68.

The study divides Garment District trucking into three parts: the handling of piece goods, garments, and cut goods. Terminal facilities are recommended only for the first group, which are primarily involved in the pickup and delivery of textiles in bolts, boxes and packages. The study considers only the movement of freight between Garment District establishments and trucks parked at the curb. No provision for off-street parking or waiting space is proposed, except for the berths at the terminal platform.

Such a terminal, therefore, while reducing curb parking, would not seem to be a solution to the over-all problem, which involves the total circulation of goods within as well as to and from the district, including vertical transportation within the buildings. A meaningful solution for a perplexing set of problems must embrace an over-all plan for the development of the district as a whole, including manufacturing, merchandising, storage, design, servicing and other activities which collectively make up the garment industry.

The Water Front

Serious traffic congestion also afflicts certain sectors of the water front. Particularly severe conditions are encountered by the motor freight carriers when serving cargo piers on Manhattan's Hudson River and East River water fronts. The situation has prevailed for a number of years and has been discussed at length in an earlier report of The Port of New York Authority.[9]

As the report pointed out, these portions of Manhattan's water front were originally created by land-fill-out beyond the natural river banks. West and South Streets were established 70 feet wide and the Marginal Way 180 feet wide, the latter intended entirely for pier service and placed under the administrative jurisdiction of the city's Department of Docks (later the Department of Marine and Aviation).

When motor traffic assumed commanding magnitudes these wide marginal areas offered convenient rights-of-way for the construction of elevated highways. The West Side Elevated Highway, a facility not related to the piers, now occupies a part of the Marginal Way. Its supporting columns and its approach and exit ramps have pre-empted much of the space formerly available for trucks moving to and from the piers and have created impediments to circulation in the space remaining. At the same time, a change took place in the nature of freight-handling operations. The horse-drawn dray was replaced by the far larger motor truck and tractor-trailer. Also, a constantly growing proportion of the freight which formerly had come to the piers by rail or water shifted to the highways.

Another factor of controlling importance is the dimensions of the piers themselves. Historically, Manhattan piers were considered to be extensions of the street system, and the oldest piers are not only aligned with the crosstown streets, which determines their spacing, but also of equal width, some as narrow as 40 feet. Piers built during the past 50 years are wider, most of them 100 to 150 feet wide. Still the majority do not provide an adequate turning radius for large trucks and tractor-trailers and have meager space for maneuvering, loading and unloading truck units inside the pier shed. Moreover, many of the piers were designed for passenger purposes and have solid façades fronting the Marginal Way with only narrow gangways for truck entrance and exit and no back-up space at the inshore end for loading and unloading.

In consequence of these conditions,

truck access is severely limited and cargo handling is seriously impeded. Long waiting lines on the Marginal Way add to the time spent in delivering and receiving freight and aggravate general street congestion. In many instances steamship companies have resorted to using the Marginal Way as an unloading platform for motor trucks, and have handled cargo to and from the pier by using pallets and forklift trucks.

The inability of the narrow piers to handle trucks without congestion has been observed and commented upon for many years. Understandably, the motor carriers have been outspoken in their criticism of the situation. Cartage charges to and from the piers are high and there are extra charges for waiting time, unfavorable to the Port of New York's competitive posture.

Piers built during the past decade and those now under construction, in most instances, have been made much wider and have been planned to provide adequate space for the accommodation of motor freight within the terminal. As Manhattan's piers and water fronts are redeveloped along modern lines, it may be expected that the more severe aspects of water-front traffic congestion will be progressively relieved.

The report cited suggests that "the Port Authority's union inland motor truck terminal program is the prototype for facilities which will reduce the number of trucks now going to the piers with part loads by consolidating freight for the same pier at sorting stations off the water front, thus eliminating many of the vehicles carrying small loads." The suggestion still merits a detailed analysis of the economics and operational feasibility of such sorting and consolidating depots, particularly in view of the probable growth of containership operations.

Containerization

Increased use of containers, in the form of loaded trailer bodies, transported by ship or rail, promises to bring about an expansion of motor traffic to and from shipside and rail piggyback yards. Highway approaches to those facilities and the staging and loading areas associated with them will become matters of increasing importance as traffic increases.

It may be expected that the shift in rail freight transport away from the boxcar will become pronounced during the next few years, and that the trailer-on-flatcar (TOFC) shipment, with its low terminal handling costs, short loading-time and ease of door-to-door delivery will take its place to a great extent. Its growth (and the growth in containerization of some of the water-borne freight) will increase the volume of local trucking.

The effect on motor common carriers is not wholly clear, for there may be conflicting tendencies. Long-haul motor freight (over 500 miles) may gravitate to the rails under TOFC Plans 1 and 5, which provide for the integration of railroad and common-carrier trucking operations (see Chapter 13). General freight moving shorter distances, say between 50 and 500 miles, especially freight moving less than 200 miles — the forte of the intercity motor common carrier — does not appear to be vulnerable to rail diversion.

The effects of TOFC upon terminal location will be dependent upon its rate of growth and upon its impact on motor carriage in general. When container loading and handling assume commanding magnitudes, a pull will be exerted upon the motor carriers to locate their terminals within easy reach of the TOFC yards. Also, the size and number of the TOFC yards in the New York Metropolitan Area will be increased (there are now 8).

In view of its local nature, consolidation and distribution of trailers may be handled by other than common-carrier trucking firms, such as pool-car distributors, freight forwarders, and shipper associations. Only the extensive development of Plan 5, now in embryonic form, would appear to have a strong positive effect upon intercity motor carriers and even here, in the interline handling of freight on a joint-rate basis, there does not appear to be a great deal of promise since the railroads themselves (under Plan 2), freight forwarders, the resurgent Railway Express Agency, and others seem to be in a position to secure most long-haul business.

CHAPTER 15

AIR FREIGHT

Air cargo appears to be on the threshold of continued major growth and expansion. It is nonetheless still a very small business when compared with intercity trucking, railroad freight service and ocean freight. In the domestic movement of freight, Interstate Commerce Commission reports indicate air cargo presently represents approximately 1/20 of 1 per cent of total domestic intercity freight. On the movements of cargo across the North Atlantic, air's share is also about 1/20 of 1 per cent of the total.

TABLE 1. TONS OF DOMESTIC AND OVERSEAS AIR CARGO HANDLED AT PORT OF NEW YORK AUTHORITY AIRPORTS

(includes freight and express moved by scheduled and nonscheduled airlines on all types of planes)

	Domestic	Overseas	Total
1948	61,737	6,854	68,591
1949	72,310	8,905	81,215
1950	92,397	10,573	102,970
1951	100,385	12,406	112,791
1952	100,724	13,906	114,630
1953	107,396	14,424	121,820
1954	104,620	18,160	122,780
1955	128,522	22,658	151,180
1956	135,490	26,074	161,564
1957	145,873	31,266	177,139
1958	131,770	36,151	167,921
1959	152,868	47,690	200,558
1960	166,744	60,304	227,048
1961	179,573	73,378	252,951

Youth is on the side of air cargo. Today it may represent only an infinitesimal portion of total domestic and foreign freight movements. Small increases in this share, however, will represent major growth in the actual volume of air cargo handled. They therefore are a matter of great interest and importance to the airlines, and in air terminal planning.

The rapid growth in air cargo in recent years has been a reflection of the great expansion which has taken place in the transportation of passengers by air and particularly the conversion from piston- to jet-propelled aircraft. Changes in aircraft design since the war have resulted in an increasing cargo capacity on passenger planes. The new jet liners, in addition to a full load of passengers (with their normal baggage), can carry three to seven tons of freight. As a consequence, the airlines have had a rapidly increasing available cargo capacity on their regularly scheduled passenger flights. However, the stringent dimensional restrictions of the cargo compartments limit the kinds of freight which can be physically accommodated. As the airlines set about developing cargo traffic to fill this available capacity they found it increasingly desirable, and even necessary, to be able to offer shippers a full range of services, including the ability to accept shipments which could not be handled in the cargo holds of passenger planes. To accomplish this, they converted "stepped down" passenger planes into "freighters."

In addition to this expansion of cargo capacity in passenger planes, much of the recent interest in and expansion of all-cargo operations has grown out of the availability of large numbers of modern piston planes, all with good service life remaining but low resale value. These planes offered an opportunity to expand cargo capacity quickly and with a minimum of new investment. This situation contributed to a faster growth of all-cargo air transport operations in recent months than would have occurred if the air carriers had to finance their cargo expansion exclusively with new aircraft.

TABLE 2. DOMESTIC AND OVERSEAS ALL-CARGO PLANE MOVEMENTS AT PORT OF NEW YORK AUTHORITY AIRPORTS

(annual totals, all airports)

	Domestic	Overseas	Total
1948	14,068	450	14,518
1950	20,957	533	21,490
1955	13,591	1,998	15,589
1958	11,260	3,027	14,287
1959	11,619	3,655	15,274
1960	14,476	3,790	18,266
1961	15,776	4,777	20,553

Air shipment is clearly of value where time is important, particularly when the cargo has low weight and high value. Air shipment is particularly adaptable to the handling of perishable and fragile freight. In other cases, the value of the superior speed of air service permits sufficient savings in inventory and warehousing costs to more than offset the higher freight charges. In these areas, the opportunities for air cargo appear promising.

In building volume cargo movements in other areas, particularly those where truck and rail can offer substantial competition, the outlook is somewhat different. Here air transportation's greatest problem will be costs. Not only are basic air transportation costs high but so are terminal handling costs, because of the need for special stowage of most ordinary shipments and for terminal handling at each

end of the air trip, in addition to the loading and unloading of the truck which moves the shipment to and from the airport. An airplane cannot get direct access to a shipper's or consignee's loading platform. By contrast, volume shippers by truck and rail can move their freight door-to-door without the need for intermediate loading, unloading or terminal handling, in addition to obtaining lower rates. However, where long distances (over 2,000 miles) are involved, it is possible air cargo will be able to offer some competitive service and rates.

The mere fact that there exists a demand for air transport service does not automatically mean that there is a market in which volume air shipment can operate successfully or profitably. The basic question is whether the service and the rates which the carrier must charge to recover full costs are reconcilable with what the shipper will in fact pay, and whether these rates will generate sufficient volume to make the whole operation economical. Available studies indicate that there are substantial markets where air cargo can thrive with rates high enough to give the carrier a reasonable financial return and the shipper a service of practical value.

KINDS AND VOLUME OF CARGO AVAILABLE

Although the total markets for domestic and overseas freight are both enormous, only small portions are actually susceptible to movement by air. The limited data available concerning the nature of intercity freight movements by all carriers indicate that over 75 per cent of all reported ton-miles represent bulk cargoes, such as grain, petroleum, coal, mineral ores, and cement, which are generally low in value and high in density. These types of cargo are exceedingly sensitive to small changes

TABLE 3. COMMODITY GROUPS OF DOMESTIC AIR FREIGHT ORIGINATING AND
TERMINATING AT NEW YORK REGION AIRPORTS IN 1950

(per cent distribution of tons originated and terminated, all airports)

	Inbound	Outbound	Combined Total
Perishable & alive	11.0	1.8	5.1
Animal & vegetable, edible but not perishable	.3	.2	.2
Animal & vegetable, inedible (except wood & fiber)	4.0	1.9	2.7
Wood, paper & plastics	9.3	18.5	15.2
Textile fibers, manufactures & wearing apparel	10.3	39.1	28.8
Metals & manufactures	4.1	2.7	3.2
Nonmetallic minerals	1.1	.4	.6
Chemical products	2.8	6.7	5.3
Machinery & vehicles	47.4	21.6	30.9
Miscellaneous	9.7	7.1	8.0

Source: Port Authority Report, "Domestic Air Freight 1950."

in cost and therefore will for the foreseeable future remain the exclusive field of those transport agencies with the lowest cost service.

The area in which there is greatest potential for air transport is in general cargo, which accounts for about 10 per cent of the ton-miles reported, but represents over 20 per cent of the revenue received. It is in this area that the competition between railroads, common-carrier trucks and private trucking is intense.

TABLE 4. PRINCIPAL COMMODITIES OF
IMPORT AND EXPORT AIR FREIGHT, 1960

(per cent distribution by weight,
all New York Region airports)

Woven wool fabrics	19.1
Automobile parts	16.4
Electrical machinery & apparatus	4.9
Wool wearing apparel	3.5
Cotton wearing apparel	3.0
Office, accounting & computing machines	2.0
Live animals	1.6
All others, each less than 1%	49.5

An indication of the kinds of domestic freight which do move by air is available from the study of air cargo at New York's airports in 1950, summarized in Table 3. Although over ten years old, it is the only available detailed record of domestic air freight movement. A somewhat similar, but more recent record, of principal commodities in international commerce moving to and from New York by air was obtained by the U. S. Census Bureau in a special study of air cargo imports and exports conducted in March 1960 (Table 4).

There is a thesis held by some students of air freight that the value per pound of a commodity is a reliable measure of the degree to which it is susceptible to transportation by air. There has, however, been no proof of this proposition.

On the other hand, a more recent thesis holds that air freight must be considered as a marketing tool contributing to lower inventory, less capital tied up in transit, lower packaging costs, fewer claims, and less stock obsolescence. Emphasis on these factors places the modern air freight developer in the role of marketing consultant to top management rather than in the role heretofore practiced of air freight salesman to specialists in traffic management. The growth of this concept will continue and be augmented to the benefit of this young industry.

ORIGINS AND DESTINATIONS OF CARGO

There are few data of this nature available. However, an origin-destination survey of domestic air cargo at New York's airports in 1950 (the only such survey available) discloses the geographic differences between points of origin and destination and the uneven flow of traffic (Table 5). A similar study of overseas air freight discloses that the problem of geographic differences between points of origin and destination also exist in foreign commerce (Table 6).

TABLE 5. ORIGINS AND DESTINATIONS OF DOMESTIC FREIGHT, 1950

(per cent distribution by weight, all New York Region airports)

	Inbound Freight Originating In	Outbound Freight Destined To
New England States	3.3	2.3
Middle Atlantic States	3.8	4.0
South Atlantic States	9.6	11.5
East North Central States	55.4	42.3
East South Central States	1.7	1.4
West North Central States	4.2	9.7
West South Central States	3.6	7.8
Mountain States	2.0	1.3
Pacific States	15.9	18.1
Canada, North Atlantic	0.5	1.6

Source: Port Authority Report, "Domestic Air Freight 1950."

The number of airports in the United States receiving jet service has been and is continuously growing, though it is increasingly evident that large airports of this nature will almost certainly be restricted to larger metropolitan areas. It is reasonable to assume, therefore, that the air carrier usually will find airports to accommodate its all-cargo aircraft in every principal metropolitan area, but there will be many areas of industrial or commercial importance having limited airport facilities. To some degree this can be offset through the use of truck services to or from the nearest airport. The time and cost of this trucking operation will, however, restrict the range of economical usefulness of air cargo for long-distance hauls.

TABLE 6. ORIGINS AND DESTINATIONS OF OVERSEAS AIR FREIGHT, 1960

(per cent distribution by weight, all New York Region airports)

	Import	Export
United Kingdom	23.8	9.3
France	20.9	5.9
West Germany	13.1	12.5
Italy	17.1	3.2
Switzerland	5.6	2.8
Netherlands	3.1	2.8
Austria	1.9	0.9
Haiti	1.4	0.8
Canada	1.2	16.4
Venezuela	0.2	6.2
Bermuda	0.0	4.4
Belgium	1.2	2.8
Sweden	1.3	2.2
Mexico	2.0	2.0

Source: U. S. Bureau of Census 1960 survey of air cargo imports and exports.

AIR CARGO OPERATING COSTS

The direct plane operating cost of an air cargo service performed by a carrier whose primary operations are for passengers depends heavily on which theory of joint cost allocation is to be used. If cargo is to be treated as a by-product of passenger transportation with all general, over-head, plane ownership and plane opera-tion costs charged to passenger service, the result will be a comparatively low level of costs. If it is to be treated semi-independently, accepting direct plane op-erating costs but without responsibility for general or overhead costs, the result will be a middle level of cargo costs. Lastly, if air cargo is to be accepted as a business standing on its own feet and meeting all costs, both direct and indirect, the result will be a comparatively high level of costs.

To date, most air cargo activities have been conducted by carriers whose pri-mary concern is the movement of passen-gers. The three principal all-cargo oper-ators (Flying Tiger, Riddle, and Seaboard & World) have found full costs to be so high as to restrict severely their operating potentials without government aid.

Changes in government policy with re-spect to these direct and indirect financial aids can have major impact on the total cost of air cargo service, and thereby in-fluence its future development. This is evidenced by the recent federal govern-ment proposal for the institution of a 5 per cent federal excise tax on air cargo.

The operating costs of piston-engine cargo planes and of passenger planes con-verted into all-cargo planes certainly do not offer prospects for profitable all-cargo operations in a mass market. The direct operating costs for nonstop flights of about 1,000 miles seem to center around 9 cents per available ton-mile. Allowing for indirect costs, a profit margin and an optimistic 70 per cent average annual load factor, this would probably require a basic rate level of about 20 to 22 cents a ton-mile (excluding ground transporta-tion costs) for balanced bidirectional traffic flows and 28 to 30 cents in cases of unbalanced flows.

The newly offered turbine-powered cargo aircraft promise large reductions in operating costs, according to their manu-facturers, which may range as high as 50 per cent, yielding a cost of around 5 cents per available ton-mile. Because of the more efficient design of all-cargo fuselage permitting larger sized shipments, heavier floor loading and easier loading and un-loading, there seem to be good prospects for substantial savings in indirect opera-ting cost to the point where basic rate lev-els of 10 to 12 cents on bidirectional and 15 to 17 cents on one-directional flows seem possible.

A crucial factor in achieving such low operating costs is the assumed plane util-ization which can be obtained under normal operating and traffic conditions. Fixed cost (amortization, interest, insur-ance) for the CL-44 and the DC-8 Jet Trader may amount to as much as $2,000 a day, so any inefficiency in utilization will have a major impact on costs.

Utilization is heavily dependent upon the available market, the constancy of de-mand and the availability of efficient ter-minal facilities, in order to provide readily available loads and to reduce terminal handling and turn-around time of the aircraft to a minimum. The utilization figures of 3,000 hours per year or 10 hours a day, 6 days a week, which underlie the low costs used here certainly would not be realized if terminal operation time were to exceed one hour or so, or if cargo demand fluctuated so that the plane could not be kept in steady, year-round operation un-der load.

TERMINAL OPERATING COSTS

A principal cost of service, and a major problem to any operator seeking the de-velopment of a volume air freight serv-ice, is and will remain the terminal operation. In order to realize the low rates needed for major penetration into the general cargo market for shorter hauls (under 1,000 miles) in the face of existing competition, it will be necessary to lower terminal costs substantially.

The estimated terminal cargo-handling cost of $35 to $65 per ton presently being incurred by airlines indicates the severity of terminal cargo-handling costs. The total $70-per-ton cost of handling one ton of freight at two terminals (origin and destination at $35 each) is equivalent to the direct cost of transporting that ton of cargo 1,000 miles by air at 7 cents per ton-mile. Air cargo rates will remain relatively high so long as they must absorb terminal costs of this magnitude, in spite of the improved efficiencies of newer all-cargo craft.

Aircraft builders have given much thought and attention to the problem of terminal handling and have designed systems which will, it is claimed, make large cost reductions possible. These systems require major capital expenditures, so that the degree of saving will be related to the continuity and intensity of use that can be achieved under actual working conditions. These systems can be used for the newer all-cargo planes but are not particularly adaptable to the converted piston planes now in widespread use, and are of limited value in handling cargo for normal passenger planes (including the newest jets).

Terminal costs might be reduced through the use of standard containers which are loaded by the shipper and transferred directly between truck and plane without additional airport terminal handling. The size of container which has been set as "standard" for general freight interchange by the American Standards Association (8 by 8 feet in 10-, 20-, 30- and 40-foot lengths) is not well suited to plane use, irrespective of the weight factor. The smaller units will fit some of the newer all-cargo planes (with a loss in available cubage) but will not fit converted piston planes nor the cargo holds of passenger planes. One version of the 8 by 8 by 10 feet approved interchange container is reported to have an empty weight of 500 pounds.

The development of the C-141 military cargo craft promises to reduce terminal handling costs. This high-wing plane permits highway trucks to back directly to its rear loading gate for acceptance or delivery of cargo without using expensive or complicated handling machinery. Equally important, this plane will accept the transportation interchange containers of the standard dimensions recommended by the American Standards Association.

AIR FREIGHT RATES

All of the various factors which influence the movement of freight and which govern the interests of the operator come into play when actual freight rates are set. How the air transport industry evaluates and relates these conditions is best answered by a comparison of existing rates, shown in Table 7. These were rates in effect on November 1, 1961, and for air transport reflect the new "very low" rates announced by the major airlines a month previous.

Machinery and parts were selected for the comparison in Table 7 because this is a commodity which is susceptible to volume air movement (see Tables 3 and 4). The three cities were selected to give short-, medium- and long-haul mileage ranges. These air cargo rates, when converted to ton-miles and with the pickup and delivery charges omitted, range from a high of 64.5 cents per ton-mile for small

TABLE 7. RATES FOR SHIPPING PACKAGED MACHINERY OR PARTS FROM NEW YORK TO BOSTON, CHICAGO AND SAN FRANCISCO BY DIFFERENT MEANS OF TRANSPORTATION

(per 100 pounds; includes pick up and delivery)

	Boston	Chicago	San Francisco
Volume Rates (24,000 to 30,000 lbs. and over)			
Truck	$ .59	$ 1.43	$ 5.58
Rail	1.07	2.09	5.12
Air cargo	6.35	8.95	22.20
Freight forwarders	a	1.43	5.58
REA express	3.67	5.04	10.76
Small Shipments Rates (Less than 5,000 lbs.)			
Truck	$ a	$ 3.93	$ 7.75
Rail	2.01	3.86	9.67
Air cargo	7.75	11.40	26.60
Freight forwarders	a	3.93	6.92
REA express	3.67	5.04	10.76

ªNo rates offered.
Source: Tariffs on file at Port Authority as of 11/1/61.

shipments to Boston to a low of 16 cents per ton-mile for large shipments to San Francisco.

THE FUTURE OF AIR CARGO

There are several domestic and overseas air cargo traffic projections, but these are based on more or less arbitrary evaluations of the many factors involved. Apart from simple trend projections, only limited assumptions can be made as to the share of the total market which air cargo can attract, based on known trends in costs and rates. As explained in Chapter VI of "A Report on Airport Requirements and Sites in the Metropolitan New Jersey-New York Region" published by the Port Authority in May 1961, although air cargo may enjoy a rapid build-up in the future, "a relatively small number of flights into and out of major airports will be needed to handle the volume. No all-cargo airports will be justified for the New York area . . ." This conclusion stems in part from the "surplus" cargo capacity available on passenger jets, and in part from the capacity of New York Metropolitan Region airports to handle all-freight plane movements in off-peak passenger hours.

Air freight service has an importance to the business and industry of the New York region that cannot be measured wholly by the number of tons transported or by the number of all-cargo planes to be accommodated; the aggregate value of the goods transported by air is far out of proportion to the aggregate tonnage. As has been pointed out in an earlier paragraph, its role promises to be that of an important tool in distribution, one that increases the opportunities for efficiency and economy in the over-all flow of materials to the producer and of products to the consumer.

PART III

Transporting People

CHAPTER 16

INTERCITY TRAVEL AND ITS FUTURE

The vitality and the wealth, the industrial, financial and cultural leadership which have made the New York Region one of the great metropolitan regions of the world stem from many and diverse roots, but prominent among them is its accessibility. Although both freight and passenger transportation are vital, passenger transportation is of particular significance because of the Region's executive office and marketing functions which rely upon ease of assembly of business leaders, buyers and sellers and professional personnel. If the New York–New Jersey Metropolitan Region is to maintain its leadership as the national and, perhaps, the world-wide nerve center, it must be endowed with extensive and high-quality intercity travel services.

New York's intercity passenger transportation network consists of a complex of interstate highways, airways, railways, and bus lines and their supporting terminals. These in turn are intricately linked to local systems of urban and suburban highways, streets, subways, railways and bus lines, which perform the regional collection and distribution function. This mix and its many interrelationships are by no means stable; just as there have been many changes in the past there will continue to be physical changes and shifts in demand in the future as the business and social life of the city develops, perhaps along new and unforeseen lines.

Whatever physical form the intercity passenger transportation complex may take in the future, its effectiveness and value to the community will be measured by its ability to move people freely into, out of and throughout the Region, and to or from other metropolitan areas with which its functions are intimately related. Access must be equally convenient, economical and attractive from the nearby centers such as Philadelphia, Binghamton, Albany and Boston as it is from more remote points such as New Orleans, Los Angeles or London, since all such near and remote centers are, in reality, the sources of New York's strength and vitality.

The past two decades have seen sweeping changes in the means for transporting people from one urban area to another, and New York has benefited from most of these changes. The air transport industry has grown from a fledgling to the nation's largest common carrier of intercity passengers. Great increases have been achieved in speed, comfort and reliability of air transportation while there have been but small increases in fares (particularly if measured in constant dollars). The growing networks of superhighways are making possible intercity travel by automobile and bus with unprecedented ease and speed. With each passing year they serve more communities, making automobile and bus travel more accessible and easily available to more people.

The railroads, once the nation's principal intercity carrier of passengers, have fallen sharply in patronage and railroad passenger service has been curtailed. In the East, particularly, the railroads' financial integrity is in hazard. The decay of rail passenger services is impairing the service level of passenger transportation between New York and the smaller nearby cities such as Albany, Hartford, Providence, Wilmington and Harrisburg. Although there are air and bus services available to and from these points, in many instances they do not provide the full span of center-to-center service with the speed or convenience that the railroads have provided. Bus and automobile travel are slowed during peak traffic periods by congestion on the highway approaches to the city. Similar congestion in the ground approaches to and from the airports is diminishing the speed advantage of air travel, particularly on these shorter trips.

The general outlook is for each form of intercity common-carrier travel in the future to establish its dominance within a particular travel-distance bracket. Air travel will dominate in longer mileage travel, say trips of more than 500 miles. The dominance of the railroads will lie in the bracket of, say, trips of 100 to 500 miles — in the shorter distances they will face stiff competition from intercity bus and in the longer distances competition from air travel. A still shorter mileage bracket will be the province of the bus, say, from 50 to 200 miles. These provinces will overlap, of course, and intermodal competition for the traveler's patronage will prevail in the overlapped mileages. The competition will find its expression in fares, comfort, frequency of schedules and running times.

Private transportation, primarily by automobile, will also vie with common carriers, particularly in the shorter trips, although the competition will be not wholly economic. In the shortest intercity trips, say, those of less than 50 miles, the automobile will probably dominate.

[1]For instance, the intercity passenger miles by automobile as reported for 1959 by the Interstate Commerce Commission is equivalent to 64 per cent of the *total* automobile passenger mileage for that year as reported by the Bureau of Public Roads.

In this competitive arena, the position taken by the federal government will exert a powerful force. Federal assistance has throughout the nation's history played a major role in the development of all intercity transport modes: canal, rail, highway and air. A relatively recent example is the use of military research and development funds to finance the cost of air transport equipment development, much of which is adaptable to commercial use. A combination of federal programs will undoubtedly finance most of the enormous development costs of supersonic air transport.

During recent years federal expenditures have been of considerable importance in the construction of highways and airports and in the construction, maintenance and operation of inland waterways and airways. There are direct operating subsidies for air carriers for the maintenance of service at selected local stations and over selected local routes.

In the field of intercity passenger transportation the federal government plays a crucial role, and its outlook, policies and methods will have far-reaching effects upon the form and nature of future developments.

INTERCITY TRAVEL VOLUMES

It is virtually impossible to project into the future the total demand for intercity travel in quantitative terms. We do not even know what the magnitudes are today, or what they have been in the past, with any satisfactory degree of reliability. The published statistics are often in disagreement and occasionally appear unreasonable.[1] Except for air travel, they present national totals and their applicability to intercity travel to and from the New York Metropolitan Region is questionable.

For example, there are no data on the number of intercity passenger trips or passenger miles flown in private aircraft. Intercity travel by automobile must be estimated. For common carriers, the data reported to the ICC, required by that agency to aid it in its regulatory functions, do not lend themselves to analysis of travel behavior. As a result, intercity travel by bus is also of unknown magnitude, except for some data on bus-trip lengths compiled by the bus industry in 1947. Generalized data on rail travel are plentiful but identification of intercity magnitudes is difficult and trip-length data are incomplete. Data on airline travel present fewer problems.

The University of Michigan, for the purpose of its National Travel Market Survey series started in 1955, defines an "intercity trip" as travel having a one-way "crow's flight" distance of 100 miles or more. The same definition, modified by the requirement that an overnight stay be involved, was used by the U. S. Census Bureau for its "1957 Survey of Travel." The 100-mile limit excludes daily home-to-work commuting, routine shopping trips and Sunday pleasure drives, but it has the weakness of excluding also such trips as those from New Haven to New York, Philadelphia to New York, and similar shorter intercity trips in the more densely populated sections of the country, while at the same time including shopping trips into town from remote ranches in the West and Southwest. Nevertheless, the 100-mile criterion is reasonable and there are certain data available which can be fitted to it. These data, while far from complete, provide some approximate measures of quantity.

Despite the impossibility of providing a solid statistical base for analysis, certain developments of the recent past are clear: travel by air has been growing rapidly; travel by rail has been declining; bus travel has shown no strong trend either way; travel by automobile has risen to high levels.

The primary source of data on intercity travel is the Interstate Commerce Commission's annual report of passenger miles traveled by various modes of transport.

TABLE 1. U. S. DOMESTIC INTERCITY PASSENGER TRANSPORTATION
BY VARIOUS MODES OF TRANSPORTATION

(billions of passenger miles)

Year	Automobile	Bus	Railway	Air	Waterway
1935	178.3	7.6	14.4	0.3	1.2
1940	245.8	10.2	20.8	1.1	1.3
1945	179.8	26.9	93.5	3.4	2.1
1950	337.3	20.9	32.5	8.0	1.2
1955	585.8	25.1	28.7	19.8	1.7
1956	617.7	25.2	28.6	22.4	1.9
1957	644.8	25.0	26.3	25.3	1.9
1958	629.5	20.8	23.6	25.3	2.1
1959	659.4	20.4	22.4	32.6	2.0
1960	677.6	19.9	21.6	34.0	2.1

Source: Annual Reports of the ICC.

Table 1 shows data from their annual reports. In preparing its report, the only data available to the ICC are financial reports for the rail, air and water carriers. For automobile travel, the ICC has combined the estimates of automobile miles operated on rural roads and of "intercity automobile miles" operated on urban streets, prepared by the U. S. Bureau of Public Roads, using an average of 1.7 passengers per vehicle. Bus passengers are estimated by the ICC from incomplete data and include intrastate, charter and other special service operations. It cannot be claimed, therefore, that the travel magnitudes reported by the ICC reflect faithfully intercity travel within any strict definition of the term.

It is to be noted, nevertheless, that aggregate common-carrier travel reported by rail, bus, air and water rose steadily, with a wartime bulge, until 1955, since when the common-carrier total of passenger miles has not deviated much from about 75 billion passenger miles a year.

There is no comparable series showing the *number of passengers* carried by the different modes of transportation. However, there are several independent sources which can be used to piece together a series showing passengers carried or trips made by common carriers (Table 2).

Although these data are widely accepted as a record of intercity travel, they have many shortcomings. First, they include a large volume of short-distance travel which should not properly be classed as intercity travel. Although commuters using multiple-ride tickets have been excluded from the railway data, the reported volumes include an unknown number of transit passengers[2] and suburban passengers using one-way and round-

[2]There are a number of standard railroads which operate transit services, such as the Staten Island Rapid Transit Co.

TABLE 2. PASSENGERS MAKING DOMESTIC INTERCITY TRIPS BY COMMON CARRIER

(millions of trips)

Year	Bus[a]	Railway[b]	Air[c]	Water-way[d]
1935		186.3	0.8	
1940		224.6	2.5	
1945	556.7	571.7	6.6	
1950	366.0	209.1	17.3	4.0
1955	255.4	183.6	38.0	3.8
1956	238.5	181.5	41.7	3.7
1957	226.4	162.0	48.5	4.1
1958	201.6	139.8	48.1	3.9
1959	204.8	129.9	54.8	3.4
1960	201.0	122.7	56.1	e
1961	201.2	118.5	e	e

[a]Bus Facts, 30th Edition, p. 12.
[b]ICC Transport Economics, April 1962, p. 4.
[c]FAA Statistical Handbook of Aviation, 1961, p. 84.
[d]ICC Transport Statistics, Part V for years shown, Class A and B carriers only.
[e]Not available.

trip tickets. Bus data are strongly influenced by the ICC definition of intercity travel as being any revenue passenger riding on a commercial nonschool bus operating over both urban and rural roads. Further, neither the bus nor the rail records are corrected to remove the duplication of counts resulting from passengers making a single trip involving the use of more than one carrier; the passenger is counted each time he uses the services of a different company.

The Future of Intercity Travel

The amount of intercity travel in the future and the need for specific types of transport facilities to accommodate it will depend on economic, technological, demographic, social and cultural factors that now can be but dimly foreseen. All long-range studies of future economic activity agree in projecting healthy increases in industry and commerce. The implication is that intercity travel undertaken for business purposes will grow correspondingly. As transport has become faster and more convenient in the past there has been a generating effect on travel behavior, and the technological advances in transport in the future will undoubtedly have a similar consequence. As the nation becomes one largely of city dwellers, intercity and intermetropolitan linkages will assume greater and greater importance. As national income rises, and as leisure-time opportunities increase, travel undertaken for purely personal reasons — social or recreational — will rise. The prospect is for a growing demand for intercity passenger transport.

The probable need for travel facilities of a particular kind, however, and the likelihood that the needed facilities will be available, cannot be stated with assurance. The public-policy framework will be of strategic importance but is not now predictable.

Railroad Intercity Passenger Service

Future intercity passenger services by railroad will depend upon railroad financial strength, management methods, the turns that public policy might take as to taxation, regulation and promotion of transportation, the interplay of competitive interests, and the strength of public demand for railroad service.

Passenger miles traveled by railroad have been declining steadily throughout the postwar period, and the decline in first-class travel has been especially marked. Between 1949 and 1959 the miles

of railroad used for passenger service declined by 41 per cent, and there was an equal drop in train-miles operated. In the heavily settled northeastern part of the country, where the railroads, with their extensive networks of controlled rights of way and their ability to handle large passenger volumes, are well suited to provide for intercity travel on trips up to 300 or 400 miles, the railroads display greatest financial distress and pose the threat of further service curtailment or outright discontinuance.

The Doyle report[3] states that railroad passenger service has been self-supporting for only 4 out of the past 30 years, the wartime years 1942–1945, and part of its costs have had to be provided from freight earnings. The critical point has been reached, says the report "where sufficient freight earnings, at least for the passenger-heavy and highway-plagued Eastern railroads, are simply not available."

The term "railroad passenger services" covers considerably more than the intercity movement of people. By Interstate Commerce Commission definition it includes U. S. mail (both first-class and bulk mails); express, newspapers and milk; suburban and commuter coach services; intercity coach services; Pullman (parlor and sleeper) services; and dining car services. The passenger service losses that have been publicized so widely cover all the "passenger services" enumerated and are not confined to the intercity movement of passengers. The total losses reported are so large[4] that the question is often raised as to whether they are in fact "real" losses or merely bookkeeping charges. It arises because the railroads perform such a variety of different services using common facilities, that there is necessarily much apportionment and allocation of common and general expenses.[5] This subject has been studied many times,

[3]Prepared for the Committee on Interstate and Foreign Commerce, U. S. Senate, by the Special Study Group on Transportation Policies in the United States.

[4]The 1959 reported passenger service losses for all Class I railroads in the United States was $543.8 million. For the Pennsylvania Railroad, the reported loss was $37.7 million, and for the New York Central $24.8 million.

[5]The ICC reports that in 1960, 24 per cent of all primary passenger service expenses were apportioned; many subaccounts are allocated but not so identified.

and each study has reached the conclusion that, with minor variations, the deficits do exist, approximately as reported.[6] Nevertheless, these losses are in part an accounting phenomenon. As so many items of cost are apportioned among different kinds of service, intercity passenger service "costs" are to some degree dependent upon the volume of freight and other kinds of traffic handled on the same line. Thus, for example, if freight tonnage declines, the assignment of fixed and overhead costs to intercity passenger service may increase. And when passenger trains are withdrawn, the load falling on the remaining trains becomes greater. Evidence has been presented which indicates that strict intercity passenger service accounts for less than half of the total reported passenger service losses.

At the heart of this discussion is the question of the essentiality of rail passenger service, whether the alternatives are equally economical, practical and effective. Of course, parts of the country are living without railroad passenger service today, and at one point the Doyle report states, "Railroad intercity passenger service meets no important needs that cannot be provided for by other carriers and possesses no uniquely necessary service advantages." But however supportable this view might be as a generality, the intercity transportation demands of the Washington–New York–Boston megalopolis are exceptionally great and cannot be so easily disposed of. Some measure of the "need" or "demand" for railroad service for this area can be judged from estimates of the number of common-carrier passengers to and from New York (Table 3).

More definitive data on rail and bus in-

[6]Investigation by the Interstate Commerce Commission, Case 31954, "Passenger Train Deficits," "Cost Data for the Management of Railroad Passenger Service," Dwight R. Ladd, Harvard University, 1957. "Avoidable Costs of Passenger Trains Service," Aeronautical Research Foundation, 1957.

TABLE 3. ESTIMATED PASSENGER TRIPS BETWEEN NEW YORK AND SELECTED CITIES BY AIR, RAIL AND BUS ON AN AVERAGE WEEKDAY, 1960

	Air	Rail	Bus
Philadelphia	150	6,000	3,000
Washington	1,700	3,000	—
Chicago	2,000	500	—
Cleveland	800	100	—
Syracuse	450	150	—
Albany	180	700	—
Providence	320	1,000	—
Boston	2,400	2,400	1,200

Source: Air passengers from CAB Origin-Destination Survey. Rail and bus passengers estimated except as indicated by dashes.

tercity travel are not available, but general observation leads to the conclusion that there is still a demand for rail service on trips up to about 300 to 400 miles in length, particularly between cities in the Washington–New York–Boston travel corridor.

In the densely settled Northeast, and particularly around New York, railroad service has some tremendously important assets:

1. Exclusive, high-speed, high-capacity rights of way already in existence.

2. Potentially, an ability to serve more than one traffic center within the Metropolitan Area, such as the Pennsylvania Railroad's stations in Manhattan and Newark, as intra-urban movement is not impeded by competitive traffic.

3. Capability of higher speeds than are practicable on the highway.

The railroads' passenger service financial problems appear to stem as much from high costs as from inadequate traffic. The deterioration in quantity and quality of service offered, the continued operation of over-age equipment, the reduction in schedules, and the failure to replace worn-out physical plant are consequences of a business situation in which costs exceed revenues.

The railroads have been subject to close regulation by federal, state and local governments, and the regulatory bodies have been slow to recognize that the railroads are no longer monopolies.[7] They have been subject to property taxation much like other businesses, though in many instances their taxes have been disproportionately high. Statutory as well as administrative measures have established work and pay rules and the number of employees required for many operations, and have required the retention of little-used branch lines and the continuation of low commutation fares.

Also, over the years there has been little effective cost control by railway management, which can be traced in part to the ICC accounting requirements. While these requirements do not prohibit the keeping of additional cost accounts which would be more useful for management purposes, the railroads generally have not chosen to set them up. The conclusions of the Doyle report put emphasis on the need for important changes in railroad management and operating methods, directed toward recognizing the importance of passenger service within the entire railway framework.

The present prospect is for railway intercity passenger service to continue its general downward traffic trend, for the near future at least, reflecting the continued deterioration of equipment, corporate financial weaknesses, and travelers' preferences for other forms of transportation.

The clue to the future of intercity railroad passenger services will be given by

public policy decisions in regard to the New Haven Railroad, for that railroad's bankruptcy is causing a critical analysis of the future of the Boston–New York passenger service. The decisions may be influential in determining the future of the Pennsylvania Railroad's New York–Washington service. These two high-traffic-density services will probably be the first to show whether there will be any change from the present downward course. It is possible that improvement or modernization of rail services between Boston and Washington could be followed by rehabilitation and modernization of other intercity rail services.

Commercial Air Transport

Air travel has grown to the point where it now represents more than half of all common-carrier intercity passenger-miles involving trips of over 100 miles, and dominates heavily common-carrier long-haul travel of more than 1,000 miles. At New York, its growth rate, in percentage terms, has been greatest in the longer trip ranges. However, in spite of this dramatic performance of long-haul travel, the greatest volume of domestic air travel to and from New York and two-thirds of its total growth have been in trips of 1,000 miles or less (Table 4).

TABLE 4. DOMESTIC REVENUE PASSENGERS ARRIVING AND DEPARTING METROPOLITAN NEW YORK COMMERCIAL AIRPORTS, 1960

Trip Length	No. of Passengers	Per Cent of Total
0–249	2,870,000	28.7
250–499 miles	1,464,000	14.6
500–999 miles	2,609,000	26.1
1,000–1,999 miles	2,049,000	20.5
2,000 miles and over	1,011,000	10.1
All trips	10,003,000	100.0

Source: CAB Origin & Destination Survey.

---

[7]This subject is discussed at length in the Doyle Report, pages 119-163. Also see Meyer, Peck, Stenason and Zwick, *Competition in the Transportation Industries,* Harvard University Press, 1959, pp. 12–14.

In long-haul travel air travel is already dominant and its principal opportunities for future growth are restricted to population increases and to growth in long-haul travel behavior. Available information[8] indicates that trips under 500 miles represent a major part of total intercity travel, and in this mileage bracket the airlines have had a smaller share of the total traffic. Shorter-trip travel, therefore, seems to offer the principal potential for air travel growth but its realization will have to overcome some serious problems.

The airlines have been seeking means for developing their short-haul travel business more effectively and economically by experiments with no-reservation coach services on short-mileage trips with what so far appear to be favorable results. Over the long term, however, the future performance of air transport in volume markets up to 500 miles will be governed by (1) ground access to airports, (2) development of suitable and economical short-haul aircraft, (3) availability of adequate airport capacity, and (4) competition from other forms of transportation.

At present, most service to points within a 250-mile radius of New York is offered on propeller aircraft, with turbojet equipment used only when the flight is one stage of a longer trip. As the airlines continue to add jet craft to their fleets and phase out obsolete propeller airplanes,

virtually all airlines operating at New York will have all-jet fleets.

For the airlines to provide an effective economical volume service for trips within a 250-mile radius of New York, which includes Boston and Washington, the problem of equipment needs to be solved. Whether existing jet aircraft as the Caravelle, Boeing 727, or Convair 880 can be economically supported if used exclusively in such short-haul turnaround service at present fare levels is as yet undetermined.

The aircraft manufacturers are cognizant of this problem and have designed smaller fixed-wing jet aircraft especially for short-haul operations. The British Aircraft Corporation has designed and anticipates delivering its BAC 111[9] turbojet beginning in 1964, the Dutch are planning deliveries of the Fokker F-28 short range jet in 1965-66, and the Douglas Aircraft Company has designed a "compact" jet 2086 which it will put into production after sufficient orders are received. These planes are designed to seat only 50 to 70 passengers.

Manufacturers are also considering two other kinds of aircraft specifically designed for short haul service: (1) "VTOL"[10] aircraft, such as a larger (50 to 70 passenger) and more efficient turbine-powered helicopter and (2) "STOL" craft.[11] After studying the possibilities of such aircraft types, R. Dixon Speas Associates, a consultant to the Port Authority, concluded that "There is no technical basis for acceptance of VTOL or STOL aircraft in significant replacement of fixed wing aircraft for any scheduled air transport function performed in the New Jersey-New York Metropolitan area for the years 1960-1975 . . ."

The airlines will probably continue to experience the pressure of rising costs, possible airway user fees,[12] possible higher airport charges, and increased operat-

[8]An estimate of U. S. common carrier passenger-miles (excluding commuter travel) by trip length for the year 1960 shows: 0–50 miles 12%; 51–250 miles 33%; 251–500 miles 22%; 501–1,000 miles 16%; 1,001–2,000 miles 10%; over 2,000 miles, 7%. (Table 3.8 in "National Requirements for Aviation Facilities: 1956–75" Aeronautical Research Foundation, 1957.)

[9]This plane has been recently ordered by Mohawk and Braniff.

[10]Vertical Take-Off and Landing aircraft, such as helicopters.

[11]Short Take-Off and Landing aircraft.

[12]The FAA reports that a fuel tax of about 11 cents per gallon would be required in 1962 to recover the full $302.4 million civil share of the cost of the domestic federal airway system. "A Study of User Charges for the Domestic Federal Airway System," FAA, April 1961, Tables 9 and 14.

ing costs.[13] Unlike what has occurred during the past 15 years, these cost increases are not likely to be offset in the near future by new developments which will increase dramatically the speed, comfort or attractiveness of air travel. Although basic seat-mile costs have been falling steadily, they probably will level off in the near future and may even climb slightly as the jet planes grow older and require more maintenance. The combined effect of these forces is likely to be greatest on short trips, already the least profitable and frequently unprofitable component of air travel service.

The prospect is that air travel will continue to compete with surface travel on trips up to 400 to 500 miles in length. The extent to which the commercial air transportation industry can successfully solve its economic and operational problems in the shorter-trip service, under 250 miles, and the kind of rail and bus services offered, will largely determine the future levels of commercial air traffic in the New York region.

General Aviation

There are more than 1¼ billion plane-miles of "general aviation" flown a year,[14] representing an estimated 3.6 million passenger miles, most of which is assumed to be intercity travel. Although there is a scarcity of information concerning this kind of travel, it is reasonable to expect that it will continue to grow. As private

[13]There are no developments in sight which hold any promise of reducing seat-mile costs. There are, however, many which will work to increase costs. In addition, the growing size of the commercial plane fleet, coupled with the peaking characteristics of air travel will work to lower the average annual load factor per plane as measured both by actual use and by available time. This in turn will require the airlines to assume a larger fixed cost burden. Also see Peter Masefield's "Sixth Henry Royce Memorial Lecture" on the future outlook for Civil Aviation, as reported on page 622 of *The Aeroplane*, November 9, 1961.

[14]"General aviation" is defined by the FAA as including every form of civil flying other than commercial air transport. Of particular interest here is the use of private or corporate aircraft and of air taxis for intercity travel.

aviation has many characteristics similar to other forms of private transportation, it can be assumed that its future growth will be governed by similar factors and conditions, even though the private plane is a more sophisticated and expensive vehicle than the automobile or motor truck.

As the airlines continue to equip themselves with jet planes, there will be a growing number of secondhand propeller planes available for purchase by industries and "air taxi" operators. The probable consequence is that an increasing number of business travelers (who now represent the principal market for commercial air travel) will travel by private or charter planes. Pilot examination rules and physical requirements may become more stringent, as the growing volume of air commerce requires higher pilot performance standards, and the cost of private flying may increase as the result of higher airport charges, airway user fees, and added cost of air navigation devices, but large increases in private air transportation are still to be expected. While the increases may be large, the diversion from commercial air travel service is not expected to be significant in relation to the total.

Intercity Bus

Intercity buses share the highways with the automobile and the motor truck. If the over-all speed on the highway is slow, so is the speed of the bus. There is a marginal improvement in speed over automobiles, but this advantage is offset by lower standards of comfort. The various states regulate the maximum size of buses, and at the widths and lengths allowed it is difficult to provide full seat comfort and also economical seating capacity at present fare levels. A moderate relaxation of the width restriction would permit a material improvement in travel comfort.

Also, there are other potentials for improvement of the quality of service. Buses are relatively small transport units, 50 passengers or so per bus, and if traffic volumes should be great enough, it is entirely possible that a bus could be loaded for destination, for let us say Wilmington. It would have to compete with the rest of the urban travel demands on the highway system at both the New York and the Wilmington ends of the journey, but could bypass Newark, Trenton and Philadelphia. A bus loaded for Baltimore could avoid the problems of Wilmington as well.

Some consideration has been given to allocating to suburban and intercity buses for their exclusive use special lanes on some of the major highways leading to urban centers. If this were to be done, intercity bus travel would have time advantages over automobile travel for the center-to-center traveler.

Despite current limitations bus travel has supplanted rail travel for many of the short-distance intercity trips, and has its own economy market for those of longer distance. The likelihood is that intercity bus travel will rise.

Highways and Automobile Intercity Travel

Highways serve a multitude of different purposes. They are built to accommodate both travelers and freight, journey-to-work travel and leisure-time travel, bus travel and automobile travel, short and long trips. One of their outstanding functions is to provide access to domestic and to economic establishments.

Much of today's intercity automobile travel, specifically that portion which is for social or recreational purposes, would not be undertaken at all if the automobile and the highway system were not available, and is not to be considered as potential to common-carrier travel. Its fu-

ture will reflect the level of personal incomes, the amount of leisure time available, and the ability of the highway system to accommodate it.

Highway usage reaches its highest intensity as the urban centers are approached, and consequently intercity passenger travel by automobile is slowed in the close-in urban areas during periods of peak demand, for they coincide with weekday peak work-travel hours and with week-end peak periods of local recreational travel (such as Friday afternoons and Monday mornings). Consequently the future growth of intercity automobile travel will be influenced by the highway and terminal capacities in the urban areas. If the urban (and suburban) portions of the intercity trip should become slower, growth of automobile travel between cities would be discouraged.

PUBLIC POLICY, PLANNING, REGULATION AND ASSISTANCE

It is often contended that each form of transportation should stand on its own economic feet, that it should stand or fall in terms of its ability to survive in a competitive world. But we do not have a situation of only competitive economics to deal with. Our transportation system is a mixture of private and public properties — privately owned and operated rights of way and equipment in the case of the railroads; publicly owned rights of way and equipment and operation in the case of rail rapid transit lines; public rights of way and private equipment and operation in the cases of waterway, airway, over-the-road freight and bus transportation. Common carriers and private vehicles use the public rights of way and pay charges for their use in some instances and not in others. Automobile travel is hardly to be considered in terms of business economics at all.

There is an equally complex mixture of functions and objectives the transportation system is expected to serve. The common-carrier company's objective is to operate a profitable business. The business traveler's need is for a transportation system which will yield the maximum degree of accessibility to all points of economic activity throughout the country. The traveler on a social or recreational trip wants comfort, convenience and economy. The community wants to strengthen its transport linkages with other communities. The owner of property wants the value of his property to be sustained by ease of access, whether he himself ever travels or not.

It is not to be wondered at that a great number of contending interests participate in the shaping of public policies dealing with transportation. Even the producers of particular kinds of transportation equipment or construction materials for this or that type of transportation facility are not silent. There is no single arena for this contest and where the over-all public interest lies is not always plain. One result is that there are a number of transportation policies, not only without coordination but frequently in conflict.

But planning is becoming a more widely used tool of government and transportation planning will probably play an important role in the future. Public sentiment is opposed to government ownership and operation of common-carrier transport. The alternative is a concept of transportation control in which planning, regulation and public assistance are coordinated and administered so as to bring about a pattern of use of the different means of transportation that will yield the maximum of public service and benefit.

If intercity railroad passenger service should continue to deteriorate, or even become unavailable, the results could be far-reaching. The strongest impact would fall on the travel linkages between the New York–New Jersey metropolitan area and the moderate-size cities within a radius of 200 to 300 miles. Albany, Utica, Binghamton and Harrisburg, for example, are not likely to become traffic generators of sufficient strength to warrant point-to-point air service, nor is air transport likely to prove economically successful for this short travel distance except under exceptional circumstances. There is no present prospect of the establishment of bus service that would be equivalent to rail service in comfort and speed. The cities referred to would suffer reduced accessibility and could easily be disadvantaged economically through lessened location value. The ultimate consequence could be a remapping of the economic activities of the northeastern part of the country.

CHAPTER 17

DOMESTIC AND OVERSEAS AIR TRAVEL

A Revolution in Transportation

In less than thirty years, air transportation has changed from an experimental novelty to an accepted, routine way of travel. From its early role at the county fair it has grown into a major transportation industry. Equipment has changed from open-cockpit, slow-flying, planes to high-speed "flying living rooms." Not only has the air transport business itself changed, but it has brought about changes in travel patterns, in business organization and in recreational preferences. Large amounts of additional travel have been generated. Air transportation has helped the United States to become a single market, for buyers and sellers from distant points can meet at common points and on brief notice can conduct face-to-face negotiations. It has also made the world smaller by greatly facilitating travel between countries and continents and over long distances.

The New York area has shared in this aviation expansion, for almost one of every four domestic air trips begins or ends in this region. New York is, by far, the greatest aviation hub in the world. Of the ten largest domestic air routes, New York figures in nine. Of this country's eleven trunk airlines, nine (including all of the big four) serve New York, and of the 14 major international airlines, 13 serve New York.

Growth of Domestic Air Travel

The most inclusive measure of air travel is the number of passenger-miles flown. Table 1 reveals that scheduled domestic

revenue air passenger-miles for all United States airlines has been following the typical growth pattern of new industries. As is common in many new industries, in the

TABLE 1. United States Scheduled Airlines Domestic Revenue Passenger-Miles, Total, First Class and Coach, 1930–1961

(in thousands)

Year	First Class	Coach	Total
1930			73,093
1931			92,605
1932			110,524
1933			150,938
1934			163,437
1935			279,376
1936			388,242
1937			411,545
1938			479,844
1939			682,904
1940			1,052,156
1941			1,384,733
1942			1,418,042
1943			1,634,135
1944			2,178,207
1945			3,362,455
1946			5,947,956
1947			6,109,508
1948	5,976,158	4,835	5,980,993
1949	6,501,334	251,288	6,752,622
1950	6,946,732	1,056,093	8,002,825
1951	9,293,850	1,272,332	10,566,182
1952	10,182,641	2,345,677	12,528,318
1953	11,042,371	3,717,938	14,760,309
1954	11,447,466	5,321,240	16,768,706
1955	13,102,845	6,716,376	19,819,221
1956	14,287,771	8,074,053	22,361,824
1957	15,829,214	9,510,346	25,339,560
1958	15,267,627	10,075,760	25,343,387
1959	16,966,172	12,303,720	29,269,892
1960	16,096,114	14,417,502	30,513,616
1961	13,904,170	17,108,572	31,012,742

earliest stage of development absolute growth is small, for the industry itself is small, but the percentage rate of increase is high; next, absolute growth picks up, for the industry is now larger, but the percentage rate of growth slows; finally, when the industry is established and most of the readily available market has been captured, growth is more or less in line with the country's general economic situation. Air travel has gone through the first of these stages. It is not yet clear whether it is still in the second or has already entered the third phase.

Although passenger-miles is for most purposes the most meaningful measure of passenger transport accomplishment, the number of passengers served determines the task of the airport operator. At airports it is the movement of people on and off planes that determines the work load. Passenger counts, however, are more difficult to define, particularly when a passenger changes planes in the course of a trip.

Different air travel statistical series issued by the United States government treat such transferring passengers differ-

TABLE 2. UNITED STATES DOMESTIC ENPLANED AIRLINE PASSENGERS, 1948–1961

(in thousands)

1948	13,168
1949	15,081
1950	17,345
1951	22,652
1952	25,010
1953	29,282
1954	32,922
1955	38,635
1956	42,104
1957	48,999
1958	48,804
1959	55,629
1960	57,165
1961	57,601

ently, and from time to time at least one series has shifted its definition. Enplanements is the most inclusive definition and is the more appropriate measure of airport activity.

The history of enplaned passengers follows the history of passenger-miles. There is the same slow beginning, a steeper rise during the 1950's and signs of wavering during the past few years.

GROWTH OF OVERSEAS AIR TRAVEL

During the 14-year period from 1948 to 1961 the volume of United States international passengers more than tripled, from 1,745,000 in 1948 to 5,487,000 in 1961. As indicated in Table 3, the rate of growth from year to year showed no consistent pattern:

TABLE 3. TOTAL UNITED STATES INTERNATIONAL PASSENGER VOLUMES, 1948–1961[a]

(in thousands)

Year	Passengers	Annual % Increase
1948	1,745	—
1949	2,000	14.6
1950	2,155	7.8
1951	2,328	8.0
1952	2,652	13.9
1953	2,786	5.1
1954	3,032	8.8
1955	3,544	16.9
1956	3,985	12.4
1957	4,366	9.6
1958	4,619	5.8
1959	4,934	6.8
1960	5,480	11.1
1961	5,487	0.1

[a]Includes all civilian passengers to and from foreign countries except on trips originating or terminating in Canada. Also excludes all passengers traveling between Port of New York and insular and territorial possessions of the United States and all United States military personnel on military transports and commercial planes. Cruise passengers included only since July 1958. Total cruise arrivals and departures in the July-December, 1958 period were 58,346; in 1959, 172,056. Air passengers between United States and Mexico included only since January 1958.

It is significant that this growth was attained mainly in air travel which recorded a fivefold increase during this period. Sea travel showed a slight increase in the first ten years of this period but began to decline in recent years leaving an accumulated increase of only 30 per cent in the period from 1948 to 1961. As shown in Table 4, air's share of the total international market grew constantly to the point where it represented 80 per cent of the total in 1960.

TABLE 4. DISTRIBUTION OF UNITED STATES INTERNATIONAL PASSENGER VOLUMES BY AIR AND SEA, 1948–1961

(in thousands)

Year	Air	Sea[a]	Total	Air as % of Total
1948	899	846	1,745	51.5
1950	1,157	998	2,155	53.7
1952	1,558	1,094	2,652	58.7
1954	1,880	1,152	3,032	62.0
1956	2,736	1,249	3,985	68.7
1958	3,451	1,168	4,619	74.7
1960	4,380	1,100	5,480	79.9
1961	4,489	998	5,487	81.8

[a]Does not include cruise passengers.

AIR TRAFFIC AT NEW YORK

Passenger data for the New York airports are available only from 1948. Since that year, the pattern of growth of New York's air passenger traffic has closely paralleled the growth of air travel in the nation. The ratio of New York's airport passengers to the national total of air passengers has remained relatively stable.

The number of passengers handled is a good measure of the work that an airport performs. But some of the functions of an airport (such as runway services) are related to the number of plane movements rather than the number of passengers.

The two are closely related but they have diverged over the years as a result of the increasing size of aircraft.

It is appropriate, therefore, that some attention be given to data on plane movements. Between 1948 and 1961, while the number of domestic scheduled revenue passengers at New York airports increased by 319 per cent, the number of plane movements increased by only 126 per cent. In the same period international passengers increased by 723 per cent, while the number of overseas plane movements increased by only 172 per cent. Facilities for landing, takeoff, handling, and storage of aircraft therefore have not had to keep up with the increase in passenger flow, but rather with the more modest growth of plane movements.

These two measures of domestic commercial transport activity are shown in Table 5. This table also shows how the increasing size and load capacity of transport planes is resulting in a slower growth in plane movements than in passengers handled.

It can be seen from these data that scheduled passenger transport plane movements now represent only 55 per cent of all domestic plane movements (excluding flying schools) at Port Authority airports.

CHARACTERISTICS OF DOMESTIC COMMERCIAL AIR TRAVEL

In attempting to reach some estimate as to the future growth of air travel, it is desirable to know something of the characteristics of the people who actually travel by air, their reasons for so doing, and the purpose of their trip. Over the past seven years much information of this nature has been gathered through the medium of five National Travel Market Surveys based on home interviews of a

TABLE 5. AIRLINE PASSENGERS AND PLANE MOVEMENTS
AT PORT OF NEW YORK AUTHORITY AIRPORTS

	Passengers	Revenue Passenger Plane Movements	Average Passengers per Revenue Plane Movement	Total Plane Movements[a]	
				Excluding Flying School	Including Flying School
Domestic					
1948	3,134,608	158,249	19.8	279,708	425,947
1950	4,294,060	176,392	24.3	286,213	428,310
1952	5,742,214	218,629	26.3	341,392	484,364
1954	7,871,458	271,730	29.0	448,794	573,884
1956	10,161,259	344,332	29.5	541,182	677,316
1958	11,174,063	361,285	30.9	582,014	698,156
1960	12,930,756	374,609	34.5	654,947	766,756
1961	13,126,152	357,338	36.7	647,821	745,447
Overseas					
1948	352,784	16,357	21.7	21,805	
1950	538,596	17,691	30.4	20,447	
1952	864,024	22,833	37.8	32,029	
1954	1,098,906	27,565	39.9	35,489	
1956	1,529,595	35,632	42.9	45,797	
1958	2,091,065	47,273	44.2	56,127	
1960	2,821,469	45,494	62.0	55,620	
1961	2,904,030	44,572	65.1	55,469	

[a]Includes, where applicable, scheduled all-cargo and nonrevenue movements, movements of domestic non-scheduled airlines, business and private aircraft, air taxi and government aircraft.

representative sample of the nation's population.

From these surveys it has been learned that the people most likely to travel by air are concentrated: (1) In people having incomes of $10,000 per year or more; (2) In those having better education; (3) In those employed in the professions or in the management and sales functions of industry. Further, it has been learned that the majority of reported trips (53 per cent), are made by a comparatively small number of people (13 per cent of all air travelers) who travel frequently, and that more air trips are made for business (67 per cent of all reported trips) than for nonbusiness purposes.

When measured in terms of the total population, the Surveys disclosed that the number of people who accounted for all the air trips taken during the year has slowly increased from 6.7 per cent of total adult population in 1955 to 8.8 per cent in 1957, and 11.0 per cent in 1961-62.

An analysis of domestic commercial air travel to and from New York's airports over the past 14 years discloses significant differences in the growth pattern for trips of varying mileage ranges.

On trips of 500 miles and over (principally Chicago, Miami and transcontinental trips) air has apparently captured the lion's share of common-carrier travel, and has had success in competing with the private automobile. On trips of between 250 and 500 miles air has made substantial inroads into rail and bus travel, but appears to have had only moderate success in com-

TABLE 6. GROWTH OF DOMESTIC AIR TRAVEL TO AND FROM NEW YORK, BY TRIP LENGTH[a]

Trip Length	Passengers 1947	Passengers 1960	Increase	Per Cent Increase
0-249 miles	1,343,000	2,870,000	1,527,000	114
250-499 miles	490,000	1,464,000	974,000	199
500-999 miles	655,000	2,609,000	1,954,000	298
1,000-1,999 miles	534,000	2,049,000	1,515,000	284
2,000 miles & over	231,000	1,011,000	780,000	338

[a]Trips originating or terminating at New York airports.

peting with the private automobile. On trips shorter than 250 miles (primarily to Boston and Washington) air travel has had its smallest percentage rate of growth.

During the more recent years, since 1955, there has been no significant change in the proportions of New York's passengers going to distant and to nearby places. If one goes back a few years earlier, however, and compares the 1947 pattern with that of 1960, he finds that there has been a relative decline in the portion making trips of 250 miles or less. This decline reflects the greater relative growth in long-haul air traffic during this period, when the airlines were diverting long-haul traffic from the railroads and creating new travel. By 1955 long-distance railroad passengers apparently had been reduced to or near a nondivertable hard core, so that thereafter all segments of air travel shared about equally in the growth in total intercity travel. During the past six years about one-third of New York's traffic has been to or from places less than 300 miles distant, another third to or from destinations 300 to 800 miles away while the remaining third has been to or from places more than 800 miles from New York.

Trips of less than 800 miles now represent some 67 per cent of air travel to and from New York airports and trips of less than 500 miles, 43 per cent. As air travel already handles the lion's share of the longer trips, its prospect for growth in that travel bracket lies primarily in population increase and in a general increase in travel habit. For the shorter trips, air transport now accounts for a smaller proportion of total travel, and therefore it is in this bracket that its major opportunity for future growth lies, either through diversion from other forms of transportation or by the creation of new markets.

CHARACTERISTICS AND DISTRIBUTION OF INTERNATIONAL AIR TRAVEL

The basic source data indicate that from 1948 to about 1955 international travel by United States citizens increased faster than did travel by foreign citizens (aliens). From 1955 to 1960, however, this trend seemed to reverse itself and the growth rate in travel by foreign residents

TABLE 7. INTERNATIONAL TRAVEL TO AND FROM THE UNITED STATES BY CITIZENS AND BY ALIENS, 1948–1960

(in thousands)

Year	U. S. Citizens Number	% of Total	Aliens Number	% of Total
1948	1,003	57.5	742	42.5
1952	1,679	63.3	973	36.7
1956	2,608	65.4	1,377	34.6
1960	3,328	60.7	2,152	39.3

TABLE 8. MARKET DISTRIBUTION OF TOTAL U. S. INTERNATIONAL
PASSENGER VOLUMES, 1948 AND 1960[a]

(in thousands)

Geographical Market	1948		1960		Average % Growth Per Year
	Number	% of Total	Number	% of Total	
Transatlantic	808	46.3	2,821	51.5	11.5
Bermuda	77	4.4	234	4.3	9.5
Central and South America	221	12.7	679	12.4	9.5
Caribbean	533	30.5	1,294	23.6	7.5
Pacific	106	6.1	452	8.2	13.0
Total	1,745	100.0	5,480	100.0	10.0

[a]Combined air and sea. Excludes cruise passengers and travelers to and from Mexico and Canada.

showed some significant increases (Table 7). A similar pattern in the growth rates for citizens and aliens is indicated by Immigration and Naturalization Service statistics when travel by air and sea are studied separately.

As shown in Table 8, the transatlantic market has been, and continues to be, the most important of the five major international markets, representing about half of all international passenger travel to and from the United States. In terms of rate of growth, rather than absolute volumes, it is important to note that travel to and from the Pacific area increased at a faster rate than any other area.

As indicated in Table 9, the proportion of American citizens traveling to each of the several geographical markets changed in recent years. As these data show, United States citizens seemed to have shifted from travel to Bermuda and the Caribbean in favor of trips to Europe.

To indicate the importance of New York as a major gateway for international travel, Table 10 shows the volume of international passengers traveling through New York by air and sea in 1960 and the share it represented of total United States international volumes in each geographical market.

In 1960 the New York gateway accommodated 85 per cent of the total United States air and sea transatlantic traffic. The

TABLE 9. DISTRIBUTION OF UNITED STATES CITIZEN TRAVEL
AMONG INTERNATIONAL MARKETS, 1948–1960[a]

(per cent)

Year	Transatlantic	Bermuda	Central and South America	Caribbean	Pacific	Total
1948	40.8	6.4	12.9	32.8	7.1	100.0
1952	45.6	8.5	10.1	29.3	6.5	100.0
1956	44.8	7.0	8.5	32.1	7.6	100.0
1960	53.2	5.9	8.7	24.6	7.6	100.0

[a]Combined air and sea. Excludes cruise passengers.

TABLE 10. INTERNATIONAL AIR AND SEA PASSENGERS THROUGH NEW YORK, 1960[a]

Geographical Market	Number of Passengers	% of Total U. S. International Passengers
Transatlantic	2,398,000	85.0
Bermuda	190,000	81.0
Central and South America	162,000	24.0
Caribbean	269,000	21.0
Pacific	–	–
Total	3,019,000	55.0

[a]Excludes cruise passengers.

relationship between transatlantic volumes and total United States international volumes remained relatively constant from 1948 to 1960; however, there was not a similar relationship between New York's transatlantic passengers and total United States transatlantic volumes. The rather constant downward trend in New York's share of total transatlantic passenger movements is essentially the direct result of a decline in New York's air passenger volumes vis-a-vis the total United States transatlantic movements by air, despite the fact that air captured most of the New York market.

Initially, almost all transatlantic air travel to and from the United States was channeled through New York. The range of economical performance of the available aircraft was rather limited, at least with respect to the operational requirements of the transatlantic routes. With the advent of long-range piston-engine aircraft, such as the Lockheed 1049G, the 1649A and the Douglas DC7C, it became operationally and economically feasible to operate direct nonstop transatlantic service to other major United States traffic markets such as Los Angeles and San Francisco (via the Arctic route)

and Chicago. Soon these possibilities were included in some of the bilateral air agreements with European countries, and this resulted in the opening of other major United States transatlantic traffic potentials to direct overseas services, such as Boston, Detroit and Houston. The inauguration of these direct services (bypassing New York) resulted in the diversion of some traffic formerly served exclusively through New York. While New York served from 87 to 90 per cent of total transatlantic traffic to the United States in the postwar period until 1954, this share declined to approximately 82 per cent by 1956. Current data seem to indicate that in recent years New York's position has been stabilized at this lower level. The current stabilization in the trend of New York's share is not necessarily of a permanent nature. Both in the technological and economic trends in aircraft design and in international aviation policy, there are elements which conceivably may induce a further decline in New York's share of transatlantic air traffic.

Immigration and Naturalization Service statistics indicate that of total travel between the United States and countries on the transatlantic route by air and sea, the share represented by United States citizens went up from approximately 50 per cent in the late 1940's to 63 per cent in 1960. The main change in this pattern took place from 1948 to 1953 when United States tourism to Europe increased rapidly, while European travel to the United States was still severely hampered by the currency restrictions in the economic aftermath of World War II. Since the middle 1950's however, as a result of the general economic recovery in Europe, travel to the United States by Europeans primarily of a business nature, has been growing rapidly.

Published data indicate clearly that the

bulk of travel between Bermuda and the United States is concentrated in the New York area. While travel in this predominantly tourist market represents only about one-twentieth of total United States international travel, four-fifths of the passengers traveling between the United States and Bermuda are accommodated at New York. The published statistics for Bermuda travel understate the true importance of this market because they do not include "cruise" passengers arriving in the United States on United States flag carriers.

The Central and South American market has maintained a rather constant share of total United States international travel. It appears, however, that New York has not fared as well, its share declining from more than one-third of the total market in 1948 to less than one-fourth in 1960. A closer investigation of this market's traffic through New York indicates that this loss in New York's share of the total, particularly in recent years, results from the declines recorded in sea travel. While air passenger volumes through New York represented about the same per cent of total United States air travel to and from Central and South America in 1960 as in 1948, sea travel declined from about 60 per cent in 1948 to about 25 per cent in 1960. Air travel to Central America and the north coast of South America was well within the range of technical, and to some extent economical, performance of the aircraft in use by the airlines shortly before and during World War II. Travel by sea was time-consuming, therefore advantages of air travel were evident; thus air travel in this region got a good start in the early stages of commercial aviation. A dense network of air connections was developed in this area by Pan American Airways shortly before and during World War II, which covered most of the countries of Central America and the north coast of South America, with connections provided to major cities in other parts of the South American continent. The steamship lines which operated substantial passenger services in this area could not compete and began to decline in importance steadily except for cruises.

Between 1948 and 1960 the Caribbean market lost some of its importance in terms of its share of the total United States international travel market. New York, however, saw a marked increase in its share of total United States–Caribbean passenger volumes. This substantial increase in the volume and share of the Caribbean market accommodated through New York is due to the tremendous increases recorded in air travel. In the late 1940's and early 1950's almost all travel to points in the Caribbean went via Miami. With technological improvements in aircraft, more and more direct services to and from New York have been introduced both by United States and foreign flag airlines. This resulted in an increase in New York's share of total air travel between the United States and the Caribbean from less than 4 per cent in 1948 to over 22 per cent in 1960. It has virtually wiped out sea travel (except for cruises) in this market.

The only recent data available concerning travel between the mainland and Puerto Rico are those compiled by the Puerto Rican Bureau of Labor Statistics which are obtained from interviews of all arriving and departing air passengers at San Juan airport (these surveys began in 1957), and from the Puerto Rican Transportation Authority, showing volumes of passengers carried by various air carriers. Although little current information is available concerning sea travel between the United States and Puerto Rico, there is no question that sea travel constitutes a negligible amount of travel in that market. By 1950 air travel between the United States and Puerto Rico already represented over 95 per cent of total air and sea passenger volumes. As regards New York, there was no direct air service to Puerto Rico until 1946, then in a short span of five years virtually all the travel between New York and Puerto Rico was by direct air service.

Factors of Future Growth

Three distinctly different kinds of factors will influence the future rate of development of commercial aviation. In addition to those relating to general economic and social developments here and abroad and the competitive relationships between the various forms of transportation, there are trends and developments within, or closely related to, the aviation industry itself, including ground access to airports, developments of new types of aircraft and fare trends.

Speed of Air Travel

The average speed of domestic scheduled airline service was 142 miles per hour in 1935 and had risen by 1960 to 236 mph. The first turbojets were placed in commercial domestic service in 1959; 10 per cent of the airlines' fleets were jets by the end of 1960. As the ratio of jets to propeller planes becomes greater, average speed will increase and should encourage air travel further. However, much of the traffic generation attributable to increased speed has taken place, for the jet planes are already in use on the longer routes. As shorter routes come to be served by jets, the total time savings will be relatively smaller and cannot be expected to

[1] Transport Aircraft Development Trends and Passenger Schedule Patterns, 1961.

produce significant increases in traffic.

If supersonic aircraft should come into service in the 1970's they would almost certainly be used only on transcontinental and transoceanic routes. They might have a substantial impact on traffic volumes.

Another possibility is the use of helicopters or other vertical take-off and landing craft capable of operating from city-center to city-center on shorter intercity routes. In an exhaustive study of the subject[1] R. Dixon Speas Associates, however, concludes that there is little likelihood that such aircraft will replace fixed-wing planes on any intercity routes into or out of New York by 1975.

Fares

Air fares remained about constant from 1935 to 1959, while the prices of other consumer goods more than doubled and per capita disposable personal income about quintupled. The result was a drastic reduction in the cost of air transportation relative to people's incomes and to other things the public buys. This accounted for many more people becoming air travelers during the 1935-1959 period. In the past few years, however, domestic fare increases have been introduced, which have raised domestic airline revenue per passenger-mile by 15 per cent between 1957 and 1960. Further increases in fares were instituted in 1961, and still more applications for fare rises are pending. Turbojet aircraft have reduced seat-mile operating costs, but as occupancy has been low, passenger-mile costs have risen. This has resulted in financial losses for both domestic and overseas airlines, and is the source of pressure for fare increases on their part.

While the direction of domestic fare changes in recent years has been upward, there has been a considerable amount of experimentation with promotional fares.

Coach service has been increased, shuttle and air bus services have been introduced, a transcontinental excursion fare has been tried, and a special youth fare and a reduced fare for elderly people.

The upward cost trends in the economy will be felt by air transport in the future, plus probable pressure for the airlines to pay a larger share of the cost of installing and operating airways, controls and airport facilities, and there is likely to be a reflection in air transport fares.

In overseas travel the picture is somewhat different because average fares are still inching downward through the introduction of higher-density seating and off-season excursion rates. These low fares are generating new and increased volumes of overseas travel. With continuing increases in personal leisure and income both here and abroad the result is expected to be continued growth in international travel.

Safety

The 1935-1961 period was one in which accidents declined greatly: passenger fatalities per hundred million passenger miles flown by domestic scheduled air carriers dropped from 6.0 to 0.4. It is quite possible that a similar improvement will be made in the record in the next twenty years. It is reasonable to suppose that improved safety will result in greater public confidence in flying and thereby promote travel by air.

Service

The volume of air travel is strongly influenced by the amount of service offered by the air carriers. Between 1938 and 1960, the number of cities served by domestic scheduled air carriers increased from 286 to 721.[2] The number of cities

[2] Includes cities outside continental United States, but excluding places in Alaska.

served has not increased in recent years, however, and it is doubtful that it will rise further in the near future. All the large cities have air service now and so any additional cities to be served would be small ones, whose traffic generation would be light.

If the airlines should provide greater frequency of schedules for the cities now served, or if more nonstop intercity services should be introduced, increased air travel volumes could result.

Ground Access to Airports

To the passenger, the journey to and from the airport is part of his trip. Airports must serve large geographic areas having a multitude of different traffic-generating centers. Inescapably, there must be travel between the airport and its traffic-generating centers. In New York, as in most cities, this travel has been by private automobiles and taxicabs on the highways, with "limousine" bus service to Manhattan and a few other points. The highways, however, must serve many functions. The advent of the faster jet plane has resulted in a peaking of air travel coinciding with the peak load on highways for regional home-to-work travel. At the hours of peak demand for airport access, the highways are used intensively. As a result, the time required for the ground portion of the air traveler's journey has been increased.

Popular attention has been directed toward the helicopter as a means of travel between airport and air traffic generating centers. Limited service is now available in New York, Chicago and Los Angeles and elsewhere. Although useful, the helicopter is not a complete solution of the basic problem. For example, landing space requirements are such as to limit their usefulness in built-up areas; New York's intown heliports are located on

TABLE 11. LOCAL DESTINATIONS OF INBOUND AIR PASSENGERS
AT NEW YORK'S COMMERCIAL AIRPORTS

(Average Daily Volume — Summer 1959)

County of Destination	La Guardia	Newark	N. Y. International	
			Domestic	Overseas
New York	3,140	960	2,450	1,200
Bronx	250	40	140	170
Kings	240	80	340	270
Queens	670	150	340	300
Nassau	510	50	360	130
Suffolk	110	30	70	40
Westchester	430	90	180	130
Fairfield	90	60	110	70
Union	20	250	60	70
Essex	50	470	90	60
Hudson	40	90	10	a
Bergen	120	210	50	60
Passaic	20	120	10	40
Morris	50	130	70	a
All Others	260	370	320	410
Total	6,000	3,100	4,600	2,950

(The column header "Airport Where Passenger Arrived" spans La Guardia, Newark, and N. Y. International.)

Source: Surveys by P. A. Aviation Economics.
aIncluded in "All Others".

piers out of the main stream of traffic. Operating experience has demonstrated the high costs of this service, and the need for operating subsidies because fares cannot be raised high enough to cover full costs.

Although the traffic volumes involved in airport access are sizable, the volume on any one route is small when related to urban transportation magnitudes.

To the extent that they can, passengers minimize the airport-access time through choice of airport. For example, air travelers bound for Bergen County use Newark more than they use La Guardia. However, it is not economically or physically possible to maintain equal service to all destinations at all the region's airports. Thus the problem of providing convenient access to each airport from all parts of the region remains. Airport-access travel is distributed over a large number of travel paths and the volume on any one route is far from enough to warrant investment in an exclusive airport-access highway.

The impact of travel time, inconvenience and cost in airport access is greatest when the air trip is short. A passenger traveling between New York and Los Angeles is more tolerant of these difficulties than is a passenger traveling to Boston or Washington. But it is in the short-mileage trips that the greatest potential for the future expansion of air travel lies. It follows, therefore, that the growth of air travel will be strongly influenced by the nature of airport-access transportation in the future.

The Future Growth of Air Traffic

The relatively short history of commercial air transport is of limited usefulness in indicating the industry's future. An assumption that the rate of growth experienced in the past decade, for example, will continue into the future would not be warranted. As mentioned earlier, domestic air passenger traffic has clearly gone through the first of the three development stages that are typical of industry growth, and appears to be somewhere in the second. But there is no clue in the traffic data to when or at what level its rate of growth will begin to taper off. The slow growth during the past two years could be interpreted either as the beginning of the mature period in air travel's development or merely as a temporary interruption in its continued rapid increase.

As the past trend of air travel, by itself, is inadequate as a base for projecting future volumes, additional pertinent information must be introduced. It would be advantageous if the various travel influencing factors that have been discussed — fares, service levels, and the like — could be evaluated in terms of numerical gains and losses in traffic, but not enough is known about their individual impacts.

There are some social and economic factors, however, that are related to air travel behavior and which can be projected into the future with reasonable confidence. The Port of New York Authority was one of the sponsors of a survey in 1955 of the travel behavior of the United States population. The survey disclosed that the proclivity to travel by air was closely related to the traveler's income and occupation. For domestic personal travel, age was also a closely related factor, and for business trips the industry the traveler represents. By projecting into the future the composition of the nation's population as to age, income, education and industry employment, using U. S. government projections to the extent possible, a projection of air travel has been made. The methodology has been presented in "Forecast of the United States Air Passenger Market, 1965-1975," published by the Port Authority in 1957.

A modification of this methodology was used to project overseas air travel which is presented in "Forecast of the Overseas Air Passenger Market through New York, 1965–1975" published by the Port Authority in 1958.

Coupled with this procedure for estimating the future growth in air travel that can be expected to result from future changes in the economic and demographic composition of the United States population, was an extrapolation of the rate at which people will become first-time air travelers. At the time the forecast was prepared, no more than 25 per cent of the United States adult population had taken an air trip. It has been assumed that this percentage will increase as air travel becomes a more accepted means of transportation.

All projections that have been made of future air transportation demands in the region indicate clearly the need for additional airport capacity within the planning horizon of this report. Acquisition of the necessary land at an early date is imperative in view of the rapidity with which vacant land throughout the region is being developed for residences, industrial and commercial establishments and public facilities, or committed for parks and recreation space. The Regional Plan Association has estimated that the Region's growth by 1985 will have brought about the development for these purposes of 2,800 more square miles if existing zoning laws remain in effect. This is equivalent to the utilization of some 100 square miles of vacant land a year and a total urbanized area in 1985 more than twice the urbanized area of today. Each year that goes by will see a diminution in the amount of land available to accommodate growth in air transportation.

An indication of the land area requirements of a major airport facility is contained in Chapter IX of "A Report on Airport Requirements and Sites in the Metropolitan New Jersey–New York Region" published by the Port Authority in May 1961. A "prototype airport plan," as described in that report, indicates that some 10,000 acres would be required for runways, buildings and other construction, and aircraft noise considerations.

The Port Authority has a long-standing policy that the residents of communities in the vicinity of airports must be protected from excessive aircraft noise. In 1951, the Port Authority Board of Commissioners adopted a regulation, which is still in force, which states "No jet or turbo-prop aircraft may land or take off at an air terminal without permission." Under this regulation, permission for jet operations has been granted only after noise tests of the aircraft involved have shown that it could be operated at the particular airport under specified conditions without subjecting neighboring communities to intolerable noise levels. Any future airport, or any future aircraft designed to operate into the metropolitan region, would have to be designed to conform with this limitation.

CHAPTER 18

PASSENGER SHIP TERMINAL REQUIREMENTS

Ocean steamship passengers using the terminal facilities of the Port of New York in 1961 totaled 946,906. Some of the ships they traveled upon were designed and built especially for passenger service, a few accommodating more than a thousand, some were built to carry cargo as well as passengers, most with accommodations for fewer than 500, and some were built primarily for the transportation of cargo, with limited, and incidental, passenger accommodations.

Included in the total of 946,906 were 242,446 passengers who were embarked on cruises. Generally speaking, the cruise passenger may be identified as one who stays with the ship during a round-trip voyage, using it as living quarters when at the various ports of call. The cruise clearly can be considered as pleasure rather than as business travel. Several of the steamship lines serving the port specialize in serving the cruise trade, mostly to Bermuda, the Bahamas, and the West Indies. Many of the other steamship companies place one or more of their transocean liners in cruise service during the late fall and winter months, which are slack season for transocean travel. Some of the companies have a ship or two continuously in cruise service in addition to those in liner service.

The port's passenger terminals cannot be distinguished neatly from the cargo terminals, for many terminals accommodate both passenger and cargo vessels. With few exceptions the lines operating passenger ships operate cargo ships also and they generally use a single terminal for both services, although one or more berths may be singled out and specially equipped for passenger service.

Nevertheless, there are several terminals, providing 17 berths altogether, on the Manhattan shore of the Hudson River, which can be considered the primary steamship passenger terminals of the port. They account for a preponderant share of the steamship passenger volume. In this chapter attention is directed to these primary passenger terminals. Berths used by combination passenger-cargo ships and those through which the passenger volume is minor and only incidental to cargo operations, have been included in the analysis of cargo terminal needs discussed in Chapter 10.

STEAMSHIP PASSENGER VOLUMES

The number of overseas passengers, by both steamship and by aircraft, as officially reported by the Immigration and Naturalization Service, for the period 1948-1961, is presented in Table 1. The figures must be used with caution, for over the years there have been several changes in the method of compilation. Prior to July 1958, for example, cruise passengers were excluded but have been included since then. Air passengers to and from Mexico are excluded prior to 1958. All civilian travelers to and from Canada are excluded. Travel to and from United States possessions is excluded, as is the travel of military personnel by air or by military sea transport. Civilian passengers on military aircraft, however, are included.

Despite the difficulties in making accurate year-to-year comparisons the data in-

TABLE 1. PORT OF NEW YORK: OVERSEAS PASSENGERS BY SEA AND AIR, 1948-1961

| | Sea | | | Air | | |
	Arrivals	Departures	Total	Arrivals	Departures	Total
1948	352,396	266,920	619,316	239,996	141,626	381,662
1949	428,250	325,665	753,915	224,660	156,769	381,429
1950	443,503	347,229	790,732	229,354	195,680	425,034
1951	440,373	316,388	756,761	270,440	234,286	504,726
1952	453,075	387,555	840,630	328,671	296,866	625,237
1953	429,317	402,760	832,077	390,931	339,580	730,511
1954	461,183	415,836	877,019	441,414	386,831	828,245
1955	481,841	420,710	902,551	533,277	478,943	1,012,220
1956	505,299	429,361	934,660	631,867	525,553	1,157,420
1957	460,133	407,121	867,254	751,099	611,988	1,363,087
1958	460,173	435,144	895,317	868,942	771,523	1,640,465
1959	460,151	463,904	924,955	951,594	859,094	1,810,688
1960	477,893	491,795	969,688	1,163,800	1,046,497	2,210,297
1961	461,304	485,602	946,906	1,199,286	1,092,567	2,291,853

Source: Immigration and Naturalization Service, United States Department of Justice.

dicate clearly several important trends. Total overseas travel has been increasing steadily during the past decade. Overseas air travel has been rising strongly. Steamship travel, exclusive of cruise travel, had a rising trend through 1956 but appears to have faltered thereafter. If the cruise travel volume reported for 1961 is deducted from the total sea-travel volume for that year, transocean travel trips by sea were 704,460, considerably less than the comparable figure for 1956. Nevertheless, even without cruise travel, there has been a steadily rising trend of total transocean trips, by air and by transocean liner.

The European area has consistently accounted for the major proportion of the noncruise sea travelers, as Table 2 indicates. Its dominance has been heightened since World War II by the replacement of steamship travel by air travel to all other areas. Travel to and from Asia, Australasia, Africa and North and South America has become air travel to an ever-

increasing degree and today there are few liner sailings from the Port of New York to those areas. Steamship travel to the Far East and to Australasia is now largely through Pacific Coast ports.

Cruise travel has been growing, presumably in response to increased leisure time and increased personal incomes. It has been estimated that its volume through the port in 1948 was no more than 50,000, and that it had increased to 100,000 or more by 1956. In 1961 the volume was 242,446. Most cruises are of rather short duration, from 7 to 15 days; the prime region of travel is to the area of Bermuda, the Bahamas, the West Indies and the north coast of South America. In 1959 there were 205 cruise sailings from the Port of New York, of which 106 were by the three vessels of the specialized cruise operators, to Bermuda and the Bahamas.

Most of the remaining cruise voyages were made by vessels operated by the major transatlantic passenger carriers,

TABLE 2. PORT OF NEW YORK: DISTRIBUTION OF SHIP PASSENGERS BY
MAJOR AREA OF TRAVEL 1950, 1955 AND 1961

	1 9 5 0		1 9 5 5		1 9 6 1	
	Passengers	Per Cent of Total	Passengers	Per Cent of Total	Passengers	Per Cent of Total[a]
Europe	668,802	84.6	792,301	87.8	639,485	90.8
Asia	10,806	1.4	7,619	0.8	17,593	2.5
Africa	3,811	0.5	7,577	0.8	2,875	0.4
Oceania	283	—	95	—	1,047	0.1
North America[b]	78,144	9.9	71,712	7.9	30,543	4.3
South America	28,886	3.7	23,247	2.6	12,917	1.8
Cruise	n.a.	n.a.	n.a.	n.a.	242,446	—
Total	790,732	100.0	902,551	100.0	946,906	100.0

[a]Excluding cruise passengers.
[b]Includes Caribbean.
n.a.: Not available.
Source: Immigration and Naturalization Service, United States Department of Justice.

taken out of transatlantic service during the winter months. The Trans-Atlantic Passenger Conference has reported that the winter cruise sailings of its member lines (the major lines providing regular passenger service to and from European and Mediterranean ports) carried 35,986 passengers in the 1957-1958 season and 43,838 in 1959-1960.

Air transport has penetrated deeply into the overseas travel market. Overseas air travel caught up with and passed trans-

TABLE 3. PORT OF NEW YORK:
TRANS-ATLANTIC CONFERENCE
PASSENGER MOVEMENTS[a]
1953-1961

	Arrivals	Departures	Total
1953	330,471	312,825	643,296
1954	382,787	325,337	708,124
1955	384,238	327,259	711,497
1956	400,726	334,589	735,315
1957	377,412	334,660	712,072
1958	366,190	350,127	716,317
1959	327,793	321,884	649,677
1960	327,892	332,472	660,384
1961	302,193	314,104	616,297

[a]Exclusive of cruise passengers.
Source: Trans-Atlantic Passenger Steamship Conference.

ocean steamship travel in 1955 and has been widening its lead ever since, particularly since the introduction of economy air fares in 1958 and of jet planes in 1959. The extent of air transport's penetration, however, has been unevenly distributed over the different geographic areas of travel. It has supplanted much of the noncruise steamship travel to all areas other than Europe and has probably generated a large amount of new travel to those areas. For travel to and from European and Mediterranean ports, however, the steamship lines still show strength, as the data presented in Table 3 indicate.

Travel to and from Europe accounts for an overriding share of steamship travel, nearly 91 per cent of noncruise passengers in 1961, while it accounted for 66 per cent of overseas air travel.

The future prospects for overseas travel volumes appear to shape up as follows: As population, income and leisure time are all expected to increase, the total amount of overseas travel is likely to increase. Travel by air is expected to continue its rising trend and may soon account for virtually all overseas travel except travel to and from European and Mediterranean ports. Travel to and from those ports will probably account for virtually all noncruise steamship travel. Cruise travel, however, should increase and, in consequence, steamship travel as a whole should show a modest rise.

For passenger movements through the region's commercial airports it has been projected that the volume of transatlantic passengers will increase some fourfold by 1980, and that Bermuda, Puerto Rico and Caribbean travel will more than double.

The outlook for steamship passengers is a much more modest rate of increase, from 946,906 in 1961 to perhaps 1,200,000 by 1980. It is assumed that the Port of New York will continue to be the key East Coast port for ocean travel, particularly for regularly scheduled transatlantic service. Virtually all of the growth to be expected, however, will be in cruise passengers.

It is noteworthy that the long-time directional imbalance of transocean steamship passenger travel through the port, more arrivals than departures, has declined greatly in recent years. In 1959, 1960 and 1961, indeed, departures exceeded arrivals. The total overseas passenger volume, by sea and air, however, continues to show an excess of arrivals. The relative strengthening of steamship passenger departure volumes may reflect a growing practice by transatlantic passengers of traveling one way by sea and the other way by air.

Primary Passenger Ship Terminals in 1962

All of the piers now used primarily for passenger ship movements are on Manhattan's Hudson River water front. They comprise Pier 40, newly completed for the Holland-America Line, and Piers 42, 84,

86, 88, 90, 92, 95 and 97. Together, they provide a total of 17 berths equipped for passenger service.

The United States Line occupies Pier 86 and the Cunard Line Piers 90 and 92. In both cases they are exclusive tenants. The American Export Line and the Italian Line share Pier 84, and the French Line, the Greek Line and the North German Lloyd share the use of Pier 88. Until January 1962, Pier 42 was shared by the Norwegian American Line and the Incres Line, the latter a specialized cruise ship operator. Since then Incres has also shared Pier 88. Piers 95 and 97 are used by the Furness Withy group of lines as cruise ship terminals and are shared with five other lines in the transatlantic and cruise trades. The intervening Pier 96 is used by Furness Withy as a cargo terminal.

There is little difference between the terminal requirements of transoceanic and cruise-ship operations. Both require facilities for baggage handling, for customs, immigration, public health and other regulatory agency inspections, for taxicab access and automobile parking, and amenities for embarking passengers and visitors. In addition, the regular liner services need facilities for the handling of express cargo.

Passenger Terminal Utilization

The 19 steamship lines which used the 17 berths in these primary passenger terminals operated 53 passenger ships into and out of the Port of New York in 1959. All regularly scheduled liner sailings from these terminals were in the transatlantic service. More than half of the cruise sailings were to Bermuda, the Bahamas and the West Indies.

There was an average in-port ship population in 1959 of 6.8, with a recurring

peak of 12 ships at these primary terminals. The cruise ships had a much shorter
average stay at berth, 2.5 days, than the
transatlantic liner ships had, 3.2 days. The
three specialized cruise ships, *Nassau*,[1]
Ocean Monarch and *Queen of Bermuda*,
operated on tight schedules, frequently
moving into and out of the port on the
same day. Few of the liners turn around
in less than 2 days.

The 8 berths comprising the terminals
operated under exclusive occupancy conditions, as a group, had an average in-port
population of 3.1 ships. Peak occupancy,
however, was 8 on a single occasion when
all berths were occupied; on three occa-
sions there were 7 ships. The 9 berths
comprising the terminals at which occupancy was shared by two or more lines as
a group, had an average in-port population of 3.7 ships. Peak occupancy was 9;
frequently these terminals accommodated
6 ships at one time.

These peak occupancies did not coincide in time, however, as the over-all peak
of 12 ships indicates.

In general, the berths in these terminals
averaged less than one ship departure per
week in 1959. One accommodated more
frequent sailings, Pier 42 with 69 departures during the year, 36 of which were of
the cruise ship *Nassau*.

THE OUTLOOK FOR 1980

Since 1959 there have been a number
of new ships in the passenger fleet serving
the Port of New York in transatlantic service, such as *Rotterdam*, of Holland-America, *Leonardo da Vinci*, of the Italian Line,
and *France*, of the French Line, as well
as new ships in cruise service. Some have
been replacements of overage vessels and
some have represented additional entries
into ocean passenger service. There also

[1]The *Nassau* has since been withdrawn from New York
service and has been replaced by the *Victoria*.

have been announcements of shipbuilding
plans by the various steamship lines for
both replacements and new entries. When
we consider only the steamship lines that
in recent years have tenanted the primary
passenger terminals of the port, there appears to be a prospect for a net addition
of three to five ships to the 53 that sailed
from those 17 berths in 1959.

It is to be expected that the newer ships
will have somewhat faster cruising speeds,
making possible an increased number of
sailings in the course of a year. Virtually
all of the increase in passenger traffic is
likely to be in cruise travel, which exhibits
a high degree of berth utilization, and,
occurring during the cold-weather season,
should not add to the transocean peak.
For transatlantic liners, improved facilities for handling of mail and express cargo should also permit some reduction in
turn-around time. As a result, berth utilization should be improved by 1980, each
berth should accommodate more annual
sailings and more passengers, and there
should be no increase in the total number
of berths required.

If we set 50 years as the presumptive
useful life for steamship piers, all the primary passenger terminals in the harbor,
except the newly constructed Pier 40, will
be overage or will closely approach the
end of their useful lives by 1980. Piers 88,
90 and 92 will be 46 years old; Piers 84
and 86 will be 54 and 62 years old, respectively; Piers 42, 95 and 97 are super-
annuated already. Thus, an extensive reconstruction program for the port's major
passenger terminal facilities may be
needed during the next two decades.

Present facilities are badly outmoded in
their amenities for steamship passengers,
particularly when compared with the
breadth and quality of services available
to overseas air passengers. A major criterion for terminal reconstruction should

be accommodations for passengers and visitors that would be more commodious, more attractive, better designed and better equipped than those now available. The facilities that would be desirable might prove to be uneconomical at a terminal serving no more than one departure a week, but at a joint or consolidated terminal those facilities could be used in common by a number of steamship lines and the usage might be enough to make them worthwhile.

The modest increase in ocean travel that has been projected for 1980 should result in a correspondingly modest increase in the number of sailings. For reasons presented in an earlier paragraph, notably the expectation that there will be a reduction in berth occupancy time, there should be no increase in the number of berths required. If, as an extreme case, all the passenger operations of the steamship lines now occupying primary terminal facilities should be provided for at a single consolidated terminal, with all berths available to all steamship lines, twelve berths would be required. The maximum number of ships in port at any one time should be no greater than the number today. If a single facility for the terminal accommodation and servicing of steamship passengers should be assumed, however, it would have to provide for about three sailings and three arrivals a day, as an annual average. Several thousand passengers and probably twice as many visitors would pass through the terminal daily and more during peak travel season. Such a terminal would probably be unwieldy and impractical; moreover, it would have to be more than a mile long.

At a more modest level, a joint terminal for those lines that already share terminal occupancies would require nine berths, the number used today by those lines. As an average, fewer than two sailings and

two arrivals a day would have to be provided for. Such a consolidated terminal would still be large but perhaps not too large to be practical of operation. Efficient taxicab service could be arranged for and ample parking space could be made available. Amenities and services for departing and arriving passengers and for visitors could be made comfortable and attractive. An opportunity would be afforded to provide for expeditious baggage handling and for customs, immigration and public health inspections.

Such consolidation, however, would require that the cargo ships that are also operated by the passenger lines be provided with separate facilities, in other locations. The steamship lines, in other words, would have to split their terminal operations, one terminal for their passenger ships and another for their cargo ships. The evaluation by steamship line management of such a split operation may vary from line to line. Some of them already berth their cargo ships in other parts of the harbor. Consolidation would also mean the loss of identification of a particular pier location with a particular steamship line, an identification which is usually held by transportation line managements to be of some commercial value.

In any event, one of the major passenger lines, Holland-America, has entered into a long-term commitment for the occupancy of a new terminal, Pier 40, for both its passenger and its cargo ships. Another, Cunard, has contracted for an expansion of its present terminal facilities, a new Pier 94, primarily for cargo operations but available to relieve any pressure that might come on Piers 90 and 92.

In summary: An extensive reconstruction program for most of the port's major steamship passenger terminals will be called for within the coming two decades. Assuming that the three major steamship lines now enjoying exclusive occupancy of their terminals will continue to require terminals of their own in the future, they will need a total of eight passenger-ship berths, the number they now utilize. If the lines now sharing terminal tenancy should occupy a consolidated passenger terminal in the future, they would require a total of nine berths, also the number they now utilize. Consolidation of their terminal operations, however, would make possible greatly improved steamship passenger comfort and amenity. If there should be no more joint terminal usage than now obtains, 15 new or reconstructed berths will be needed by 1980.

CHAPTER 19

REGIONAL GROWTH AND REGIONAL TRAVEL

A century ago New York had outstripped its nearest rival, Philadelphia, and was the most populous city of the United States. Its pre-eminent position as the nation's commercial capital was established. Its corporate boundaries coincided with the shores of Manhattan Island, and the built-up portion of the city extended from the Hudson to the East River and from the Battery to the southern edge of the newly acquired Central Park.

New York was not the only city of importance, however, in what future generations would know as the New York Metropolitan Region. There were also Brooklyn and Jersey City and Newark, and smaller communities such as Hoboken, Paterson, Passaic, Yonkers and Jamaica. Altogether, in 1860, some two million people made their homes in the Region, and the land occupied by urban population aggregated some 30 square miles.

Over the years that followed, urban growth yielded progressively larger figures for both population and area occupied. Typically, the course of growth was outward from the urban centers, converting rural land into urban land at the steadily advancing edges of the cities, accented by extensions of the urban masses along the principal arteries of transportation. It was interrupted only by the Region's numerous water courses and marshlands. Each decade added urban development in areas that formerly had been farmland or urban fringe.

THE URBAN GROWTH PATTERN

By 1900 the Region's population had grown to more than five and a half million

and occupied 140 square miles of urbanized land. Nearly all of Manhattan was built up, and more than half of Brooklyn. There was little open land left in Jersey City or Newark, and the smaller cities and towns of the Region were growing toward each other along the connecting railroad lines.

Transportation facilities had improved remarkably since 1860. Extensive networks of streetcar lines had been developed in the Region's cities and New York City itself was served by a steam-operated elevated rapid transit railroad system. The intercity railroads carried "commuters" from outlying settlements into the central core, where most of the Region's employment was concentrated. The urban dweller's travel orbit had been enlarged. He could live farther away from his work place and from his other frequent destinations. His travel was faster and required less personal effort. Land at a distance from a city's center, provided it was served by the mechanized transport lines, had become suitable for urban development.

The Region's growth pattern during the latter decades of the nineteenth century reflected the influence of these transportation improvements. The main urban mass expanded rapidly, and its tentacles extended far out along the transport lines. The density of settlement of the urbanized portions of the Region in 1860 was about 65,000 people per square mile; by 1900 the over-all density was less than 40,000 per square mile. Urban area had increased far faster than urban population.

Even more profound forces affecting the pattern of urban growth were ushered in with the twentieth century. Motorized transportation and hard-surfaced highways became available, slowly at first and then with a headlong rush in the third and fourth decades of the new century. Central-station electric power, together with economical transmission and distribution, provided power-using industries with wide choices of site location. Telephone communication freed many businesses from the need to locate in close proximity to other enterprises with which they were linked commercially.

The consequences of these new forces were far-reaching. By increasing so strikingly the accessibility of the cities' hinterlands, the technological developments in transport, in power and in communication made hundreds of square miles of open land available for urban growth. The desire for more elbowroom led to residential development at densities still lower than those of the preceding decades. Suburbia took on steadily increasing importance in the metropolitan complex. The open spaces between the smaller cities began to fill up.

Manufacturing establishments also began to seek outlying sites. The multistory factory building in the heart of the built-up cities was obsolescent. The new sites were spacious, to accommodate the new assembly-line processes and to provide room for future expansion. Suburbanization of industry gathered pace, and carried with it a suburbanization of employment.

By 1940 the urbanized area of the New York Metropolitan Region aggregated 640 square miles. Its population totaled 12,500,000. In the 40 years since the turn of the century, each additional million of population had brought about the urbanization of about 70 square miles. The Region's population had become two and a quarter times as great, but it occupied

four and a half times as much area. The old urban core cities — Manhattan, Brooklyn, Jersey City, Newark — were fully developed and no longer contributed to the Region's population increase.

Since 1940 the tendency of the urban fabric to thin out and to spread farther has intensified. Between 1940 and 1954 each additional million of population was accompanied by the urbanization of 185 square miles of land. The cities of the Region enveloped about 33 square miles of open country a year. The 1960 census data show that the Region's population growth during the past decade was accounted for entirely in the outlying areas (Table 1). In fact, the central-core counties, with the exception of Queens, had absolute declines. The metropolis of 1960 was profoundly different in configuration from the group of compact cities which featured the Region a century before.

THE INFLUENCE OF ADVANCING TECHNOLOGY

Decentralizing influences have been operative for a long time; they are firmly based on technological advance. Only recently have they come into full flower and brought to our attention problems we consider new.

When the energy of falling water was relied upon to do the heavy work of grinding grain into flour or to provide power for other simple factory processes, mill sites were limited in number. This restraint on the choice of location was characteristic of all industrial activity about a century ago.

Steam power removed these restrictions. Power could be generated at any location, subject only to the limitations of fuel transport costs and to the adequacy of condensing water. Cities could enlarge their industrial activities and expand geographic extent. When electric power came along, together with central-station generation, the transformer and high-voltage transmission, most of the remaining limitations on industry's locational choices were removed. Power-using activities could be sited almost anywhere, as far as power considerations were concerned.

When face-to-face contact or messenger service were the only means of communication, urban activity had to take place within a restricted area. Spatial extent and city form were limited by what communication could accomplish. The telephone, teletypewriter, radio and television removed those limitations. Again,

TABLE 1. POPULATION OF NEW YORK METROPOLITAN REGION
(in thousands)

	1950	1960	Changes 1950 to 1960
Entire region	13,951	16,141	+ 2,190
Central-core counties			
Kings	2,738	2,627	− 111
New York	1,960	1,698	− 262
Queens	1,551	1,810	+ 259
Bronx	1,451	1,425	− 26
Hudson	648	611	− 37
Inner-ring counties			
Nassau	673	1,300	+ 627
Essex	906	924	+ 18
Westchester	626	809	+ 183
Bergen	539	780	+ 241
Union	398	504	+ 106
Passaic	337	407	+ 70
Richmond	192	222	+ 30
Outer-ring counties			
Fairfield	504	654	+ 150
Suffolk	276	667	+ 391
Middlesex	265	434	+ 169
Monmouth	225	334	+ 109
Morris	165	262	+ 97
Orange	152	184	+ 32
Dutchess	137	176	+ 39
Somerset	99	144	+ 45
Rockland	89	137	+ 48
Putnam	20	32	+ 12

one location became about as good as another as far as communication was concerned, except for some forms of cultural activity, certain specialized marketing functions and those enterprises that required either personal confrontation or group presence to achieve their full values.

The same story can be told of the influence of advancing transport technology. Each step along the way of providing more mobility for the individual has widened the choice of location, of residence, of work place, of leisure-time activity. The steam railroad, the electric streetcar, the motor vehicle, the airplane and the helicopter have extended the range within which cooperative urban activity can take place. The feasible journey-to-work radius has been greatly extended. Intercommunity relationships have been strengthened, and cooperative activity now can encompass a great region containing many individual urban communities.

The railroads freed industry from its need to locate at tidewater or on a navigable river or canal, and permitted inland sites to be used productively. The motor truck opened up additional areas, and industry can now utilize sites not formerly accessible for the receipt or shipment of goods.

As advances in the technology of power, communication and transportation have made possible the dispersal of industrial establishments, technical advances in production methods have motivated manufacturing industry to seek new sites. More extensive mechanization, heavier machinery and horizontal assembly methods have called for one-story, ground-level industrial architecture, with its great demand for acreage. Suitable sites at tolerable costs have been found in the urban outskirts more easily than in the old central-core areas. In some instances the horizontal dimensions have precluded accommodation within the traditional city block pattern. In others, the time and expense involved in assembling the land required from a number of owners of small parcels has swung the balance of choice toward locations in areas not so encumbered.

THE DISPERSAL PHENOMENON

The desire of the growing family for living accommodations with plenty of elbowroom, stifled for a while by the wartime restrictions on residential construction, has led to a booming period of single-family, suburban housing development, occupying land extensively rather than intensively. The increased rate of family formation in the postwar era strengthened the trend.

Retailing has shown a tendency to follow the new metropolitan population to the suburbs. The suburban shopping center is a prominent feature of the expanding metropolis. With department stores, specialty shops and professional offices, they have become much more than neighborhood facilities for convenience shopping; they are evolving into subregional commercial centers.

There has been a hundred-year history of growth of urban area outpacing growth of urban population, moderately at first but with a rapidly widening lead during more recent years. There is virtually no evidence of any reversal of the trend toward rapid territorial expansion of the metropolitan mass. The Regional Plan Association in 1957 estimated that 700 more square miles would have to be developed for urban uses to accommodate the next 20 years' growth.

Some students of the American city and the forces shaping it have presented a dramatic picture of what seems to lie ahead. It is that of the "megalopolis," a continuous city, extending from Boston to Washington without a break. It is a startling prospect, but it seems a likely prospect. A map of the eastern seaboard showing today's urbanized areas reveals few extensive gaps, and they are rapidly filling.

IMPACT ON TRAVEL BEHAVIOR

The changes in urban form that have taken place in the Metropolitan Region during the past decade have been reflected in changes in travel behavior. Although comprehensive data on travel behavior covering the entire Metropolitan Region and all forms of transportation do not exist, the travel that takes place across the Hudson River may be considered a sample of it.

In the ten-year period, 1950–1960, the total number of person trips across the Hudson River, by all modes of transportation, including long-haul travel, increased by 24.9 million, from 266.7 million to 291.6 million. The number of trips made by automobile increased greatly, the number by bus increased moderately, the number by railroad declined sharply, and ferry travel by other than railroad passengers approached the vanishing point.

These general facts have suggested that there has been a massive diversion of New Jersey commuters from the railroads to automobiles. Gross statistics often conceal more than they reveal, however. Total intraregional travel is a complex mixture of trips having different purposes, different destinations and different origins, trips made on different days of the week and at different times of the day, and trips made by residents of different parts of the region. When trans-Hudson travel volumes are analyzed in appropriate segments and each segment is studied separately, it appears that there have been over-all increases in those categories of travel which the automobile has dominated for a long time and which are not, and probably cannot be, adequately served by common carrier. Conversely, there have been over-all declines in those categories which have been, and still are, the mainstays of the public transportation systems.

To begin with, 17 million, more than two-thirds of the decade's increase in trans-Hudson trips occurred on Saturdays, Sundays and holidays. The increase in automobile travel in this component, 18.9 million, is striking but not surprising. Private transportation clearly has captured the leading position in leisure-time travel. Much of the week-end and holiday travel is family travel, for which the automobile offers superior convenience and greater economy than do the common carriers. Destinations are widely scattered and there is a correspondingly wide dispersion of travel paths, a situation not well suited to common-carrier service. Much of the 1960 automobile travel in this category was travel that would not have taken place at all if the automobile had not been available.

The increase in weekday trans-Hudson travelers was 7.9 million between 1950 and 1960. The number of New York residents represented can be estimated by utilizing sample counts of automobile license plates for the automobile travelers, by assuming that railroad, bus and ferry passengers traveling eastbound in the afternoon or westbound in the morning rush hours are New York residents, and that mass transportation passengers at other hours are divided in the same proportion between New York and New Jersey residents. On this basis there was an increase of 1.6 million in the number of New York residents crossing the river on weekdays and an increase of 6.2 million New Jersey residents.[1]

The rise in the number of New York residents crossing the river on weekdays was accompanied by a disproportionately large increase in the number traveling by automobile, a moderate rise in the number traveling by bus and a sharp decline in the number traveling by rail.

The weakening of rail travel may have been in response to shifts in the foci of employment from the Jersey City, Hoboken, and Newark core areas to more scattered points in Bergen and Passaic counties, or to changes in the New York residence patterns of workers in New Jersey establishments, or to the relative costs of rail travel and car pool travel, or to a combination of these factors.

The rise of 6.2 million New Jersey residents crossing the river conceals the fact

[1]In the interest of simplicity of phrasing, the term "New Jersey residents" is used even though in strict accuracy the term should be "residents of areas west of the Hudson River." We do not know where the trans-Hudson travelers really live, but infer that they live west of the Hudson if they travel eastbound during the morning rush hours or if they travel in automobiles bearing license plates of New Jersey or states to the west of the Hudson. "New Jersey residents," therefore, include all long-haul rail and bus travelers residing west of the Hudson. Rockland County residents traveling by railroad or bus are counted as "New Jersey residents."

that those destined for, or returning from Manhattan's Central Business District *declined* by 5.1 million. The number going to, or coming from points outside the CBD, to upper Manhattan and beyond to the north, or to Brooklyn and Queens and beyond to the east, rose by 11.4 million. This non-CBD-oriented travel is another component of regional travel which had relied heavily on the automobile even in 1950, and private transportation further strengthened its position during the decade.

The travel segment represented by New Jersey residents traveling on weekdays to Manhattan's CBD is the travel segment that the New Jersey commuter railroads were laid out to serve. Most of the 5.1 million decline occurred during off hours. The New Jersey railroads and the Hudson River ferries took the brunt of the loss, while the bus lines showed strong gains. As the data include long-haul passengers, without separation, an unknown portion of the railroad loss can be attributed to the diversion of intercity travel from the railroads to the airlines.

Despite the rise in total automobile travel, the common carriers — rails and buses — in 1960 still occupied a strongly

TABLE 2. COMPONENTS OF 1960 TRANS-HUDSON TRAVEL

	Total Travelers (millions)	Per Cent of Total		
		By Auto	By Bus	By Rail (Plus Ferry Pedestrians)
Annual Total	291.6	52.1	29.0	18.9
Saturdays, Sundays and Holidays	92.8	72.3	22.4	5.3
Weekdays	198.8	42.6	32.1	25.3
New York residents	60.0	64.2	20.4	15.4
New Jersey residents	138.8	33.3	37.2	29.5
To points other than CBD	46.6	67.2	20.0	12.8
To CBD	92.2	16.1	45.9	38.0
During off hours	25.5	30.2	45.7	24.1
During rush hours	66.7	10.8	45.9	43.3

dominant position in serving the New Jersey resident's travel to and from Manhattan's Central Business District on weekdays. They handled 88 per cent of it during the rush hours and 70 per cent during the off hours.

The automobile was the principal reliance for Saturday, Sunday and holiday travelers, for residents of New York and for New Jersey residents traveling to points other than Manhattan's CBD. These three segments together accounted for 90 per cent of the rise in automobile usage during the 1950–1960 decade.

The number of trans-Hudson travelers comprising each of the foregoing segments and the proportionate uses of each mode of transportation are presented in Table 2.

What has happened in regard to the utilization of trans-Hudson transportation facilities has been a consequence of what has happened to the locations of population and of industry and commerce, both inside and outside the central core of the metropolis. New Jersey job opportunities have been increasing, as they have been in all the noncore areas. Manhattan's Central Business District employment has changed but slightly in total magnitude but there has been a northeasterly shift in its geographic distribution. Population increase has been largely confined to the outskirts, and it has occupied new residential areas developed at relatively low density. Many suburban residents have found suburban jobs.

Mass transportation is performing much the same task it always has, carrying workers to and from the Metropolitan Area's central core, but that task involves a proportionately smaller share of the Region's total transportation. The other travel components, widely dispersed over both space and time, are less well served by mass transportation, and as they are of increasing magnitudes, individual transportation is becoming of growing importance.

THE FUTURE PATTERN OF URBAN GROWTH

Despite the general history of dispersal of population and employment, the forces of centralization are still vital and must be reckoned with, probably to a greater degree in the New York Metropolitan Region than in the other great urban centers of the country.

Although the decentralizing trend is plainly evident in manufacturing, even there it is selective. The newspaper printing plant, the small or newly born enterprise able to afford only rented quarters, the fabrication of certain consumer items, and certain other categories of industrial activity still appear to have a legitimate home in the central core of the city. Wholesale marketing, business service activities, finance, insurance, executive management, professional service, and cultural activities show little tendency to seek the wide open spaces; and one of the most important observations to be made about the changing character of our metropolitan economy is the healthy growth rate displayed by these nonmanufacturing activities. We can expect their expansion approximately to compensate for the central area's loss of manufacturing.

Moreover, it is possible that we may see a re-evaluation of the advantages of living closer to the central urban core, at higher residential densities, as the median age of our population increases, as the typical household becomes smaller.

In any event, the metropolitan New York of the future will be subjected to both centralizing and decentralizing influences. A good working assumption is that the central-core area will not be less important than now, although there may be profound changes in its character, but that the increment of growth, in both jobs and population, will be accounted for largely by suburban expansion.

Consideration of the changes that have been taking place in the distribution of people and jobs entered into the estimates of population and of employment for future years made by the economists engaged in the New York Metropolitan Region Study. They made projections of the Region's employment and of its population for 1965, 1975 and 1985. Revised population projections, made by the same technicians after 1960 census data became available, are presented in Table 3.

Population

According to the revised estimates the Region's population will rise from

TABLE 3. CURRENT AND PROJECTED POPULATION
OF THE NEW YORK METROPOLITAN REGION
(in thousands)

	1960	1965	1975	1985
Entire region	16,139	17,180	19,700	22,170
New York City	7,782	7,750	7,640	7,625
Core total	8,171	8,090	7,860	7,740
Kings	2,627	2,600	2,500	2,450
New York	1,698	1,625	1,525	1,475
Queens	1,810	1,875	1,925	1,925
Bronx	1,425	1,400	1,350	1,350
Hudson	611	590	560	540
Inner-ring total	4,945	5,395	6,140	6,370
Nassau	1,300	1,400	1,500	1,550
Essex	924	940	960	950
Westchester	809	890	1,000	1,100
Bergen	780	920	1,100	1,200
Union	504	560	640	660
Passaic	407	435	460	485
Richmond	222	250	340	425
Outer-ring total	3,023	3,695	5,840	8,060
Fairfield	654	750	1,065	1,420
Suffolk	667	910	1,295	1,660
Middlesex	434	535	845	1,145
Monmouth	334	400	745	1,155
Morris	262	320	530	730
Orange	184	205	350	540
Dutchess	176	200	320	425
Somerset	144	170	315	550
Rockland	137	170	320	350
Putnam	32	35	55	85

15,092,000 in 1955 to 22,170,000 in 1985.[2] Over that 30-year period it is estimated that the core counties[3] will decline in population by 507,000, that the inner-ring counties[4] will increase by 1,971,000, and that the outer-ring counties[5] will increase by 5,614,000.

According to this projection, Manhattan, Brooklyn, the Bronx and Hudson counties will continue their decline, slowly but continuously, over this 30-year period. Queens will reach its maximum growth and population stability by 1975. All the inner-ring counties will continue to grow but will be nearly filled up by 1985.

The great growth potential, particularly in the third decade of growth, lies in the outer ring. By 1985 the core, the inner ring and the outer ring will each account for about a third of the Region's population. This will be strikingly different from the proportions they represented in 1955, particularly for the core, which then accounted for more than half, and for the outer ring, which accounted for less than a sixth. Clearly, there is no expectation that the trend toward *extensive* urban growth will slow down. In this prospect more than 80 per cent of the Region's developed area will be of a suburban character and more than half of the metropolitan population will be suburbanites.

Employment

A similar, though less drastic shift in the geographic distribution of regional employment is projected. The total of the Region's jobs is expected to increase from 6,402,600 in 1956 to 8,846,000 in

[2]The 22-county N.Y.–N.J.–Conn. Metropolitan Region.
[3]Core counties–New York, Bronx, Kings, Queens, Hudson.
[4]Inner-ring counties–Nassau, Richmond, Westchester, Bergen, Essex, Passaic, Union.
[5]Outer-ring counties–Dutchess, Orange, Putnam, Rockland, Suffolk, Middlesex, Monmouth, Morris, Somerset, Fairfield.

1985 (Table 4). It is estimated that New York City's job opportunities will increase moderately, but by 1985 it will provide but about 48 per cent of the Region's employment, compared with its 61 per cent share in 1956. At the other end of the scale, the outer-ring counties, which accounted for 12 per cent in 1956, will be providing 23 per cent of the Metropolitan Region's jobs in 1985. The inner-ring counties are expected to strengthen their position slightly, from 23 per cent to 26 per cent.

TABLE 4. TOTAL EMPLOYMENT IN NEW YORK METROPOLITAN REGION
(in thousands)

	1956	1985
Entire Region	6,402.6	8,846.0
New York City	3,894.8	4,240.2
Essex	402.1	428.3
Westchester	216.9	377.6
Bergen	208.1	411.6
Fairfield	240.7	414.8
Nassau	274.2	457.8
Union	190.9	327.5
Passaic	161.4	277.8
Hudson	279.2	287.9
Middlesex	130.8	334.7
Suffolk	105.6	375.2
Monmouth	66.1	231.8
Morris	58.1	179.7
Dutchess	53.6	132.9
Somerset	35.3	131.3
Orange	49.6	132.9
Rockland	29.7	86.5
Putnam	5.5	17.5

The prospect for job distribution is plainly also one of dispersal; the counties outside the traditional employment centers of New York City and Essex and Hudson counties in New Jersey will increase their share of the Region's employment from some 29 per cent to about 44 per cent.

Central Business District Employment

No projection of employment in Manhattan's Central Business District has been made for the New York Metropolitan Region Study. The expectation in that study, however, is for an increase in jobs in New York City in the business and professional services and the finance and real estate categories of about 375,000. The major part of this growth will probably occur in Manhattan. The unknown quantity is the probable extent of the decline in manufacturing employment and in jobs in other categories which may transfer sites of operations to some other New York City borough.

A study of employment distribution in New York City, published in May 1961 by the New York City Planning Department, shows that the number of jobs in Manhattan's Central Business District declined by about 242,000, or 10.6 per cent, between 1950 and 1958. During that period significant gains were registered in all other parts of the city, including the non-Central Business District portions of Manhattan. For the city as a whole, the level of employment in the eight-year period was virtually stable.

This 1950–1958 decline in Manhattan's employment is consistent with the travel survey reported in the Regional Plan Association's Bulletin No. 91, "Hub-Bound Travel." In the eight-year interval 1948 to 1956 the number of persons entering Manhattan's Central Business District between 7 and 10 o'clock in the morning, by all means of transportation, from all quadrants, decreased by about 9 per cent. It is true, of course, that the number traveling between 7 and 10 a.m. cannot be equated with the number of workers. Also, with department store openings at a somewhat earlier hour, the figures for 1948 may have included more shoppers than the figures for 1956. It is even possible that

the change implies that a larger proportion of Central Business District jobs is now held by workers who do not have to enter the district at all, because they live there. But the magnitude of the decline, some 146,000, seems large enough to warrant the inference that there has been a decline in the number employed in Manhattan south of Central Park.

In any event, there is but a small range between the probable maximum and the probable minimum of Manhattan Central Business District employment in the years that lie ahead. Future magnitudes are not likely to be greatly different from those of today.

Suburban Employment

By far the largest proportion of the Region's employment increase will be accounted for by the outlying and suburban areas. Thus, the outlying areas will account for most of the Region's growth, both in residential population and in economic activity. As there is no reason to expect any reversal of the trend toward land development at a low density, we must expect a vast increase in the Region's urbanized area. If the land requirement for each additional million of population is no larger than it was during 1940 to 1954, the projected population increase of 8,600,000 for the 30-year period, 1955 to 1985, will entail the conversion of 1,600 square miles of open land to urban uses. Wide dispersal of all new foci of urban activity will yield a metropolis strikingly different in configuration from the urban region in the past. The urban fabric will be thin over most of the Metropolitan Area.

The whole pattern of living will be deeply influenced by the prospective changes in the way the Region's land is developed, by the dispersal of residences, places of employment and economic activity. It will be characterized by even more mobility than that observed today. Because of lower land-use density, points of origin and destination will be farther apart. Orientation of urban life toward the central core of the metropolis will become relatively weaker, while intersuburban relations will be stronger.

There will be a great increase in homes and jobs outside the high-density urban core. Some of the residents of the new areas will, to be sure, have their employment in Manhattan's Central Business District; others will find jobs in their own or in other outlying counties. Some of the new jobs in suburban areas will be filled by workers living in the metropolis' central core, who will travel *outward* going to work, and *inward* going home.

The linkages between points of origin and destination of travel will form a far more complex pattern than we have known heretofore. Travel paths will multiply in number, although the intensity of use of the new paths may be moderate.

CHANGING MANHATTAN

There may be changes of some importance in the pattern of work trips to Manhattan's Central Business District brought about by the redistribution there of business locations. That district is large, five miles long from the Battery to Central Park and two miles wide at its midpoint, and the several major subareas of job concentration are not equally accessible to all the present and prospective residential neighborhoods of the Region.

The years following World War II have seen a striking program of office building construction in the midtown area, largely east of Fifth Avenue, and north of 42nd Street, which has significantly shifted the geographic distribution of employment within the CBD. Owing to the configura-

tion of the commuter railroads and the rapid transit lines, the new concentrations are less favorably located with respect to residential areas west of the Hudson River than are the older centers of economic activity near the southern tip of Manhattan, while workers living in Brooklyn, Queens and other Long Island counties, or in the Bronx and in the counties to the north have found the new employment centers more accessible. Perhaps an important factor in the decline in usage of the New Jersey commuter railroads in recent years, in contrast to the relative stability in the patronage of the commuter lines from Long Island and from Westchester and Fairfield counties, has been this northeasterly shift in the location of CBD work places.

It is not possible to foresee the location of the new Manhattan office buildings to be constructed over the next 20 years. If the midtown boom continues, particularly if it continues to favor the East Side, while the total of CBD employment remains approximately the same, the depressing effect on work-travel linkage with New Jersey residential areas will persist, while the linkages with the Bronx and Westchester and Fairfield counties will continue to strengthen. On the other hand, there are some signs that large-scale commercial development may be getting under way in downtown Manhattan. If it should bring about a rise in the number of downtown job opportunities, or if new midtown development should take place within easy reach of the Sixth Avenue line of the Hudson Tubes, there will be a stimulus to work-travel from New Jersey.

FUTURE TRAVEL BEHAVIOR

Low-density residential development by itself implies a high rate of automobile ownership, and the number of automobiles in the Region will increase faster than population. Suburb-to-suburb travel, largely by automobile, already important on both sides of the Hudson River, will increase markedly as the new outlying employment centers draw on the work force living in the new suburban neighborhoods. As the speed and ease of travel improve, trips tend to lengthen, and accordingly the journey-to-work trip is likely to become longer. Within his travel time tolerance the worker will have a greater radius of coverage, within which he can choose a home location to fit his tastes and his pocketbook. As total trip mileage, particularly during peak hours, is the determinant of the total amount of route capacity required, the need for travel facilities will increase faster than population and employment.

An increase is also to be expected in the volume of work-bound travel in a reverse direction, between a home in the central core of the metropolis and a work place in the outskirts. New Jersey employment, for instance, will present more opportunities for Manhattan and Bronx residents. This component of metropolitan travel will be strong if the residents of the central core neighborhoods are unsuited, by limited education, low skill level or other handicap, for employment in the headquarters type of activity foreseen for the Central Business District.

Clearly, this work-travel pattern will be far different from the historic pattern comprised principally of a morning flow inward from the outer residential areas to a central focus of economic activity and a corresponding reverse flow in the evening.

Trips undertaken on business days for purposes other than work travel — for shopping and entertainment, for example — will also be influenced by the new metropolitan make-up. The likelihood is that the number of travel trips in both these purpose categories will be about in proportion to future population, but in increasing degree they will be trips between home and neighborhood shopping center or home and neighborhood theater, and less and less oriented toward the primary or even the secondary centers of metropolitan activity. These trips also will become longer as travel facility improves, and total trip mileage for these purposes, too, will increase faster than population. It is not likely, however, that this component of metropolitan travel will represent a controlling magnitude for facility planning.

More important for planning is the travel that will take place on week ends and holidays. It has its own characteristics, different from those of work travel, or shopping or entertainment travel. In total magnitude it has grown strikingly in recent years, as travel opportunities have enlarged and the amount of leisure time has increased. The timetable of its demand on travel facilities reflects the seasons and the weather. Demand is heaviest in the spring and summer months, when travel is oriented toward the outdoor recreation areas. Peak volumes occur on the more prominent annual holidays, Independence Day, Labor Day and Christmas. Although there is considerable anticipation of the week-end holiday by departures on Friday afternoons, which adds to the normal afternoon home-from-work travel peaks, maximum volumes are most frequently encountered on fair, warm Sunday afternoons and evenings. Moreover, leisure-time travel is typically family travel and is dominantly by automobile.

The amount of leisure time available in the future is likely to increase, as it has increased steadily in the past, but the form that the increase will take is not yet clear. Some have spoken of a four-day work week, with three-day week ends. Others foresee shorter working days instead. Still others think that there will be more frequent holidays and longer vacations, while the five-day week and the eight-hour day continue in force. There is little challenge to the view, however, that the total number of hours worked during the year will come down and leisure hours will go up. It is to be expected, therefore, that the leisure-time component of the region's annual travel mileage will assume even greater proportions in the future.

The prospects for changes in population and employment magnitudes and in the configuration of the metropolitan region and for the impacts of those changes on metropolitan transportation are in large part continuations of the trends of recent metropolitan history. Increases in population in the past few decades have been accommodated in outlying areas, in neighborhoods developed at low density. Industry has become more and more suburbanized, as have the goods-handling phases of wholesale merchandising and much of the region's retailing. New jobs have been as dispersed as new homes. And the transportation impacts have already been experienced.

Accommodating Future Travel

The role of transportation facilities in serving the regional travel pattern of the future is reasonably clear. The pattern of regional travel is becoming more diffuse, less distinct. More points of origin are becoming linked with more points of destination, but the links do not form any continuous linear arrangement. Travel paths are growing in number, and channelization is being eroded by dispersal. The opportunities for group travel diminish, the demands for individual travel increase. The role of mass transportation

is more and more limited to serving the rush-hour travel to and from the Central Business District. An ever more extensive network of highways is needed to accommodate regional travel demands. The costs may easily strain the capacities of state and local finance.

Is there any alternative prospect? Is there any way that public policy can intervene so as to make the task of accommodating regional travel less difficult and less costly? Can more opportunities for group riding be created and the demand for individual travel be held in check?

Just as the travel trends of the recent past have been the consequences of the evolving metropolitan composition, the transportation tasks of the future will be determined by the evolving form and structure of the region. If public policy is to intervene it must find appropriate ways to influence the metropolitan growth pattern.

The technological factors influencing the location of industry and other goods-handling activities are too deeply rooted and too strong to be challenged head-on. Population growth, also, is unquestionably going to take place predominantly in the suburban counties, for the simple reason that the land in the older, more central areas is all filled up; even redevelopment, desirable as it is, is not likely to endow these areas with more residents. Retail activity, save specialty and high-quality merchandising, will follow the population, especially the higher-income population. Decentralization is not to be turned back.

The Challenge to Planning

But decentralization does not need to become sheer scatter. If the future suburban landscape is to be peppered with homes, factories, warehouses and stores without spatial organization of any sort, with no particular concentrations of work places or residences, we can expect that there will be little usage of mass transportation. There will be few strong travel-generating points, and the many travel routes will each be used so thinly that individual transportation will be the only kind practicable. If new work sites should be clustered, however, there would be the possibility that at least a few routes would build up enough traffic density, from residence area to employment area, to warrant the establishment of bus service. Employment clusters may have to be large enough to account for 5,000 to 10,000 workers, which means industrial parks instead of scattered factories, to make bus transportation practicable for the journey to work. If residential areas are also more distinct, if they form clear clusters of homes, and if each cluster accommodates a large enough population in an area that is not too extensive, the opportunities for group travel will be further increased.

Perhaps such an ordering of the manner in which the newly urbanized land is to be used can be brought about by the utilization of the planning and land-use-control tools now available. Perhaps new tools will have to be devised. Perhaps new authority will have to be granted to planning bodies to permit them to be effective in such a task. The fact is that there is precious little experience today, and not even much theoretical doctrine, to guide metropolitan planning.

The transportation facilities we shall be building during the coming decade, particularly the interstate expressways, will themselves exert an influence on the Region's growth pattern. Interchange locations will tend to establish the areas in which new development can be expected. Although our understanding of the pre-

cise effects of new highways on land development is less than we should like, there is no doubt that highway planning can be used to some extent to guide metropolitan growth. It is imperative that highway planners and land-use planners learn more about how the tool can be used and that they collaborate in using it to the maximum of its potentialities.

The Point of Diminishing Returns

But we must nevertheless speculate on the consequences of an inability to provide a transportation plant that would give maximum mobility to an unpatterned expanse of urban settlement. What happens if all the highways deemed necessary cannot be built? Certainly, at times of peak demand, say, during the journey-to-work hours, travel will be slower, more congested and probably more costly than it would be if facilities were more ample. But what ultimate values are involved?

The principal dimensions of travel facility are time and cost. Convenience, too, is important but in the last analysis it is made up largely of time factors, compounded with certain intangible elements such as annoyance or discomfort. Each traveler has his own limit of tolerance as to how much time he is willing to spend in going to work and how much he is willing to pay for the journey. But when thousands and thousands of workers are taken into account, there is an average, a median or some other measure of typical behavior that can be observed.

It is known that when travel speeds are high and costs are low, travel trips are typically longer than when speeds are low and costs are high. When travel facility improves, trips lengthen. Thus, independent of any increase in the *number* of trips, total trip mileage is greater when travel is made easier, faster and cheaper. Total vehicle mileage rises and, consequently, more lane-miles are necessary to accommodate it. Trip frequency is also increased by increased travel ease and adds to the demand for highway space. These are the factors that underlie the often observed phenomenon of a new high-grade highway facility being "prematurely" used to its capacity.

Conversely, when travel is impeded, trips are shorter. With specific reference to the journey to work, workers do not live so far from their jobs. Travel to the more distant destinations is less frequent. When the worker's travel orbit is restricted, his breadth of choice as to where he will live in relation to where he will work is curtailed. If his work place is fixed, there are fewer neighborhoods among which he can choose in seeking a home in keeping with his tastes and his pocketbook. If his home is already established, there is a limited number of employers who can compete for his services. The employer, similarly, is limited as to the areas from which he can hope to enlist his employees. Clearly, employer and worker are best off in this regard when travel facility is at its highest.

There is a point of diminishing returns to this, however. If the worker's opportunities to choose among a number of residential neighborhoods are already fairly great, or if the reachable market for his services is already fairly broad, there comes a point at which the cost to the community of further broadening his areas of choice is greater than the value he will derive from it. Free flow of travel at high speeds at all times in urban areas can be extravagance. For example, transportation facilities that would make it possible for a resident of Plainfield to travel to work every day to a job in White Plains and to spend no more than 45 minutes on the trip may be a luxury the region cannot afford.

The final consequence, therefore, of a restricted highway network is a restriction on the choices individuals may make as to where they will live, work, shop or seek recreation. Extending the areas of those choices creates a value shared by all, but may cost more than it is worth. There is no neat calculus available to us by which we can compute this point of diminishing returns in facilitating travel. It may be that the speeds attainable today at the peak hour on our transportation network approximate those that would be yielded by economic calculation. If that be so, our goal for the future should be the maintenance of the present level of travel ease and the prevention of its impairment as total travel volumes rise with the growth of population and employment. Such a goal will itself make no small demands on our resourcefulness as well as on our resources.

CHAPTER 20

MASS TRANSPORTATION AND THE AUTOMOBILE

For about half its history, New York had no common-carrier passenger transportation. The first horse-drawn omnibus service was introduced around 1830, on Broadway, by Humphrey Phelps, providing transportation between Bowling Green and Bleecker Street. Lossing, in his *History of New York City* remarks:

"The hint was instantly acted upon, and when the system was fairly inaugurated there were three rival lines, and Phelps left the field to his competitors. Before the advent of these vehicles, citizens who could not afford to own a coach depended on their own natural powers of locomotion.

"The omnibuses were few in number. They were finely decorated, and bore the names of distinguished American citizens emblazoned on their sides. There was the 'Lady Washington,' the 'Lady Clinton,' the 'George Washington,' the 'De Witt Clinton,' the 'Benjamin Franklin,' the 'Thomas Jefferson,' etc. These vehicles were drawn by four matched horses.

"Very soon a fourth line of omnibuses was established by Asa Hall, a hatter on Dey Street, which started from the corner of Pine and Nassau Streets, went up Broadway to Canal Street, thence to Hudson Street, and by the green fields and gardens until it reached the village of Greenwich, the terminus of the route being (present) Charles Street. The fare was 25 cents each. This afterward famous Greenwich Line of stages Hall sold to two enterprising young men, Messrs. Kip and Brown. They made money rapidly. Kip became the soul of enterprise and good

deeds in Greenwich Village. The business of the route was finally ruined by the building of the Eighth Avenue Rail Road. Kip lost his fortune in litigation with the huge monopoly, and died poor."

Technological change made public transportation of passengers a risky business even a century ago.

COMMON CARRIER TRANSPORT IN 1960

Since those early days both private and public transportation facilities in the New York area have been developed extensively. The private coach and "natural powers of locomotion" have been succeeded by the high-power, all-weather automobile, owned by about three-fourths of the region's families, and the omnibus has been succeeded by the motor bus, the subway and the commuter railroad.

In 1962 there are the New York City subway system and the Hudson & Manhattan Railroad, electrified rapid transit rail lines. (The H & M Railroad on September 1, 1962, was acquired by the Port Authority Trans-Hudson Corporation, a subsidiary of The Port of New York Authority and was redesignated the Port Authority Trans-Hudson system, abbreviated PATH.) There are the electrified and the diesel-powered railroads providing for both regional and interregional travel; the suburban bus lines, linking the suburbs to each other and to Manhattan's Central Business District; and the local bus lines, in New York City and in other urban and suburban portions of the Metropolitan Area, operating on city streets and providing for short-distance travel. Until recently there were trolley coaches in certain sections of New York City, and there were even a few electric streetcars still operating. Finally, there are the taxicab and the traveler's own automobile operating on the extensive system of highways and streets.

From among these different modes of transport the regional traveler makes his choice, trip by trip, on the basis of the locations of trip origin and trip destination, purpose of travel, time of travel, cost of travel, and many other factors.

The Rapid Transit Lines

The most important passenger carrier in the Metropolitan Area is the New York City subway system, comprising 237 route miles of electric-railway rapid transit in Manhattan, the Bronx, Brooklyn and Queens. Currently the system has an average daily patronage of 3,666,000. In 1960 the system accommodated 1,345,000,000 revenue passenger trips. Although there have been modest upturns recently, there was a mild but steady decline in the system's usage over a number of recent years, following the more drastic drops that followed the fare increases of 1948

TABLE 1. NEW YORK CITY TRANSIT
AUTHORITY RAPID TRANSIT LINES
ANNUAL REVENUE PASSENGERS[a]

(millions)

1953	1,552
1954	1,416
1955	1,378
1956	1,363
1957	1,355
1958	1,319
1959	1,324
1960	1,345
1961	1,363

[a]Year ending June 30.
[1]See Chapter 19.

and 1953, as is indicated in Table 1.

The PATH system, an interstate rapid transit line, is of strategic importance in linking together the New Jersey and the New York sectors of the metropolitan region. With 8.5 route miles of electric railway, it provides local service between Manhattan, midtown as well as downtown, and the New Jersey Hudson River communities, Jersey City and Hoboken. Service as far west as Newark is provided by a joint service of PATH and the Pennsylvania Railroad. Most importantly, PATH gives an all-rail entry into Manhattan to the patrons of the Erie-Lackawanna Railroad from its terminal in Hoboken and downtown access to Pennsylvania Railroad passengers from the station at Newark. Under the present plans for the provision of a connection at Aldene and the routing of New Jersey Central passenger trains over the Pennsylvania Railroad's tracks to its station in Newark, PATH, from across the platform, will provide Jersey Central passengers an all-rail entry to Manhattan also.

Over the past 30 years the patronage of this system has also declined. First, usage of the system by residents of the New Jersey river-front communities, who at an earlier date traveled to the railroad's Jersey City and Hoboken terminals by local streetcar and bus, gave way to through bus service between the residential neighborhoods of those cities and Manhattan. Second, the declining usage of the commuter railroads has been reflected in a gradually diminishing patronage by transfer passengers. Third, the usage of the system has been affected by the over-all decline in the number of New Jersey residents who travel across the Hudson River to New York[1] on weekdays. The past few years have shown a slight upturn from the earlier trend, however, or at least a leveling out of the long decline.

The annual volumes of the system's revenue passengers are shown in Table 2.

TABLE 2. HUDSON & MANHATTAN RAILROAD
(PATH) ANNUAL REVENUE PASSENGERS

(millions)

	Total Interstate	Rail Transfer	Local	PATH-Penn Joint Service
1940	63.2	15.2	35.2	12.8
1950	49.3	12.8	26.8	9.7
1951	45.3	12.2	24.0	9.1
1952	38.7	10.6	19.8	8.3
1953	35.9	10.3	18.2	7.4
1954	34.9	10.3	17.7	6.9
1955	35.0	10.7	17.8	6.5
1956	34.8	11.1	17.4	6.3
1957	27.9	8.6	14.5	4.8
1958	28.9	9.0	15.1	4.8
1959	30.0	9.0	16.0	5.0
1960	30.1	9.0	16.4	4.7
1961	30.2	8.7	16.7	4.8

There are some nonstandard physical features of PATH which must be noted. The tunnels were built to dimensions which do not provide clearance for standard-size railroad or rapid-transit passenger coaches. The cars, therefore, are narrower than standard cars. Also several of the tunnel curves are far sharper than modern railroad design practice approves and consequently the cars are shorter than standard cars and their operating speed is less than it otherwise might be.

Nevertheless, even at its present level of usage, with some 55,000 passengers each way on a weekday, about 23,000 an hour in one direction during the peak periods, the system is an essential link in the metropolitan passenger transport network.

The Suburban Railroads

Seven electrified or diesel-powered railroads serve the suburban counties of the metropolitan area and provide access to New York City for both regional and interregional passengers. The Long Island Rail Road, serving the counties to the east, gives direct access to Manhattan at Pennsylvania Station, and to Brooklyn at its own terminal on Atlantic Avenue. The New York Central and the New Haven, serving the northerly sector, give direct access to Manhattan at Grand Central Station. Of the rail lines serving the New Jersey sector, only the Pennsylvania provides a continuous ride into a Manhattan terminal, Pennsylvania Station. The others, the Jersey Central, the Erie-Lackawanna and the Susquehanna, transport their passengers to terminals at the Hudson River where transfers are made to the PATH system, to trans-Hudson ferries or to buses which reach Manhattan via the Lincoln Tunnel.

The railroads serving the eastern and the northern suburban counties have experienced a slowly declining trend in patronage during the past decade, as indicated in Table 3. The New Jersey railroads, on the other hand, have lost passengers sharply and steadily since 1943, a wartime peak year. While there are some current signs of a slackening of the sharp decline of the past decade, by 1961 their combined passenger volumes aggregated not much more than half the volumes of ten years earlier.

Unfortunately, data are not available to permit a separation to be made in Table 3 of regional from interregional or long-haul passengers. The distinction is not particularly important for the Long Island, because its area of service is wholly within the New York metropolitan complex, but the New York Central and the New Haven are interregional railroads and the passenger figures shown in the table include travelers between New York and Chicago, Buffalo, Boston and Providence, as well as those traveling to and

TABLE 3. ANNUAL RAILROAD PASSENGERS INTO AND OUT OF NEW YORK CITY

(in thousands)

	Long Island Sector	Westchester Sector	New Jersey Sector
1950	83,586	50,160	98,028
1951	79,190	50,606	92,850
1952	76,392	51,126	84,510
1953	79,245	51,031	79,062
1954	78,022	51,221	75,314
1955	76,427	52,081	72,468
1956	75,277	54,010	72,736
1957	73,930	51,487	66,302
1958	73,609	49,067	62,124
1959	73,935	46,403	57,292
1960	64,379	45,496	54,658
1961	69,102	42,028	53,813

from White Plains and Greenwich. The Pennsylvania Railroad, also, is an important long-haul passenger carrier. The nation-wide attrition of interregional rail travel and its replacement by air and bus travel is a factor in recent passenger volume history, but the data available do not permit the measurement of its effect.

Physical Characteristics of the Rail Facilities

Except for the gauge of tracks and the height of couplings there is little standardization of the physical characteristics of these rapid transit and railroad lines. The nonstandard character of PATH has already been remarked. The Jersey Central and the Erie are not electrified, their trains are powered by diesel locomotives. The Long Island Rail Road is electrified in part and in part diesel-powered. The electrified part is supplied with 600-volt direct current, delivered by third rail. The Pennsylvania is electrified but uses 11,000-volt alternating current delivered by overhead catenary. The Lackawanna, also electrified and using overhead power delivery, operates on

3,000-volt direct current. The New York Central, like the Long Island, operates on 600-volt direct current delivered by third rail, but one has the contact shoe riding on the top of the power rail and the other riding on the bottom. The New Haven uses 11,000-volt alternating current, with overhead power, but is equipped so as to operate on the New York Central's power sources in order to reach Grand Central Terminal. Other physical features as well vary.

Diesel-powered trains can operate on electrified trackage, of course, although they are barred by law from operating in Manhattan. A few opportunities for operational integration, therefore, exist. For example, Jersey Central trains can operate over Pennsylvania tracks to Newark. But physical integration among all railroads would involve huge investments for new physical connections, repowering and re-equipping.

Motor Bus Transport

The New York City Transit Authority, which operates the city's rapid transit system, also operates a number of bus routes in Manhattan, Brooklyn, Queens and Staten Island, aggregating 537 route miles. In 1961 those bus lines served 432,-000,000 revenue trips (Table 4). Currently, they have an average daily patronage of 1,208,000 riders. Usage of this service has been virtually stable since the last fare increase, with a modest upturn in 1960.

In addition to these Transit Authority operations there are a number of privately owned bus lines serving Manhattan, Queens and the Bronx, operating under city-granted franchises. Local-service bus lines also operate in the other metropolitan counties.

Suburban bus service linking Manhattan with the New Jersey metropolitan

TABLE 4. NEW YORK CITY TRANSIT AUTHORITY BUS AND TROLLEY COACH LINES ANNUAL REVENUE PASSENGERS[a]

(millions)

1953	547
1954	449
1955	419
1956	413
1957	415
1958	413
1959	417
1960	431
1961	432

[a]Year ending June 30.

TABLE 5. ANNUAL TRANS-HUDSON BUS PASSENGERS

(thousands)

1950	62,078
1951	65,214
1952	68,025
1953	67,106
1954	67,485
1955	67,532
1956	68,862
1957	75,173
1958	76,930
1959	81,882
1960	84,699

counties is a relative latecomer but now an important part of the region's passenger transport system. Companies using the Port Authority Bus Terminal in midtown Manhattan serve the New Jersey suburban areas, principally the riverfront and northerly counties, although the Manhattan-Newark service is also heavily patronized. In 1960 bus traffic across the Hudson River totaled 3,269,000, the preponderant proportion by these intraregional services. The number of suburban passengers using the Port Authority Bus Terminal on a typical business day in that year was about 75,000 each way. Bus passengers crossing the river via the George Washington Bridge, about 28,000 a day in each direction, are now accommodated in a new bus station at the Manhattan bridgehead.

The number of passengers patronizing these regional interstate bus services has grown steadily through the years. Table 5 shows the annual number of trans-Hudson passenger trips by bus from 1950 through 1960.

TRANSPORT TO THE CENTRAL BUSINESS DISTRICT

Travel behavior in the New York Met-

ropolitan Region is a complex mixture of trips taken by all the travel modes available, at different times of the day, or week, for many different purposes, and between a gigantic number of pairs of origin and destination points. Data are not available to permit expressing the total behavior in any quantitative way, such as the total number of trips taken or the total travel mileage in the course of a day, or of a week or year, for the region as a whole, or to break down the total between common-carrier and private transportation.

There are sufficient data at hand, however, to make possible analyses of the more important travel phenomena and to provide an understanding of how the region's people travel, to permit inferences as to why they travel as they do and to form reasonable judgments as to how they will travel in the future. We know, for example, a great deal about travel into Manhattan's Central Business District[2] and about travel across the Hudson River. We have data on railroad passengers and on the travelers who use the Port Authority Bus Terminal. There are also data available on New York City's transit system, and on vehicular traffic using the

[2]Regional Plan Association (RPA) Bulletin No. 99, "Hub-Bound Travel."

bridges and tunnels of the Triborough Bridge and Tunnel Authority.

The data are consistent in their showing that the usage of common-carrier transportation relative to the usage of the automobile varies widely with the travel circumstances. The relative usages on Saturdays, Sundays and holidays are quite different from those on weekdays. Rush-hour usage differs from off-hour usage. Travel focused on Manhattan's CBD differs from that not so focused. Inferentially, we learn that journey-to-work travel differs from travel having a social or recreational purpose.

Perhaps the most important magnitude for planning purposes is the number of trips bound for the CBD, particularly during the rush hours. The CBD has been defined as the area of Manhattan lying south of Central Park, modified on the east side to permit the inclusion of the approaches of the Queensboro Bridge and all the East River subway tunnels.

The Regional Plan Association's survey of travel counted the number of travelers entering Manhattan's CBD in 24 hours on a weekday, including those entering it to pass through to a farther destination. (An unknown proportion entering via the Queensboro Bridge turned north and passed through the 60th Street cordon a block or so away.) It included also those residents of New York's CBD who work outside it, say in New Jersey, and who entered it when returning home from work during the afternoon rush hours. Moreover, a New Jersey resident traveling to a job, say, in Queens, whose travel path carried him through the CBD, was counted twice, once in the morning when he crossed the Hudson and again in the evening when he crossed the East River on his way home. Consequently, the number of travelers reported as *entering* the CBD is greater than the num-

ber who were destined for it. Trans-Hudson trips made via the George Washington Bridge were not counted, as that crossing does not give direct access to the CBD. Travelers using that facility bound for the CBD were counted as coming from the north and credited to the mode of transportation they used in crossing the 60th Street cordon.

The travel volumes observed in the survey, therefore, are not measures of *CBD-destined* trips. Nevertheless, the survey provides a valuable insight into the nature of a vitally important component of metropolitan travel.

Travel to and from Manhattan's CBD has always been strongly dominated by common-carrier transportation. In 1960, only 866,000 of the 3,349,000 people who entered the district on a weekday, or 25.9 per cent, entered by private automobile or by taxicab.

This proportion varied somewhat over the four quarters of the compass. Those entering by automobile or taxicab accounted for 31.2 per cent of those coming from the north, 21.4 per cent of those from the east, 28.4 per cent of those coming across the Hudson, and 10.2 per cent of those from Staten Island. More than half of all the automobile and taxi riders came from the north, down Manhattan's avenues, the West Side Highway and the East River Drive.

Nearly two-thirds of the travelers entering the CBD, 2,116,000, came by rail, including the New York City subway lines, the Hudson & Manhattan Railroad and the commuter railroads. (Of this last category, 21,000 of the 97,000 rail and rapid transit passengers coming from New Jersey crossed the Hudson by ferry and 76,000 by rail tunnel.)

The number entering the CBD, by mode of travel from the four quarters of the compass, on a typical business day in

TABLE 6. PERSONS ENTERING MANHATTAN'S CBD
ON A TYPICAL BUSINESS DAY IN 1960

(in thousands)

	Total	From North	From East	From South	From West
By all modes	3,349[a]	1,441	1,563	39	306
By rapid transit	1,913	760	1,098	—	55
By commuter railroad	203	81	80	—	42
By bus	243	116	26	—	101
By ferry[b]	36	—	—	35	1
By auto and taxi	866	450	325	4	87

[a]Includes 88,000 who entered driving or riding in trucks.
[b]Nonrailroad passengers.

1960, is presented in detail in Table 6.

During the going-to-work hours, even more reliance was placed on common-carrier transportation for these trips. Automobile usage, which was 25.9 per cent for the 24-hour total, was only 12.5 per cent between 7 and 10 A.M. Railroad and rapid transit passengers accounted for 78.5 per cent during that period, in contrast to the 63 per cent of the daily total. Bus passengers, ferry riders (mostly from Staten Island), and those driving or riding in motor trucks made up the remaining 9 per cent.

The number of passengers entering the CBD during the rush hours, analyzed as to sector, route and mode, is presented in Table 7 which is comparable in form to Table 6.

There were no great differences among the various sectors of the region in their degrees of reliance on private transportation for going to the CBD during the rush hours. From Upper Manhattan, the Bronx, Westchester County and Connecticut, automobile and taxicab riders accounted for 15.5 per cent, from Brooklyn, Queens and the rest of Long Island 10.7

TABLE 7. PERSONS ENTERING MANHATTAN'S CBD
BETWEEN 7 AND 10 A.M.
ON A TYPICAL BUSINESS DAY IN 1960

(in thousands)

	Total	From North	From East	From South	From West
By all modes	1,627[a]	632	833	25	137
By rapid transit	1,133	428	670	—	35
By commuter railroad	143	60	57	—	26
By bus	101	40	8	—	53
By ferry[b]	25	—	—	24	1
By auto and taxi	204	98	89	1	16

[a]Includes 21,000 who entered driving or riding in trucks.
[b]Nonrailroad passengers.

per cent, and from New Jersey 11.7 per cent. From Staten Island, only 4 per cent of the rush-hour travelers used private transportation, understandable in view of the limited transport accommodations available for private vehicles.

There was a wider difference, however, among the sectors when their relative usages of the different forms of common-carrier transportation are considered. Railroad and rapid transit riders accounted for 72.5 per cent of those from the north, nearly 87 per cent of those from the east, but only 44 per cent of those from New Jersey. New Jersey travelers made much heavier use of bus transportation, which accounted for 39 per cent of their hub-bound rush-hour trips.

TRAVEL ACROSS THE HUDSON RIVER

Data providing information as to destinations and covering a wider geographic scope are available for that component of metropolitan travel which crosses the Hudson River. On a typical business day in 1960, a total of 398,000 people crossed the river, eastbound.[3] Of this number, 184,000, or 46 per cent, were New Jersey residents destined for Manhattan's CBD. They used automobiles, buses, railroads and rapid transit lines much as is shown in the last column of Table 6. But those not bound for the CBD used the various travel modes in quite different proportions.

For the entire 24-hour period, 93,100 eastbound but non-CBD-bound New Jersey residents crossed the Hudson River: ferry, railroad and rapid transit passengers accounted for 13 per cent, bus passengers for 20 per cent, and automobile

[3]Eastbound trans-Hudson travelers were not all residents of New Jersey. About 29 per cent were New York residents, including those returning home during the afternoon rush hours from New Jersey jobs. For the day as a whole, the number crossing the river westbound closely approximated the number traveling eastbound.

drivers and passengers for 67 per cent. Common-carrier travel had a relatively weak position, for these trips had destinations widely dispersed over the New York side of the region, their origins were just as widely dispersed over the New Jersey counties, and but few of the common-carrier routes conform to the great number of travel-desire lines represented.

Of non-CBD-bound New Jersey residents crossing the river eastbound during the morning rush hours, 40,900 between 7 and 10 A.M., presumably going to work places outside the CBD, 74 per cent traveled by automobile and 26 per cent by common carrier. Table 8 gives the number of New Jersey–resident trans-Hudson travelers bound for non-CBD points on a business day in 1960, for the 24 hours and for the morning rush hours, and the modes of travel used.

TABLE 8. NEW JERSEY–RESIDENT TRANS-HUDSON TRAVELERS TO POINTS OTHER THAN TO MANHATTAN'S CBD ON A TYPICAL BUSINESS DAY IN 1960

(in thousands)

	24-Hour Total	7 A.M. to 10 A.M.
By all modes	93.1	40.9
By rapid transit, commuter railroad and ferry	11.9	5.0
By bus	18.6	5.7
By auto and taxi	62.6	30.2

The data presented so far on travel behavior deal with travel on weekdays. Travel on week ends and holidays has its own characteristics. Leisure-time purposes control the timing of travel and the mode of travel utilized. The CBD is far less important as a destination and the work-day timetable does not control the travel schedule.

Trans-Hudson data show that travel on

Saturdays, Sundays and holidays is heavily dominated by the automobile. In 1960, 72 per cent of the total trans-Hudson trips in this component of regional travel were by automobile and 28 per cent by common carrier. The common-carrier portion was shared one-fifth by the railroads and rail rapid transit and four-fifths by the bus lines.

Peaking Characteristics of Travel by Various Modes

Travel data available can be considered from another point of view, that of the variation in demand at different hours of the day. In view of the heavy fixed costs of the common carriers and their commitments to their employees, a relatively uniform demand on their services throughout the day, and the week, would be desirable. But this they do not have.

Common-carrier travel is highly concentrated in the rush hours. Table 9, constructed from the data in the Regional Plan Association's report on its 1960 survey of CBD-bound passengers, shows how highly concentrated the patronage of the common carriers is in the going-to-work hours. The survey showed that more than half of the 24-hour total of common-carrier travel to the CBD was concentrated in the three rush hours, 7 to 10 A.M.

The weekday rapid transit and railroad travel to the CBD in 1960 was concentrated to the extent of 60 to 74 per cent of the daily total in the three morning rush hours. It is to be observed that there was not much difference in this peaking feature among the four quadrants of the region — north, east, south and west.

The buses enjoyed a somewhat more even distribution of demand, with the three morning rush hours representing about 40 per cent of the one-direction 24-hour total. The more pronounced peaking of the bus travel from New Jersey, when compared with the CBD-bound bus travel from the north and east, reflects the heavy usage of buses by New Jersey commuters.

In evaluating the percentage figures in Table 9, it may be helpful to note that the three hours 7 to 10 A.M. account for one-eighth, or 12.5 per cent, of the day's hours, and that where the table shows that 74.0 per cent of the day's railroad patrons from the north traveled during those three hours, it means that the rush-hour rate was about six times the average rate for the day (74.0 divided by 12.5).

In contrast, automobile travel was much more uniformly distributed throughout the day. The greatest degree of load steadiness was displayed by automobile travelers from New Jersey, with a three–

Table 9. Proportion of 24-Hour Travel to CBD Accounted for by Travel Between 7 and 10 A.M.

(per cent of total)

	Total CBD	From North	From East	From South	From West – N. J.
By all modes	48.5	43.9	53.1	64.0	45.0
By rapid transit	59.2	56.5	61.0	—	63.5
By railroad	73.0	74.0	71.2	—	62.0
By bus	41.6	34.4	30.7	—	57.5
By ferry	69.5	—	—	68.5	100.0
By auto and taxi	23.6	21.8	27.4	25.0	18.4

rush-hour volume only 18.4 per cent of the 24-hour total, which means a peak rate about 47 per cent greater than the 24-hour average.

Automobile travelers to the CBD from all directions in 1960 were fairly evenly distributed throughout the day, with the three–rush-hour volume accounting for 23.6 per cent of the day's total.

The Port Authority's data on trans-Hudson travel are consistent with these findings. Eastbound travel, to all destinations, in 1960 had 62 per cent of its railroad and ferry trips and 52.5 per cent of its bus trips concentrated in the three going-to-work hours, 7 to 10 A.M. Of automobile travelers on all three trans-Hudson vehicular crossings, however, only 21.6 per cent of the daily total were accounted for by travel during those hours.

Trans-Hudson travel data show also that railroad and rapid transit travel peak somewhat more sharply than bus travel. In 1960, of the eastbound railroad and rapid transit passengers bound for the CBD during the course of the day, 62 per cent and 63 per cent, respectively, traveled between 7 and 10 A.M.; the CBD-bound bus passengers were concentrated to the extent of 52 per cent during those peak hours.

PEAK-HOUR CAPACITIES OF THE DIFFERENT MODES

The different forms of ground transportation — railroad, rapid transit, bus and automobile — can also be considered in terms of their respective capacities to move people, in equivalent space provisions. A modern highway lane for automobiles or buses and a railroad track take about the same amount of trunk-line space.

On an important city street, like Seventh or Eighth Avenue, with traffic controlled at intersections by signals dividing time between two directions, a single roadway lane can accommodate about 750 automobiles an hour, or about 1,300 persons an hour at an average loading of 1.75 persons per automobile. If progressive signal control is used the capacity is somewhat increased. When grades are separated at intersections, so that signal control is not necessary, capacity rises to about 1,500 vehicles, or about 2,600 persons, an hour. With a still more advanced type of highway design, a limited access highway with a median strip separating opposing traffic flows, capacity increases to some 1,800 vehicles, or 3,200 persons, an hour per lane. (In California, drivers on the freeways follow each other more closely than in the East, up to about 2,200 vehicles an hour per lane.) A six-lane expressway, therefore, can provide capacity for some 10,000 persons per hour in each direction in automobiles.

The capacity of a street or highway to accommodate passengers in buses has been the subject of claims and counterclaims. When buses are operating on busy city streets, with traffic signals at all intersections, lane capacities are low. There is no instance in the New York region of a solid traffic lane of buses on city streets, but it is likely that such a lane might be able to handle as many as 150 to 175 buses an hour, assuming buses operating in pairs, or 7,500 to 8,500 passengers an hour at 50 passengers per bus. At the Lincoln Tunnel and its New Jersey approaches, on the other hand, where traffic flow is not interrupted by intersections, impeded by the lateral entry of other traffic, or required to stop to load or discharge passengers, a single lane has accommodated more than 400 buses, or 20,000 passengers an hour, together with several hundred automobiles. Bus traffic observations lead to the view that the trunk-line capacity of one lane of an expressway, if allocated exclusively to buses, would easily exceed 600 buses, or 30,000 passengers, an hour.

At these traffic volumes, however, 400 to 600 buses an hour, capacity limitations are set by station stops and terminals and by operating methods rather than by the trunk-line highway lanes. The geometric design of station stops and terminals and the manner of operation of buses to achieve maximum capacity is an area of study which has had an inadequate amount of attention. Owing to the fact that the units are customarily operated singly, carrying capacity per trunk-line lane may be determined by the length of time a unit must devote to receiving and discharging passengers at a lane-side highway stop. If stops are to be made on the expressway and if the stop time required is 30 seconds, the number of buses that can be accommodated at such a stop is 120 an hour, irrespective of what the trunk-line headway could be. If buses operate on a skip-stop basis, the number that can pass a given point on the trunk line in an hour is increased. If instead of being operated singly, buses are operated in platoons, still greater capacity figures result. If station stops have more than one platform lane, capacity is again modified.

The various methods of bus operation will yield varying values as to passenger-carrying capacity and quality of transport service. Systematic exploration of the potentiality of bus transportation on expressways to handle large volumes of travel is an urgent need.

Rail transportation, commuter railroad or rapid transit, steam, diesel or electric-powered, has a still higher capacity to move people. An exclusive right-of-way obviates interferences from other traffic. Train operation puts a number of vehicles under single control and capacity can

easily be raised by increasing the number of cars in a train; the limitation on the number of cars in a train is the length of the station platforms. While the safe headway between automobiles may be two to three seconds, and that between buses four to six seconds, the safe headway between rapid transit trains must be somewhere between one and a half and two minutes. Block signaling does not permit any closer operation. But even at that, 30 trains an hour can operate on one track if necessary, as is demonstrated by operations of the New York subway system. At 10 cars per train this means 300 cars an hour, and if each car is crowded with standees, up to 200 passengers per car, 60,000 passengers an hour can be accommodated. With longer trains and longer platforms to match, the capacity can be further increased.

On a seated load basis, the capacity of one track of a commuter rail line is less. With 120 seats per car, as on the Long Island Rail Road, and with a 12-car train, each train can carry 1,440 passengers, and if traffic demand were great enough to demand a two-minute headway on one track, its capacity would be 43,200 passengers an hour. Longer trains would provide capacities in proportion to the number of cars. No commuter rail service in the New York area, or in the United States for that matter, comes anywhere near this one-track demand level. Long before traffic volumes like these would be reached, it is probable that terminal capacities rather than track capacities would become controlling.

But the various forms of transportation are not to be rated by comparing their peak-hour capacities. If the number of passengers to be accommodated per hour is 6,000, a capacity of 60,000 passengers an hour is a virtue without value. To build high-capacity facilities when the travel volumes to be anticipated can be accommodated adequately and economically by less costly means would be an extravagance. Each form of transportation is best suited for a range of traffic densities, from a low level well suited to automobile transport, through an intermediate volume range suitable for bus service, to high levels of traffic density which can be accommodated most effectively by rail transportation.

STRENGTHS AND WEAKNESSES OF THE DIFFERENT MODES OF TRANSPORT

Rail transportation, whether commuter railroad or rapid transit, is unsurpassed in passenger-carrying capacity relative to space requirements. Because of its exclusive use of the right-of-way and the great amount of power that can be utilized effectively, its speed can be high, and during the twice-daily peak-demand periods it is normally free from slowdowns due to congestion. Relative immunity to inclement weather gives it high dependability. The rider is free of responsibility for its operation and he can utilize his travel time for such sedentary activities as his tastes dictate. Operating costs per passenger mile are low when capacity is fully utilized; a few men suffice to operate a train carrying a thousand or more passengers. It is possible that technological developments in the future may permit a more automated train operation with a reduced crew.

There are countervailing drawbacks, however. Once established, a rail transportation route is set in location, and there is little opportunity to adjust to changes in metropolitan settlement patterns or employment distribution. Fixed charges account for a large part of the total costs and, while expanding traffic can be accommodated with little added expense,

declining traffic and declining revenue are not accompanied by any appreciable expense reduction. A high level of traffic along a given route is necessary to justify the high investment.

Bus transportation has its own strengths and weaknesses. Traversing the highway network, the bus can provide service to areas remote from the rail routes. Furthermore, should changes in population or employment distribution call for it, bus transportation can add or shift routes with ease. The use of relatively small units adds further flexibility, permitting a nice adjustment of frequency of schedule and area of service. Consequently, the bus can give closer-to-home service in residential areas than can rail service. It has a relatively low capital charge, and revenues and expenses follow each other more closely as traffic volumes vary than do the revenues and expenses of transportation systems having higher fixed charges.

Although the bus is capable of high speed, when it must share the highway lanes with automobiles and trucks it is subject to the same impediments to travel during periods of maximum travel demand. When operating on city streets it is highly vulnerable to street congestion. As there must be a driver for each vehicle, its seat-mile cost is higher than the seat-mile cost by rail, and when the route volume is high this feature of its cost structure may outweigh its advantage of lower fixed charges. It is also more vulnerable to the vagaries of weather — snow and ice particularly — and its reliability suffers thereby.

For some travel, the automobile presents values that cannot be provided by common-carrier transport. For most trips the automobile provides a door-to-door service. Departure times are at the traveler's convenience, rather than responses to timetables. Several extra passengers, and luggage and other impedimenta, add nothing to travel cost or burden. When three or more are riding together, the out-of-pocket cost per passenger mile is less than bus or rail fares. When travel is by high-quality highway and traffic is flowing freely, speeds can approach and sometimes exceed those of bus or rail travel. The automobile can reach directly virtually any desired destination, including those not served by common carriers, without transfer or interchange. At destination the automobile traveler still has a means of transportation ready at his command.

But there are serious weaknesses as well. When the automobile transports only the driver, even the out-of-pocket costs per mile are usually higher than common-carrier passenger-mile fares. Driving an automobile in an urban area, particularly during the high-traffic-volume periods, is a demanding effort and permits little opportunity for relaxation. Also, during those peak periods, on heavily traveled highways the over-all speeds achieved are considerably less than those achievable by common-carrier transport utilizing exclusive rights-of-way.

Perhaps the most important negative factor in automobile transport is its relatively low passenger-carrying capacity per highway lane, which becomes important when the one-direction demand on a particular route is greater than a critical magnitude, say, 9,000 or so persons an hour (assuming three expressway lanes in one direction). Where the travel rate is higher than this, it may be more economical in an over-all sense for the transport demand to be satisfied by a higher-capacity service, if the other circumstances of the transport need should make it appropriate. Moreover, highway space utilization per se, in an urban setting, becomes a consideration transcending money costs.

APPROPRIATE ROLES FOR THE DIFFERENT MODES

The mode of transportation used by the traveler depends on the travel circumstances — trip purpose, trip origin, trip destination, time of day and day of week, size of travel group. Travel demand is not an undifferentiated volume; travelers do not all enjoy a free choice of all modes of transportation for all trips. The various modes are by no means fully alternative. Journey-to-work travel to the CBD typically chooses one mode, recreation travel on Sundays another, midday travel between outlying points another, and so on.

Common-carrier facilities are relied upon most heavily for journey-to-work travel to the CBD. Indeed, all travel to and from the CBD is dominated by common-carrier transportation. This preference of the traveler is reasonable and sound from the point of view of transportation economics. Total volumes and route densities, particularly during the rush hours, are high, amply warranting the use of high-investment, high-capacity facilities.

In sharp contrast to journey-to-work travel to the CBD is the travel that takes place on Saturdays, Sundays and holidays. Here public transportation plays a minor role, and the automobile has established its dominance.

Between these contrasting components of metropolitan travel lie the journey-to-work travel between outlying points, and between centrally located residences and outlying work places, and off-hour and weekday travel not generated by the CBD. For all these intermediate travel components private transportation is favored over common-carrier transportation, although to a smaller degree than for Saturday, Sunday and holiday travel. Common-carrier transportation suffers in revenue, but the demand on highway facilities is not increased; the magnitude is not great enough to be controlling in design. There is ample highway capacity available during the off hours and reverse-direction travel during the peak does not usually press against capacity ceilings.

In general, we can say that common-carrier transportation is the traveler's principal choice when and where travel volumes are concentrated in time and in space, as in travel to and from the CBD. When and where travel volumes are dispersed, over the hours of the day or over the hundreds of travel paths of the metropolis, private transportation, the automobile, is the principal reliance of the traveler.

The Outlook

The need for common-carrier passenger transport in the New York region in the decades ahead and the feasibility of providing it, are intimately related to the region's prospective form and character, to the way in which homes and jobs will be distributed geographically.

There is little doubt that Manhattan's Central Business District will continue to provide the region's largest concentration of employment. The current employment trend is downward in some categories, such as manufacturing, and upward in others, such as finance and business service. The wholesaling and retailing categories seem to have been stabilized. Data on net change, or even on present levels, are sparse. From New York City Planning Department data, it appears that there may have been a modest decline during the past decade, despite the great amount of office building construction that has taken place. On balance, there is no strong evidence now pointing to either a net rise or a net decline by 1980 in CBD

employment from the 1960 level, some 2 to 2.5 million.

Nevertheless, the magnitude of the task of transporting such a great number of workers will continue to call for transport facilities of the highest capacity. The subway system of the New York City Transit Authority and the PATH system, supplemented by the surface bus lines, are well suited to the task, and the highest level of service of which the systems are capable will continue to be indispensable for the economy of the region.

Even if there is no material change in the number of jobs in the Central Business District, there is the possibility that the number of workers to be transported to it may change in the future, as a consequence of a shifting pattern of home locations. There have been conjectures that the future will see a greater number of employees living close to their work places, perhaps close enough to walk. If such a development should be realized, with an increase in the resident population of Manhattan south of Central Park, the load on the transit system will be lightened, not through a reduction in the number of riders but through a shortening of their rides. Postwar experience does not encourage this outlook. A sizable urban renewal and rehousing program, the nation's largest, still left a population decline in Manhattan between 1950 and 1960.

It has been observed that the increasing demand for executive, professional and other highly skilled personnel by Manhattan's burgeoning central-office activities must be met more by drawing on the residents of the outlying areas than on those of Manhattan. This has led some to foresee an increase in the number needing transportation into Manhattan from the suburban counties, even though many Manhattan residents at the same time may need transport in the reverse direction, to jobs in the outlying areas. In this event, transport to the Central Business District will have a greater task to perform even if total Central Business District employment remains much the same as it has been.

But the essentiality of the mass transportation system is not limited to the journey-to-work component of Central Business District travel. Off-hour usage to and from the CBD also is high and will remain high as Manhattan continues to be a magnet for specialty retailing, high-level professional services, entertainment, cultural and other activities for which it has unsurpassed advantages. The level of travel demand for this non-rush-hour service will not be controlling on transit facility capacity, but a high level of service will be indispensable nevertheless.

The residents of the metropolitan counties west of the Hudson River who travel to Manhattan's CBD rely heavily on common-carrier transportation, not only during the rush hours but during the off hours as well. It is reasonable to conclude that they will continue to do so. Those whose trips originate in the more northerly counties in all probability will rely principally, if not entirely, on bus service over the highway network, while those coming from the south and west will continue to give patronage to the commuter railroad lines and to the PATH system.

There is a mixed outlook for the commuter railroads.

The configurations and topographies of Long Island and the Bronx-Westchester peninsula bring about channelizations of Manhattan-bound travel into a few routes, rail as well as highway, and, consequently, require high-capacity facilities. Also, the terminals of the Long Island, New York Central and New Haven railroads provide convenient access to the northerly por-

tions of the CBD, which in recent years have shown great vitality in economic development.

On the other hand, the New Jersey portion of the region fans out over a 180-degree span and, except for the Bayonne peninsula, presents no great geographic restraints to wide route dispersal. Topographic features on the west of the Hudson tend to rim the metropolitan area, by the Watchungs, for example, rather than to channelize it into radial routes. The result is a relatively thin distribution of travel over a multiplicity of travel paths, rather than concentration into a few, and a tendency toward relatively low route densities. Also, there is as an inheritance from earlier years a railroad network laid out primarily to give access to downtown Manhattan, an area from which many businesses recently have been migrating northward.

The potential of the rail lines serving the New Jersey suburban areas can be strengthened by improving access to midtown Manhattan, through betterments of the PATH uptown service and through utilization of the Pennsylvania tunnels and Manhattan's Pennsylvania Station by passengers of other railroads transferring at Newark or other transfer stations. Also, if the redevelopment of downtown Manhattan yields increased employment in that area, it will add further to the New Jersey railroads' potential.

However, the total number of New Jersey residents crossing the Hudson River during the rush hours, by all modes of transportation, destined for the CBD, has been on the decline for some time. The total market for the New Jersey common carriers in serving Manhattan-bound travelers has not been increasing.

The long-run advantage in the competition in bringing passengers living in the more northerly counties (such as Bergen,

Passaic and Rockland) to the Hudson River gateways will probably rest with the bus lines.

The remaining major commuter rail lines and PATH are likely to be the principal carriers serving Hudson, Essex, Union, Morris and adjoining counties to the south and west, during the foreseeable future.

With all the commuter railroad and transit lines the principal problem is a financial one. The railroads serving the east and the north, for example, are not experiencing drastic declines in patronage, particularly during the work-travel hours, but they are in financial difficulty nevertheless, not too different from the financial difficulty in which the New Jersey railroads find themselves. Their passenger revenues do not keep up with their expenses. There are burdensome local taxes, inflexible labor requirements, and heavy investment charges. Technological advance is inhibited. Their bad load curves, reflecting the concentration of demand in a few morning and a few afternoon hours, defeat efforts aimed at profitable or even self-supporting operations.

We are not faced with any difficult engineering problem, but rather a complex problem in public policy — how to assure the continuance of an essential service, virtually certain to incur a financial deficit, and not do intolerable violence to local government tax revenues, avoid public ownership as far as possible, and at the same time command public support, including that of railroad labor itself.

A certain amount of progress has been made and the major framework of public policy is being slowly and cautiously constructed. The Port Authority has acquired the Hudson & Manhattan and is rehabilitating, re-equipping and operating it. New York State, using the Port Authority as an instrumentality, has instituted a pro-

gram of financing the purchase of new passenger cars for the Long Island, the New York Central and the New Haven railroads, and has taken steps toward relieving the heavy tax loads of the New York Central and the New Haven. Since 1954 the Long Island has been relieved of local taxes and has enjoyed considerable freedom in setting commuter fares. New Jersey's efforts have been along a different path — service contracts with the railroads calling for payments by the state to compensate, at least in part, for the losses sustained in providing commuter service. The Governors of New York, New Jersey and Connecticut have jointly established the Tri-State Transportation Committee to advance and coordinate transportation planning for the Region, with both shorter-range and comprehensive long-range objectives.

Further development of public policy within this broad framework is imperative.

There is not likely to be any strong demand for bus service linking the eastern or northern counties to Manhattan as long as the Long Island, New Haven and New York Central railroads are able to maintain satisfactory levels of service. There is a stronger likelihood that bus service will have to be expanded to accommodate New Jersey travelers, particularly from the more northerly sections. But if buses take up more of the responsibility for serving journey-to-work travel, bus operations are likely to show increased peaking and may begin to take on some of the uneconomical load characteristics which have plagued the railroads. Because of the lower level of fixed costs and greater operational flexibility, however, bus transportation may be better able to stand the strain and may be less liable to financial disaster.

There is a virtual certainty that in the

decades ahead there will be an even greater dependence than there is today on the automobile for regional transport, as intersuburban, reverse-direction and leisure-time travel continue to grow. Unless there is a drastic change in the metropolitan growth pattern, a multitude of travel paths, widely scattered throughout the region, will come to be employed as increasing numbers of workers travel from their quarter-acre home sites in an outlying county to campus-type factories, laboratories or office establishments in other suburbs. There will be limited opportunity for channelization of this travel into a few high-volume routes, and it will have to rely primarily upon private transportation.

Technical gadgetry will not yield a painless solution to the passenger transport problem. The evolving pattern of metropolitan travel is a response to deep-seated forces and in itself is neither irrational nor perverse. Wise and skillful statesmanship by civic leaders and public officials in the fields of finance, law and management, is the requirement.

CHAPTER 21

A MAJOR HIGHWAY NETWORK FOR THE REGION

An estimate of the future highway needs for the New York Metropolitan Region must give full recognition to the profoundly important forces which have been reshaping all the metropolitan areas of the United States during the past few decades. Particularly important is the prospect that in the years that lie ahead there will be further extensive urbanization of the region's land.

By increasing so strikingly the accessibility of the cities' hinterlands, technological developments in transport, in power and in communication have made hundreds of square miles of open land available for urban growth. Residential development has been at densities far lower than those of the past. Suburbia has taken on increasing importance in the metropolitan complex. The open spaces between the smaller cities have filled up.

Manufacturing establishments have also been seeking outlying sites, with large demands for space. The multistory factory building in the heart of the built-up city has become largely obsolescent. The new factory sites are spacious, in order to accommodate the new assembly line processes and to provide room for future expansion. Industry has become suburbanized, carrying with it suburbanization of employment.

Throughout the nation, millions of acres of land in outlying locations made accessible by the automobile have been pressed into service. As their development has been characteristically at low density, cities have grown in area at rates far out of proportion to their rates of population rise.

Taken as a whole, there has been a veritable revolution in the manner in which we have been using land. Made possible by advancing technologies in transportation, communication, and electric power, new land-use practices have, in turn, profoundly influenced the urban community's demands for transportation.

Urban Travel

In 1920, there were about 9,000,000 motor vehicles in operation in the nation, or 87 per thousand of population. They rolled up an estimated 45 billion vehicle miles a year, or about 5,000 miles per vehicle. The United States had developed 369,000 miles of hard-paved highway.

Forty years later, in 1960, national motor vehicle registration had grown to about 74,000,000. They were operated some 720 billion miles, or 9,700 miles per vehicle. Paved highway mileage approached 2,500,000, and the cities, the counties, the states and the federal government were hard put to provide for the steadily increasing highway demand.

The annual rate of growth of motor vehicle registrations in the past five years has been more than twice the prewar rate and every indicator of motor vehicle usage displays acceleration — automobile production, fuel consumption and traffic volumes. Moreover, projections of automobile ownership and usage look to a 20 per cent increase in the ratio of private cars to people by 1980. It is estimated that by then there will be, as a national total, about one passenger car registered for every 2.4 people. Registrations in 1980 would approximate 120 million vehicles, and 70 per cent of them will be owned in urban areas. Highway travel, too, has followed a comparable upward curve. It was more than 720 billion vehicle miles in 1960, compared to 55 billion in 1921, and has more than doubled in the post-war period.

Over the years there have been consistent increases in vehicle miles of travel and in highway expenditures. Except for the war and depression years, there have been about two vehicle miles of travel per dollar of gross national product, on a 1947 base. In fact, highway expenditures have lagged behind highway travel and gross national product since 1940. Between 1940 and 1960, highway travel increased 141 per cent (Fig. 1), gross national product 114 per cent, and highway expenditures 100 per cent.

INFLUENCES OF URBAN GROWTH ON TRAVEL PATTERNS

Comprehensive data on travel behavior covering the entire Metropolitan Region and all forms of transport do not exist, but the travel that takes place across the Hudson River may be considered a reasonably representative sample. The changes that have taken place in trans-Hudson travel behavior during a recent ten-year period illustrate the effects of the changes that have already occurred in the Region's pattern of settlement and in the geographic arrangement of economic activity.

Trans-Hudson Travel Behavior

Total trans-Hudson travel is a complex mixture of trips having different purposes, different destinations and different origins, trips made on different days of the week and at different times of the day, and trips made by residents of different parts of the region. Detailed examina-

tion of these components yields important insights as to the respective roles played today by public and private transportation, and suggests the character that urban transport may assume in the years ahead.

The decline in usage of mass transportation facilities and the rise in the use of the automobile, it appears, are parallel phenomena resulting largely from a common cause — the changes in form and structure of the metropolis. Public transportation serves principally those travel components which build up to high concentrations, as to time and as to travel path. Its greatest use is in rush-hour travel into the Central Business District in the morning and out of it at the close of the business day. Conversely, private transportation is relied upon mostly by those components of urban travel which are characterized by either time spread or route dispersal, or which involve family travel. Thus we find the automobile dominating week-end and holiday travel, off-peak travel, reverse commuting and intersuburban travel. All these travel elements reveal growth characteristics not fully shared by the travel generated by downtown employment. This growth will present serious problems in the future, problems of highway capacity, route selection, traffic control, adequacy of parking facilities at outlying points, and the levels of public expenditure.

Growth of Peripheral, or Non-Manhattan, Travel

Other traffic studies that have been made at periodic intervals at trans-Hudson crossings reveal steady growth in those segments of trans-Hudson vehicular traffic that have neither origin or destination in Manhattan. Prior to World War II, traffic to or from Manhattan comprised the major element in the trans-Hudson

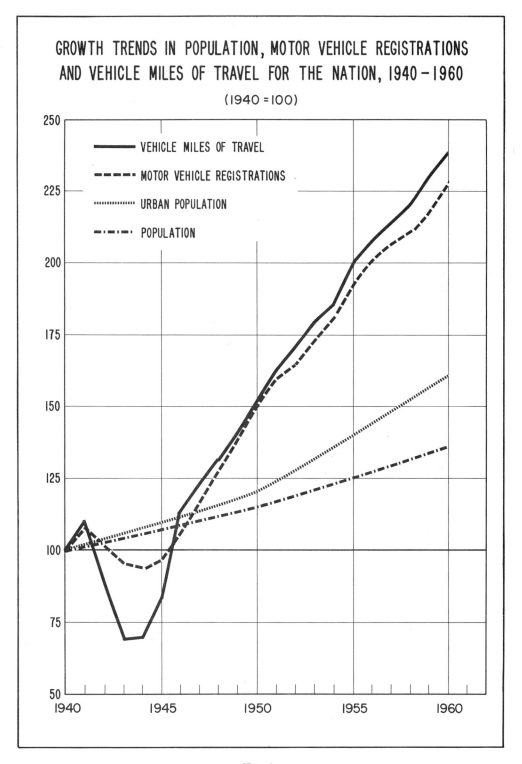

GROWTH TRENDS IN POPULATION, MOTOR VEHICLE REGISTRATIONS
AND VEHICLE MILES OF TRAVEL FOR THE NATION, 1940–1960

(1940 =100)

VEHICLE MILES OF TRAVEL

MOTOR VEHICLE REGISTRATIONS

URBAN POPULATION

POPULATION

Fig. 1

movement. Non-Manhattan traffic accounted for only about 40 per cent of the total volume. By 1949 non-Manhattan traffic had doubled in volume and accounted for 47 per cent of all trans-Hudson trips on weekdays, and 63 per cent on Sundays. A 1956 origin-destination study showed that 49 per cent of trans-Hudson traffic on weekdays and 63 per cent on Sundays was to and from areas outside Manhattan. The most recent analysis of trans-Hudson trips, in 1960, reveals that the non-Manhattan segment has grown to 51 per cent on weekdays and continues to account for approximately 63 per cent on weekends. This growth trend in the non-Manhattan components of trans-Hudson traffic is expected to continue as a consequence of continued suburbanization, and by 1980 traffic desiring to bypass Manhattan should account for about 55 per cent of the weekday movement and about 70 per cent of the week-end travel.

A Regional Highway System Concept

The prospect of the growing importance of the suburb-to-suburb, peripheral and other travel not oriented to Manhattan's Central Business District (defined as the area south of Central Park) has already led to the investment of nearly $500 million in the construction of the Narrows Bridge and the lower deck of the George Washington Bridge. These facilities will provide needed capacity on routes which will bypass the congested central core. This bypass concept is applicable not only to Manhattan, as the central core of the region, but also to the region's secondary core areas, such as Newark, Paterson, New Brunswick, White Plains, Stamford and Bridgeport.

As to Manhattan, the Holland and Lincoln tunnels and the bridges and tunnels between 59th Street and the Battery across the East River should primarily serve traffic to and from the Central Business District under this bypass concept. Traffic to and from the areas outside this central core should be able to use the peripheral crossings — the George Washington, Triborough, Bronx-Whitestone and Throgs Neck bridges on the north and the Narrows and Staten Island bridges on the south. The extent to which this concept can be realized in the future will depend in large measure upon the distributive capabilities of the regional highway system. That system, ideally, should consist of a network of major arterial highways passing through or close to the principal traffic-generating areas and interrelated with distributing highways forming a series of belt routes around the area's center. These should include an inner belt adjacent to Manhattan to distribute traffic close to the region's center, and an outer belt around the periphery of the Metropolitan Area for through traffic. In between, there should be an intermediate belt route or routes to distribute local traffic or traffic from outside the area to local destinations.

The Highway System Today

When we view the vast network of streets and highways in the New York–New Jersey–Connecticut Metropolitan Region, we can recognize the shaping influence of geographic and topographic features. Over and above origin and destination of traffic, which will be controlled by the pattern of population settlement and the distribution of economic activity, the highway network for the future will undoubtedly be influenced in a significant way by the same geographic and topographic considerations that have influenced it in the past.

The dominant orientation of the highway routes of the region is northeast-southwest, as a consequence of the general orientation of the North Atlantic coastline and the Boston-Philadelphia-Washington corridor (Fig. 2). A second important corridor leads northward from the Metropolitan Area, in general following the course of the Hudson River. Both corridors have served as important lines of communication since the early days of the nation.

The region itself is made up of three separate and distinct areas, having different geographical features important to highway development.

Long Island, because of its long and narrow configuration and its situation directly to the east of Manhattan, demands a dominantly east-west orientation in its highways. In many ways it would be geographically unreasonable to develop a highway network on Long Island in any manner other than a basic system of arterial routes extending to the east from the central core area, crossed by a series of north-south distribution roads to form a gridiron-type pattern.

Similarly, the Bronx, Westchester, Fairfield County area is roughly a peninsula extending north-northeasterly from the central core, relatively narrow at its lower end at the East River, and featured by a series of ridges and valleys running in a generally north-south direction. Formidable water barriers — the Hudson River and Long Island Sound — flank the Bronx-Westchester triangle and serve as natural deterrents to peripheral highway development. These geographic features combine to produce a highway picture which by and large shows a radial pattern with the central core area as its hub. Such important routes as the Boston Post Road, New England Thruway, Hutchinson River Parkway, Bronx River Parkway, Saw Mill River Parkway, and the Westchester section of the New York State Thruway are all of a radial character.

The geography of the New Jersey portion of the Metropolitan Area is materially different, and as a consequence the New Jersey highway pattern differs materially from those which have evolved in the Long Island and Westchester sectors. Here is a 180-degree span of land area adjacent to the region's central core. The most prominent topographic features — the Palisades ridge bordering the Hudson and the roughly parallel Watchung Mountains, 10 or 12 miles to the west — bound an extensive area of rather easy terrain. The highway pattern is irregular, with peripheral routes superimposed upon a radial system, which, in itself, stems from a much wider central core base than is the case in Westchester or Long Island. For example, the Palisades Interstate Parkway and Routes N.J. 4, N.J. 17 and U.S. 46 converge on the northern part of the central core area. Similarly, the New Jersey Turnpike and Routes U.S. 1 and U.S. 22 converge on its southern portion, while N.J. 3 is the major New Jersey feeder highway to the center.

The mountains to the west and the Palisades along the Hudson, however, have exerted a strong influence on highway location, particularly the east-west routes. Piercing the Palisades and crossing the Hudson are costly construction tasks, and as a result there is a limited number of trans-Hudson crossings. These become controlling factors in the configuration of highway routes. The several low-gradient passes through the mountains to the west have had a similar impact on the New Jersey highway network.

Application of the Bypass Concept

Taken together, the topographic features, the land-mass configurations, and

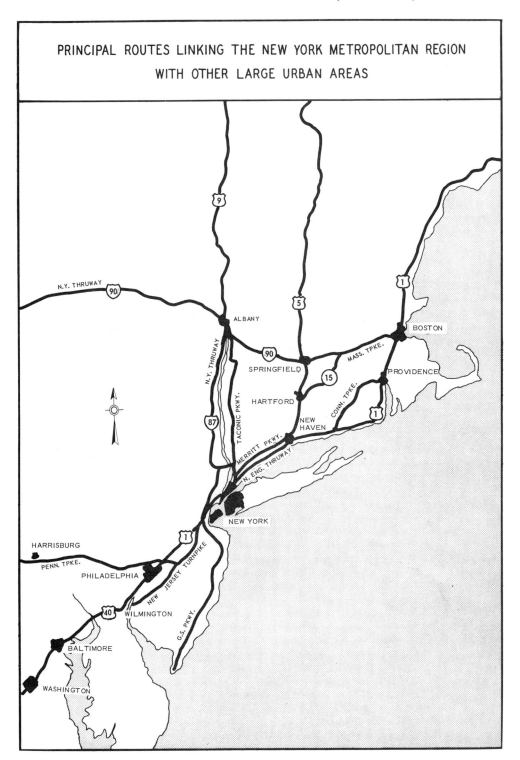

PRINCIPAL ROUTES LINKING THE NEW YORK METROPOLITAN REGION
WITH OTHER LARGE URBAN AREAS

FIG. 2

the major water barriers have resulted in a highway network which by and large has a southwest-northeast orientation through the entire area. It is also a network having prominent radial features focused on the crossings of the rivers which bound the central core. Consequently, it is a system to which the bypass principle can be applied only to a limited extent.

In New Jersey, Routes N.J. 3, U.S. 22 and U.S. 1, the New Jersey Turnpike and its Newark Bay extension — all converge on the Holland and Lincoln tunnels. The routes serving Queens and Long Island in large measure focus on the Queens-Midtown Tunnel and the lower East River crossings. Interconnection between these arterial routes and between the various river crossings is limited. In New Jersey the Garden State Parkway, it is true, provides a through north-south route skirting the edge of the Newark metropolitan area and offers a means of carrying traffic from the arterial feeders to routes serving the George Washington Bridge or to the New York State Thruway. Also, the New Jersey Turnpike, running through the heavily traveled New Brunswick–Elizabeth–Newark corridor, serves to collect traffic from the major arteries and to funnel it to the George Washington Bridge. However, both are toll routes and the Parkway is limited to noncommercial traffic.

On the New York side, the New York State Thruway, Major Deegan Expressway, Triborough Bridge, Grand Central Parkway and Van Wyck Expressway form a continuous north-south route, and the Cross Island Parkway, Whitestone Bridge and New England Thruway, supplemented by the recently completed Throgs Neck Bridge and its approaches, serve as a second north-south route. The Parkway portions of both routes, however, are limited to passenger cars.

Since the existing network is primarily oriented to Manhattan, much traffic which could reasonably bypass the congested area of Manhattan nevertheless finds it more convenient to go through the core. For instance, origin-destination studies at the Hudson River crossings show that more than half the traffic through the Holland Tunnel and Lincoln Tunnel, leading directly to Manhattan's Central Business District, on a weekday has neither origin nor destination in the central business area; over the East River crossings between the Battery and 59th Street, non-Manhattan traffic comprises nearly 40 per cent of the total. Further evidence can be found in the use made of peripheral routes via the George Washington Bridge in comparison with the use of competitive routes through the Holland and Lincoln tunnels for trips which, in view of their origins and destinations, could reasonably be expected to bypass Manhattan.

THE REGIONAL SYSTEM AS PLANNED

In recent years, highway planning and construction have been accelerated under the impetus provided by Federal Highway Aid and most particularly by the expanded program derived from the Federal Aid Act of 1956. While the greatest impact of this expanded program is the National System of Interstate and Defense Highways, increased support is also provided for the other elements of the system, the primary and secondary routes. The Interstate System will provide a 41,000-mile integrated network of the nation's most heavily traveled roadways, of which about 6,700 miles will be in the urban areas of the nation. Within the New York Metropolitan Area, these interstate routes will be key elements in the future highway system. Supplementing them are a number of other important highways planned and under construction. Assuming that all known projects are carried to completion, the resulting regional highway network when the federal program is completed in 1975 will be as shown on Figure 3.

In looking at this over-all system, the influences of geography and topography are still apparent. The Long Island and Westchester sections remain basically a radial system centered on Manhattan. In the larger, more open areas of New Jersey, where about half of the region's population growth during the next two decades is expected to settle, there is to be more peripheral route development connecting the various population concentrations and breaking through some of the historical natural barriers. For example, both I-280, an east-west radial route centering on the central core area, and I-80, an east-west bypass of the central core, will cut directly through the Watchung Mountain barrier to serve the rapidly developing areas to the west. Route I-287, a peripheral route spanning the full 180 degrees in New Jersey from Perth Amboy on the south to the Tappan Zee Bridge on the north, will also break through the Watchung Mountains as well as through the lower Ramapo Mountain barrier in northern New Jersey, which has traditionally been a deterrent to arterial highway construction.

Gaps in Bypass Facilities

These examples are indicative of the changes in the pattern of the region's highway network which are necessary to serve new areas of heavy population growth. Some of the traditional physical barriers to highway development will have to be pierced.

However, an examination of this planned network, to determine the extent to which it will provide a regional system

adequate for the anticipated future needs of the region, reveals certain apparent gaps. The resulting system would still be basically a radial system focused on Manhattan and would not provide a network that would fully exploit bypass possibilities. While the bypass routes leading to the George Washington Bridge and the Tappan Zee Bridge would be strengthened, the new routes planned are likely to encourage routing through the core of the noncore traffic that might better be led to use routes via the Narrows and Staten Island bridges.

In New Jersey, three of the five planned major expressways, the Route 24 Freeway, I-78 and I-280, would lead to the trans-Hudson tunnels. Of the other two projects, I-80, sometimes called the Bergen County Expressway, would serve the George Washington Bridge, and I-287 would lead toward the Outerbridge Crossing and thence via Staten Island to the Narrows Bridge. There are no plans for major north-south distribution roads beyond the New Jersey Turnpike and Garden State Parkway. Only a few short segments of north-south expressway are planned, unrelated to each other: a short route through Newark connecting I-280 and I-78, the completion of Route 21 Freeway between Paterson and Newark, the extension of the Turnpike to the Bergen County Expressway, and the completion of N.J. 440 in Bayonne as a freeway leading to the Bayonne Bridge.

In New York, the Long Island Expressway, together with the Queens-Midtown Tunnel, or with the Brooklyn-Queens Expressway and the Williamsburg Bridge as an alternate route, would lead traffic to the south and west directly through the central core to the trans-Hudson tunnels. The Bushwick Expressway–Southern Parkway route would further strengthen the radial aspect of the system. Never-

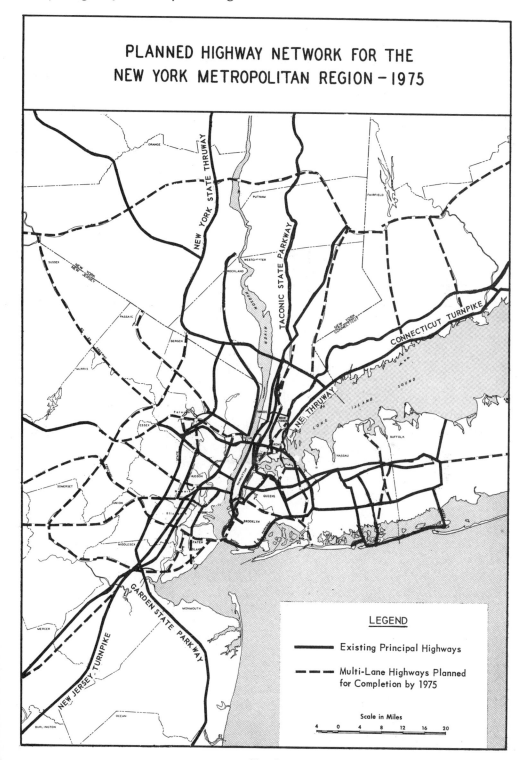

PLANNED HIGHWAY NETWORK FOR THE
NEW YORK METROPOLITAN REGION – 1975

LEGEND

———— Existing Principal Highways

- - - - Multi-Lane Highways Planned
for Completion by 1975

Scale in Miles

Fig. 3

theless these routes would provide needed capacity to serve the central core.

Crossing the radial routes would be the Cross Bronx Expressway–Throgs Neck Bridge–Clearview Expressway route and, closer in, the Brooklyn-Queens Expressway, Major Deegan Expressway and Harlem River Drive which, together with the George Washington Bridge and the Triborough Bridge and their approaches, would form an inner circumferential route. The only proposed improvement on Long Island which would favor the Narrows Bridge route is the Gowanus Expressway linking the bridge with the Brooklyn-Queens Expressway.

On Staten Island the Clove Lakes Expressway would link the Narrows Bridge with the Goethals Bridge. However, there is only a limited program as yet for the westerly extension of this route into New Jersey. The West Shore Expressway is also planned to link the Outerbridge Crossing with the Goethals Bridge, and via the Clove Lakes Expressway, with the Narrows Bridge. The Richmond Parkway would provide a more direct link between the Outerbridge and Narrows, but it is now planned that this route would be restricted to passenger cars.

Except for one short gap, the system as planned would provide an outer belt route following roughly the Port District boundary, consisting of the Tappan Zee Bridge and New York Thruway, I-287, Outerbridge Crossing, Richmond Parkway, the Narrows Bridge, the Belt System of Long Island, the Throgs Neck Bridge and Clearview Expressway, New England Thruway and Cross-Westchester Expressway. However, a large part of this route, the Richmond Parkway and the Belt Parkway system, would be restricted to passenger car traffic, and the section between the presently planned terminus of I-287 at U.S. 1, near Metuchen, New Jersey, and

Outerbridge Crossing is not presently programmed.

An inner belt would also be provided, consisting of the George Washington Bridge, New Jersey Turnpike, Goethals Bridge, Clove Lakes Expressway, Narrows Bridge, Gowanus Expressway, Brooklyn-Queens Expressway, Grand Central Parkway, Triborough Bridge, Major Deegan Expressway and Trans-Manhattan Expressway to the George Washington Bridge. Many of the requirements of an inner belt would be met but the New Jersey Turnpike segment is a toll route, and, at the same time, is too far west to serve adequately as a distributor to the close-in areas along the Hudson River and Upper Bay. The function of a distributor in those areas would still have to be performed by U.S. 1 and N.J. 440, neither of which would be adequate for the purpose.

POTENTIAL FUTURE NEEDS

The highway system as now planned does not include any new Hudson or East River crossings. The six-lane lower level of the George Washington Bridge was completed in 1962 and six lanes on the Narrows Bridge will be ready in 1965. Assuming that interstate mass transportation facilities will be maintained and improved, it is expected that these bridge facilities will meet trans-Hudson vehicular demand through 1975. Some time later there will probably be need for additional trans-Hudson capacity. However, it is not feasible to forecast at this time the location or future role of such additional capacity in the over-all transportation situation. Earlier studies have shown that any additional trans-Hudson crossing located south of 125th Street would require a new East River crossing, the location of which is equally indeterminate now. Because of this intimate relation between the Hudson and East River crossings, therefore, any discussion of future needs must proceed on the basis of existing major river crossings.

Within the scope of this report many of the needs can be defined only in general terms. It is not the intent that these descriptions be construed as specific recommendations, but rather as potential areas for future study. At the same time, the analysis must be limited to the major network within the region. Many local needs and problems within particular areas exist that cannot be included herein.

Strengthening the Bypasses

Previous discussion has shown the need to strengthen the bypass elements of the region's highway system, particularly for a southerly bypass of Manhattan. This could be accomplished by the addition of certain routes as presented diagrammatically in Figure 4. In the New York counties east of the Upper Bay and Hudson River, the most critical need appears to be a Cross-Brooklyn route connecting the Narrows Bridge directly with the expressway and parkway system serving Queens and Long Island. This would provide the added capacity needed for interstate traffic using the Narrows Bridge and destined for the Bronx, Westchester County and north via the Bronx-Whitestone and Throgs Neck bridges, and would also serve local needs for east-west capacity. On Staten Island, local and regional needs appear to call for an expressway connecting the Outerbridge Crossing directly with the Narrows Bridge across the Island, leaving the West Shore Expressway to function as a distributor serving the potential development along the water front and immediately inland, rather than functioning as both distributor and through route. This could also

bring about a better balance between the use of the Goethals Bridge and the Outerbridge Crossing. Those two crossings should have enough capacity through 1975 to meet the demands of through traffic as well as of the traffic between New Jersey and Staten Island. Beyond that time additional trans-Arthur Kill capacity may be required, but again, it is not feasible at this time to forecast location or timing of an additional crossing.

In New Jersey, the needs with respect to a strong southerly bypass include the link between the Outerbridge Crossing and the Middlesex Freeway, a link from the Goethals Bridge to U.S. 1, and a route tying the Goethals Bridge in with the routes serving the Newark metropolitan area and areas north and west.

There would also appear to be a need for strengthening the north-south distribution system through the Elizabeth-Newark-Hudson County corridor. This could be accomplished either through linkings between existing and proposed routes, or by a new through route closer to the Hudson River. Such a route would serve the function now assigned to I-95, distributing traffic between the peripheral facilities and the built-up areas extending back from the Hudson River.

The Completed Belt System

With the changes in and additions to the over-all system as outlined above, the resulting pattern, as shown in Figure 4, would contain the required balance between the radial system of arteries serving the central core area and the distribution system around the central core to meet the broader regional needs. A close-in expressway belt would be available as has been described, adjacent to Manhattan, to distribute traffic close in to the center of the region. It would consist of the expressway system through Hudson

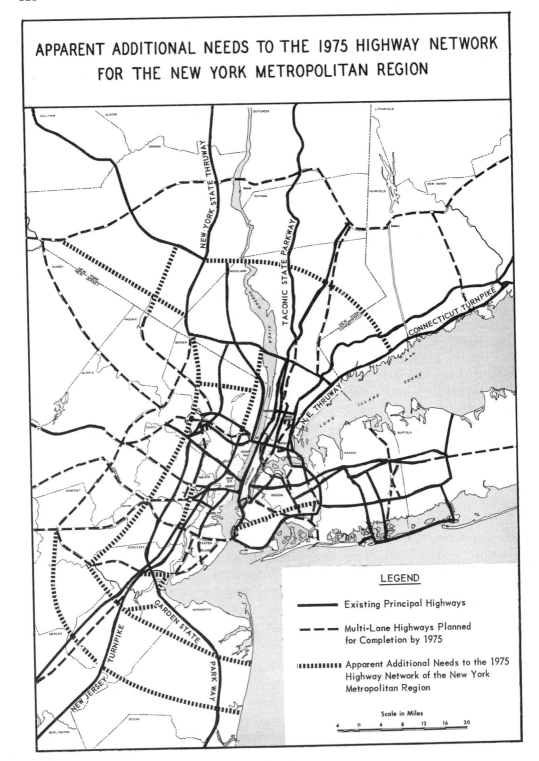

FIG. 4

County to the Bayonne Bridge, the Willowbrook and Clove Lakes expressways across Staten Island to the Narrows Bridge, the Gowanus and Brooklyn-Queens expressways north to the Triborough Bridge and then via the Major Deegan Expressway and trans-Manhattan Expressway and the George Washington Bridge.

An outer belt around the periphery of the region would exist, but to make it an all-expressway route there would have to be an extension of I-287 into the Outerbridge Crossing, an expressway linking the Outerbridge Crossing with the Narrows Bridge, and a Cross-Brooklyn Expressway.

Several intermediate belts for local traffic or for traffic from outside with local destination would also be available. One would consist of the routes connecting the George Washington, Throgs Neck, Narrows and Goethals bridges. The New Jersey Turnpike and Garden State Parkway would also fit into the over-all complex as part of the system of intermediate belt routes in New Jersey. All of these intermediate belts would be loops elongated in a north-south direction. An intermediate belt oriented in an east-west direction would also be formed by I-80 on the north and I-287, N.J. 24, I-78 and the extension to the Goethals Bridge on the south in New Jersey, together with the Cross-Brooklyn, Clearview and Cross-Bronx expressways circuit in New York.

Central Core Needs

Needs of a more limited geographic scale also warrant consideration. During periods of peak travel demand, Manhattan's Central Business District is a "saturated" traffic area. In terms of the belt concept, there are no routings of expressway capacity, existing or planned, that would provide a complete circumfer-

ence around this central core intersecting the radial routes, capable of distributing traffic to exits nearest its final destination within the core. As a result high volumes of traffic are forced to make unnecessarily long trips through the city streets. But the nucleus of such a close-in circumferential route exists in the West Side Highway and East River Drive. To develop it would necessitate upgrading the southern portions of these routes to freeway standards, or otherwise providing capacity for handling commercial traffic, and to improve the connections to the intersecting radial routes.

The Belt Concept Applied to Secondary Cores

The secondary core areas can be examined in much the same way. For example, the connecting highway between I-78 and I-280 would serve as a westerly bypass of Newark as well as a distribution route for traffic to and from the western part of its central business district. Improving the southerly part of N.J. 21 would provide a similar service for the eastern side of Newark.

In Elizabeth, two connections — from U.S. 1 to the Goethals Bridge and a section running north from the Bridge to Newark — would provide a bypass of the Elizabeth central area for traffic now using U.S. 1. This bypass to the east of Elizabeth combined with existing N.J. 439 on the west, assuming operational improvements which would increase the route capacity, would provide a complete circumferential distribution system around Elizabeth, intersecting all radial approaches.

In essence, however, these two areas are only part of a continuous belt of densely developed land that by 1980 could well be continuous from northern Bergen County south through the corridor between the Hudson River and the Watchung Mountains and embracing Hackensack, Paterson, the Oranges, Newark, Elizabeth, Plainfield, to New Brunswick and its environs, and eastward along Raritan Bay to the Atlantic Ocean. By 1980, the population within this corridor is expected to increase by almost 50 per cent, from about 3.6 million to 5.2 million, with most of the growth concentrated in Bergen, Middlesex and Monmouth counties. Numerous routes provide east-west passage through this corridor but only the New Jersey Turnpike, U.S.1 and the Garden State Parkway now provide continuous north-south routes. These routes are now carrying large volumes and additional capacity may be required, particularly along the westerly side.

Traffic flow maps made by Bergen County also show heavy north-south flows on the routes in the eastern part of the county and increasing east-west travel in the central and northern sections. Much of the anticipated growth in county population will take place in these areas and the growth will further increase travel demands. Therefore, it is likely that new north-south and east-west capacity may be required through these parts of the county. These roadways, in effect, would complete a northern loop around the whole corridor. One possibility for north-south capacity long under discussion would be an extension of the Turnpike north to the New York Thruway. There are also a number of proposals for improving the east-west county system, although a higher-type facility might be required ultimately.

At the southern end of this corridor the east-west section of I-287 would fill a vital need for distributing local traffic through the northern part of Middlesex County. However, as both Middlesex and Monmouth counties develop, traffic between them can be expected to grow. This growth, combined with increased traffic between Monmouth County and areas to the south and Staten Island, Brooklyn and Queens resulting from the completion of the Narrows Bridge, could necessitate additional capacity across the Raritan River as well as provision for additional east-west capacity from I-287 through the area south of New Brunswick into Monmouth County, thereby completing a loop around the southern end of the corridor.

Other Possible Needs

The interstate and expressway system as planned in the northern section of the region — Orange, Rockland, Westchester and Fairfield counties — would generally appear adequate for through traffic needs. One overburdened section is the New York Thruway south of Harriman. This could be relieved by the completion of I-87 on the east side of the Hudson River. Further relief could be accomplished by additional east-west capacity in the vicinity of the Harriman Interchange, by extending N.J. 208 north to tie into Route 17 or by providing additional east-west capacity parallel to the New York–New Jersey state line.

Within the Bronx-Westchester corridor, the geography and topography have produced a fan-shaped pattern of highways with emphasis on the radial or generally north-south routes. Westchester and Fairfield counties are expected to experience major population expansion. As this area continues to expand, greater emphasis will probably have to be given to improving east-west movement, such as was provided for by the Cross-Westchester Expressway.

On Long Island the pattern will probably retain its predominant gridiron character. As the growth in population extends eastward, there will be an increase in the movement between the more out-lying areas and the center of the region and other sectors of the region as well as in the more local or intracounty trips on the Island. There will be an increase in both radial and peripheral demand. However, because of controlling geo-graphic aspects, both types of demand translate into a need for additional east-west expressway capacity on the Island. The more local movement will also re-quire additional north-south capacity, both in presently developed areas and in the areas of expected future development.

As the extensive urbanization of the Re-gion progresses, there will be an increas-ing volume of suburb-to-suburb travel by automobile and a greater need for non-core-oriented facilities. This need will have to be met by a strengthening of the distribution system around the region's central core, as well as around the several secondary core areas. The system as it now exists is basically radial, serving pri-marily the central core, and even the new facilities now planned will not alter that basic character. Filling in the gaps of the distribution system is necessary to provide a highway network that will be in balance with broad regional travel patterns.

CHAPTER 22

TRANS-HUDSON TRANSPORTATION REQUIREMENTS

Automobile traffic, at nearly 73 million trips annually (83 million when the Tappan Zee Bridge is included), accounted for about 83 per cent of the total trans-Hudson vehicular traffic in 1960. Automobile traffic, in view of its potential expansion, will continue to exert a controlling influence on the future need for trans-Hudson crossing capacity. Planning for trans-Hudson vehicular traffic in 1980, therefore, must begin by projecting into the future the levels of trans-Hudson automobile traffic.

Annual trans-Hudson automobile traffic has been, and it is assumed it will be, closely related to the number of automobiles in the 18-county area comprising the Hudson River "traffic shed." The number of automobiles depends upon the number of households and the automobile ownership rates.

Based upon projections of regional population, household size and rates of automobile ownership there will probably be about 6.7 million automobiles in the 18 counties in 1980, and the trans-Hudson automobile traffic demand will be about 140 million vehicles annually. Truck traffic will also continue to increase, largely in large truck and tractor-trailer movements, and by 1980 should be about 18.9 million trucks a year. Bus traffic, although of irregular growth, should amount to about 4.2 million a year. The total vehicular demand on trans-Hudson crossings by 1980, therefore, should be some 163 million vehicles annually.

The present trans-Hudson crossing facilities should be capable of accommodating the traffic demand until about 1975.

Shortly thereafter the added capacity of the lower deck of the Narrows Bridge, already planned for, will probably be needed.

AUTOMOBILE TRAFFIC VOLUMES

The rate of growth of trans-Hudson automobile traffic between 1930 and 1960, encompassing the depression years of the 1930's, World War II with its gas rationing and tire shortages, and the postwar period, was equivalent to about 5.1 per cent a year, compounded. If an equal growth rate were to continue, the number of trans-Hudson automobile trips would double in the next 14 years and would become about 222 million by 1980, a 168 per cent increase over 1960.

But it would be unreasonable to expect a growth rate so high for the next 20 years. The prospect for regional population growth in the 18 counties over that period has been estimated to be about 25 per cent, and the growth of regional employment to be about the same. Even though experience has shown that automobile traffic generally, and trans-Hudson automobile traffic specifically, have grown more rapidly than either population or employment, a continuation of the 1930 to 1960 growth rate would outpace them far too much.

Moreover, automobile traffic cannot logically be considered to grow merely as a consequence of the passage of time, at a rate set in the past. It is more reasonable to suppose that the year-to-year increase of trans-Hudson automobile traffic has been and will be a reflection of increases in population, in households, in automobile ownership, in employment, or in some combination of these factors, as influenced by the changes in urban configuration and regional distribution of population and jobs, as discussed in Chapter 2.

Automobile Traffic and Automobile Registrations

Analysis of the data available leads to the conclusion that in the past the rising annual total of automobile traffic crossing the Hudson River has been closely related to the increased number of automobiles owned and registered in the 18 counties[1] making up what may be considered the Hudson River "traffic shed," which, in turn, has been related to the increases in the region's households, resulting from

[1]The 18 counties are: New York, Bronx, Kings, Queens, Westchester, Nassau and Suffolk, east of the Hudson, and Rockland, Bergen, Passaic, Hudson, Essex, Morris, Union, Richmond, Middlesex, Somerset and Monmouth, west of the Hudson.

population growth, and increases in the prevalence of automobile ownership.

Over the 35-year interval, 1925-1960, annual trans-Hudson automobile traffic over all river crossing facilities from the Battery to Tarrytown has been approximated closely by a formula which states that each automobile in these 18 counties, over and above a total of 550,000, accounted, on the average, for 22.7 trips across the Hudson River a year.

Over the entire 37 years of record, the correlation between annual trans-Hudson automobile traffic and the number of automobiles registered in the 18 counties has been remarkably close. The differences between traffic volumes computed by the formula and the recorded traffic have been within about 6 per cent for two years out of three. Of the 13 years in which the differences exceeded 6 per cent, six were clearly abnormal years: two depression years, two war years, and two immediate

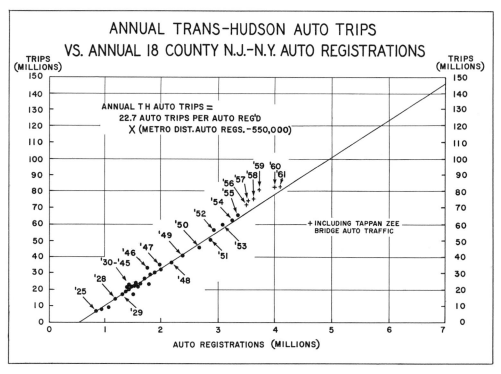

FIG. 1

postwar years. Two more years, 1926 and 1927, were before the Holland Tunnel was in operation, and the four latest years, 1956 to 1959, include the Tappan Zee Bridge traffic. Thus, the annual volume of trans-Hudson automobile traffic has been determinable in the past, within a small margin of error, by considering a single factor, the number of automobiles owned in the 18 counties, irrespective of travel volumes by any other transportation mode.

Although the immediate traffic-generating effect of the Tappan Zee Bridge must be taken into account, we cannot do better at this juncture than to assume that the relationship that has prevailed so closely for 37 years will continue to prevail during the next two decades.

The relationship between automobile registrations and trans-Hudson automobile trip traffic can be used as a tool for traffic projection provided it is possible to project the aggregate automobile ownership in the 18 counties.

Quite like the growth history of trans-Hudson automobile traffic, the growth rate of automobile registrations in the 18-county area over the past 35 years, considered in percentage terms, has been far too high to warrant the assumption that it will continue unabated in the future. Between 1925 and 1960 automobile registrations increased at a rate equivalent to 4.5 per cent annually, compounded. The continuation of such a rate would look forward to a total of 9.7 million automobiles by 1980, an increase of 145 per cent in 20 years, concomitant with a 25 per cent growth in population. The implied average ownership rate for the region would be unreasonable, 145 automobiles per 100 families.

We could project into the future the historical trend of the absolute number

²"People, Jobs and Land 1955-1975," Regional Plan Association, 1957, p. 39.

of automobiles registered in the 18 counties, either as an aggregate or as a summation of 18-county projections. Such a procedure, however, has the same logical weaknesses, of implying that time alone is the determining factor and of ignoring the many changes in the social and economic environment which are plainly influencing the number of automobiles owned in the region and in the individual counties.

A more logical projection procedure is to work from the base of prospective population, taking into account the changing relationship between population and the number of households, and between households and automobiles owned.

Population and Households

Projections of the New York Metropolitan Region's population to 1985 are presented in Chapter 2. For the 22 counties covered in those projections the total population is expected to increase from 16,139,000 in 1960 to 20,935,000 in 1980. For the 18 counties considered in this chapter the corresponding figures are 15,094,000 in 1960 and 18,805,000 in 1980, a 25 per cent increase.

The automobile is a household-ownership item and it cannot be assumed that the number of households in the 18 counties will increase in the future in proportion to the increase in population. The number of people forming a household group has been declining all over the country for at least six decades, and in the New York Metropolitan Region has fallen from an average of 4.72 in 1900 to an average of 3.18 in 1960. Paradoxically, average family size has been increasing in recent years. The Regional Plan Association has had the following to say about this phenomenon:²

"Household size is affected greatly by the changing age distribution of the population. This in turn depends on many factors: economic conditions; marriage and birth rates; the tendency toward more or fewer children per family; medical science and longer life expectancy. Household size is affected also by the ability of unmarried adults or elderly parents of adults to maintain separate living accommodations.

"The region's average household size has undergone a steady decline from 4.72 in 1900 to 3.43 in 1950. It is most striking to note that while population increased 2½ times in the past half century, the number of households increased 3½ times. The significance of this fact on the distribution of population may be dramatized by the following supposition: if the region's 1955 population were still living in the 1900 pattern of household size, there would be nearly 1½ million fewer homes in the region today and a drastic reduction in the amount of land in residential use.

"The crucial factors accounting for the actual decline in household size have been the continually aging population and the sharp drop in families with a dozen or so children. Increased life expectancy and a consequent rise in one- and two-person households have more than offset the fact that, as compared with the depression years, families with children may tend to have more children nowadays."

As a result of the declining trend of household size (Table 1), the number of households has been increasing faster than population. In the 20-year period, 1940 to 1960, the number of households in the Region increased by about 50 per cent, while population rose by 28 per cent. It is reasonable to suppose that the factors that have brought about the decline in household size in the past will also be operative in the future, and we must look forward to a more rapid growth in households between 1960 and 1980 than in pop-

TABLE 1. AVERAGE HOUSEHOLD SIZE[a]
IN THE REGION, 1900 TO 1960

1900	4.72
1910	4.65
1920	4.41
1930	4.07
1940	3.72
1950	3.43
1960	3.18

[a]Household size: Total population divided by total number of households.

Source: U. S. Census.

ulation, a conclusion concurred in by the Regional Plan Association.

The individual counties of the Region differ rather widely both in household size and in the rate at which that size has been changing. For each one a projection can be made of its probable size of household in 1980 and its probable number of households, based on its expected 1980 population. When such projections are made, on the assumption of a percentage drop in household size during 1960–1980 equal to the percentage drop experienced during 1940–1960, a projected value of 2.79 persons per household is obtained for 1980 as a regional average. The projected aggregate number of households for that year in the 18 counties is 6,748,000, a 41 per cent increase over 1960.

Automobile Registrations

How may the projected future number of households be translated into a future number of automobile registrations? If automobile ownership rates in the region, expressed as automobiles per hundred households, should remain at 1960 levels, we should expect the number of automobiles in the 18 counties to increase by 41 per cent between 1960 and 1980, equal to the projected rate of increase in households, even though only a 25 per cent growth in population is expected. But the number of automobiles registered in the region has been increasing even faster than the number of households.

In 1940 the automobile ownership rate for the 18-county district as a whole was 59.7 automobiles per 100 households, in 1950 it was 69.8, and 83.4 in 1960. The individual counties, of course, vary widely in ownership rates, ranging in 1960 from a low of 25 in Manhattan to highs of 146 in Morris County and in Suffolk County. There is a consistent tendency for areas developed at low residential densities to display high ownership rates and for high-density areas to be characterized by low ownership rates.

When the growths in automobile registrations that took place during the two decennial periods are related to the growths in households, it appears that between 1940 and 1950 the increase in the number of automobiles was equivalent to 120 for each 100 additional households; for 1950–1960, the incremental rate was higher, 140 additional automobiles for each 100 additional households. For the 20-year period as a whole, 131 automobiles were added for each 100 additional households.

Two important factors have been involved in the rise in the regional average automobile ownership rate. One is the preponderance of population gains in the suburban counties, where the ownership rate is high as a consequence of low residential density, which makes automobile ownership almost indispensable. The other is the general increase in personal incomes, and a higher standard of living, which has increased ownership rates throughout, irrespective of character of residential development. Hudson County, which has been stable in the character of its land development, increased its ownership rate from about 72 to 77 per 100 households between 1950 and 1960; its

increase in households was moderate and its population actually declined.

If we assume that the 1940-1960 relationship between the region-wide increase in automobile registrations and the region-wide increase in households will prevail during 1960–1980, the increase in automobiles, based on the projected increase in households of 1,973,000, will be 2,610,000, and the number of automobiles in the 18 counties will be 6,610,000 in 1980.

A more refined estimate results from the application of this estimating procedure to the 18 counties individually, using the 1940–1960 incremental growth rate for each county and each county's projected increase in households. On this basis the estimate for the 18-county total of automobiles in 1980 is 6,678,000, a 68 per cent increase over 1960. The implied average rate of ownership for the 18 counties in 1980 is approximately one automobile to a household.

Thus, although we look forward to only a 25 per cent rise in population, a 41 per cent rise in households is to be expected, because of the declining trend in household size, and a 68 per cent increase in automobile registrations is likely, because of increasing rates of ownership.

Future Trans-Hudson Automobile Traffic

The future magnitude of trans-Hudson automobile traffic can now be projected by utilizing its correlation with automobile registrations. An 18-county total of 6,678,000 automobiles implies a 1980 annual volume of 139,100,000 automobile trips. This is the 1980 projected annual volume for the aggregate of the Holland Tunnel, the Lincoln Tunnel, the George Washington Bridge, the Tappan Zee Bridge and the interstate component of the Verrazano-Narrows Bridge.

Back in 1930, trans-Hudson automobile

traffic on 114 Saturdays, Sundays and holidays, accounting for about 31 per cent of the year's days, was 42 per cent of the annual total. The annual average Sunday and holiday traffic was 54 per cent higher than the annual average daily traffic and 80 per cent higher than the annual average weekday traffic. In recent years, however, some of the leisure-time or recreational travel has spilled over into the weekdays, on Friday afternoons and Monday mornings. Moreover, traffic has expanded during weekday off-hours, when surplus capacity has been available on the vehicular facilities. In 1960, only about 37 per cent of annual trans-Hudson automobile traffic was concentrated on Saturdays, Sundays and holidays. Annual average Sunday and holiday automobile traffic was only 21 per cent higher than the annual average daily traffic and about 30 per cent higher than the annual average weekday traffic, a marked change in 30 years. This spreading out of trans-Hudson automobile traffic over the seven days of the week has contributed to higher annual working capacities of the existing Hudson River crossings.

The historical relationship between the annual totals of Saturday, Sunday and holiday traffic and the number of automobiles registered in the 18 counties can be established, similar in form to the relationship between total annual traffic and automobile registrations. The relationship between weekday traffic and automobile

TABLE 2. ANNUAL TRANS-HUDSON AUTOMOBILE TRAFFIC, 1930–1980[a]

(in millions)

	Weekdays	Saturdays	Sundays & Holidays	Total
Recorded				
1930	10.9	2.9	5.0	18.8
1935	13.5	3.6	5.8	22.9
1940	17.7	4.7	7.8	30.2
1945	14.8	3.4	5.3	23.5
1946	20.6	4.8	7.5	32.9
1950	27.8	7.2	10.8	45.8
1955	41.4	10.1	13.8	65.3
1956	44.5	11.4	15.6	71.5
1957	47.1	11.5	16.1	74.7
1958	48.4	11.8	15.9	76.1
1959	52.0	12.1	16.8	80.9
1960	52.2	13.2	17.2	82.6
Projected				
1965	59.2	14.1	19.0	92.3
1970	69.3	16.4	21.9	107.6
1975	79.9	18.8	24.9	123.6
1980	90.0	21.2	27.9	139.1

[a]Includes Tappan Zee Bridge and interstate traffic via Verrazano-Narrows Bridge.

TABLE 3. AVERAGE DAILY TRANS-HUDSON AUTOMOBILE TRAFFIC, 1930–1980[a]

(in thousands)

	Average Weekday	Average Saturday	Average Sunday & Holiday	Average Day
Recorded				
1930	43.5	56.9	79.3	51.5
1935	54.1	70.3	91.6	62.9
1940	70.4	91.6	124.0	82.6
1945	59.0	66.7	83.7	64.3
1946	82.2	93.6	118.5	90.1
1950	110.9	141.7	169.3	125.4
1955	165.2	197.7	218.8	179.0
1956	178.2	219.1	243.5	195.4
1957	187.4	226.2	255.9	204.7
1958	192.8	231.5	252.4	208.5
1959	206.2	241.9	267.3	221.6
1960	209.0	248.3	273.5	225.8
Projected				
1965	236.8	276.5	301.6	252.5
1970	272.2	328.0	347.6	294.5
1975	319.6	368.6	395.2	338.5
1980	360.0	407.7	442.9	381.0

[a]Includes Tappan Zee Bridge and interstate traffic via Verrazano-Narrows Bridge.

registrations also can be established. When these relationships are used for projection purposes, they indicate that differences between weekday and week-end traffic will be further reduced, and that by 1980 average Sunday and holiday traffic should not exceed average daily traffic by more than about 16 per cent, or average weekday traffic by more than 23 per cent.

MOTOR TRUCK TRAFFIC

For the period of record, motor truck traffic has also increased steadily but, unlike automobile traffic, the annual increments have shown no strong upward trend. Future increases can be approximated by using equal annual increments, approximately the average annual increment in the most recent past.

In the first 15 years (1915–1930) for which records are available, much of the increase in trans-Hudson motor truck traffic was a replacement of the shrinking trans-Hudson traffic of horse-drawn vehicles. Trans-Hudson motor trucks first exceeded trans-Hudson horse-drawn vehicles in 1921. In that year there were over 2.4 million trans-Hudson motor truck trips and 2.2 million trips by horse-drawn wagons. Between 1915 and 1930 the annual increases averaged about 150,000, and between 1930 and 1950 about 195,000. In the last 10-year period (1950–1960), the average annual gain in trans-Hudson trips was about 280,000. An annual gain of about 300,000 trans-Hudson truck trips may reasonably be expected in the future.

Table 4 shows recorded annual trans-Hudson truck trips for selected years and projections for every fifth year in the next 20 years.

TABLE 4. ANNUAL TRANS-HUDSON
MOTOR TRUCK TRIPS[a]

Recorded

1915	3,927,000
1930	6,187,000
1950	10,067,000
1960	12,872,000

Projected

1965	14,400,000
1970	15,900,000
1975	17,400,000
1980	18,900,000

[a]Includes Tappan Zee Bridge and interstate traffic via Verrazano-Narrows Bridge.

Analyses of the trends of the different classes of trucks make it appear that future expansions in truck movements will probably be limited almost entirely to trucks of over five tons capacity and to tractor-trailer combinations. Traffic of medium trucks (two to five tons) appears to be shrinking and will probably continue to shrink in the future, while that of small trucks (two tons and under) apparently has permanently leveled off.

The strong growth trend in large trucks and tractor-trailers began during World War II and has continued through the postwar period. This has come about in part as a result of a tendency for carriers to use larger units, but more important has been the strong growth trend in over-the-road trucking of freight. Recently the move toward larger units has been further reinforced by the gradual adoption by the railroads of the "piggyback" method of rail-truck coordination, and by their growing practice of substituting trucking for marine handling of freight between New Jersey and New York.

Expanding trans-Hudson movements of large trucks and tractor-trailer combinations thus may be expected in the next 20 years. It is possible, however, that the trend might be slowed down if the railroads were to adopt operating methods in the marine handling of freight that would yield significant economies and efficiencies, such as consolidation of operations of floating equipment.

In 1950, large trucks and tractor-trailers constituted about 46 per cent of total trucks, in 1960 about 63 per cent, and by 1980 they will probably make up about 85 per cent.

TRANS-HUDSON BUSES

Records of trans-Hudson bus traffic begin with 1925, when it was estimated that there were some 70,000 trans-Hudson bus trips. The volume more than doubled, to 155,000, in the following year.

Over the years, trans-Hudson bus traffic has grown irregularly, showing spurts after the opening of each new vehicular crossing, like the Holland Tunnel in 1927, the George Washington Bridge in 1931, the Lincoln Tunnel in 1937, and after the opening of the Port Authority Bus Terminal in 1950. There were also growth responses to each discontinuance of commuter rail service, particularly in Bergen County. In each of such instances, new bus lines were inaugurated, followed by gradual increases in trans-Hudson bus movements. Table 5 shows the recorded annual trans-Hudson bus trips for selected years in the past, and projected volumes for the next 20 years.

The prospect is for discontinuances or reductions of trans-Hudson railroad ferry services, and for the construction of more expressways in New Jersey. The consequence is likely to be further growth in trans-Hudson bus trips. In the next 20 years about 930,000 more annual trans-Hudson bus trips may be expected, at an average growth of about 46,500 a year.

TOTAL TRANS-HUDSON VEHICULAR TRAFFIC DEMAND

Bringing together the projections of trans-Hudson automobiles, trucks and buses, it will be seen from Table 6 that trans-Hudson vehicular traffic will probably expand from a 1960 level of 98.8 million vehicles, to a level of about 163 million vehicles by 1980, or an anticipated over-all expansion in 20 years of about 65 per cent.

TABLE 5. RECORDED AND PROJECTED ANNUAL TRANS-HUDSON BUS TRAFFIC

Recorded

1929	676,000
1937	1,129,000
1940	1,737,000
1960	3,269,000
1961	3,426,000

Projected

1965	3,640,000
1970	3,840,000
1975	4,040,000
1980	4,200,000

TRANS-HUDSON VEHICULAR CAPACITY

Since the end of the war it has been necessary to rerate the annual capacities of trans-Hudson crossings. During the earlier years of the Holland Tunnel's operation, the annual capacity of its four

TABLE 6. ANNUAL TRANS-HUDSON VEHICULAR TRAFFIC[a]

(in thousands)

	Automobiles	Buses	Trucks	Total Vehicles
Recorded				
1915	1,040	—	3,927	4,967
1925	7,256	71	5,220	12,547
1930	18,811	777	6,187	25,775
1940	30,231	1,737	7,446	39,414
1950	45,773	2,484	10,067	58,324
1959	80,898	3,186	12,651	96,735
1960	82,641	3,269	12,872	98,782
1961	83,310	3,426	13,126	99,862
Projected				
1965	92,300	3,640	14,400	110,340
1970	107,600	3,840	15,900	127,340
1975	123,600	4,040	17,400	145,040
1980	139,100	4,200	18,900	162,200

[a]Includes Tappan Zee Bridge and interstate traffic via Verrazano-Narrows Bridge.

lanes was rated at about 15 million vehicles, or about 3.75 million vehicles per lane, and in its early years the annual capacity of the George Washington Bridge, with six lanes, was rated at about 15 million vehicles, or about 2.5 million vehicles per lane. In later years, the ratings of their annual capacities have been raised several times. The Holland Tunnel's annual capacity is now rated at about 22 million vehicles, or about 5.4 million vehicles per lane. The George Washington Bridge's annual vehicular capacity with eight lanes was rated in 1961 at about 40 million.

Why have the annual capacities of the trans-Hudson vehicular crossings become greater over the years? The lanes themselves have not changed.

Fundamentally, the only true measure of the capacity of a highway lane is the number of vehicles it can accommodate safely and comfortably in a relatively short time interval, say an hour. If traffic demand were uniform throughout the 24 hours of each day, the seven days of each week and the 52 weeks of the year, a lane could accommodate in the course of a year its hourly capacity multiplied by 8,760, the number of hours in a year. But traffic demand is not uniform. Such a theoretical annual capacity must be reduced by three factors, all reflecting the time aspects of travel behavior, in order to arrive at a publicly tolerable annual load. The three factors are (a) hourly variations in the course of a day, (b) daily variations in the course of a week, and (c) seasonal, or weekly, variations in the course of a year.

From data assembled on hourly, daily and seasonal volumes of traffic flow at the trans-Hudson crossings, these three load factors may be derived and the rated annual vehicle capacity of each crossing may be computed. The factors involved are not unique for the trans-Hudson cross-

ings, for similar factors may be observed at other highway facilities in the New York region as well as in other parts of the United States. Over the years, however, the variations in traffic flow as among the hours of the day, the days of the week and the weeks of the year have become narrower, and as a result the annual capacities of trans-Hudson crossings have become greater.

In the 1930's, the George Washington Bridge, with a maximum hourly capacity of about 1,300 vehicles per lane, had an absolute annual lane capacity of about 11.4 million vehicles; that is, if each lane had carried 1,300 vehicles an hour for the 8,760 hours of the year, its yearly total would have been 11.4 million vehicles, or 31,200 a day. But the hourly pattern of flow was such that a day's average hour was only about 50 per cent of its peak hour. This meant that if the peak hour absorbed the hourly capacity, the traffic for the day would be only about 50 per cent of that, or 15,600 per lane.

Similarly, weekday traffic was far lighter than Sunday traffic, so that the average day of the week came to only about 60 per cent of the maximum day volume, and seasonal variation was such that the average week was only about 73 per cent of the year's maximum week. Thus, the hourly, daily and seasonal factors reduced the annual working capacity of a bridge lane to about 22 per cent of its absolute capacity, or to about 2.6 million. The six lanes of the bridge were thus rated at about 15-million vehicles capacity annually.

In 1961 the absolute capacity of each George Washington Bridge lane was not materially different from what it was in the thirties, about 11.4 million vehicles annually. With eight lanes the Bridge had an absolute annual capacity of about 90 million vehicles. Its hourly, daily and seasonal load factors, however, were about 60 per cent, 90 per cent and 82 per cent, respectively, with another step-up in the hourly load factor resulting from the five-lane–three-lane operation during peak hours. Its annual working capacity, consequently, was about 40 million vehicles, or 5 million per lane instead of 2.6 million. Its composite load factor was about 44 per cent of the absolute instead of the 22 per cent which was the composite factor in the thirties.

This rating also assumes that there are a certain number of hours in the year, perhaps as many as 100 on some 40 days, during which traffic demand is somewhat more than can be accommodated immediately and that during those hours there is some back-up. It would be inordinately costly, and quite uneconomical, to provide enough capacity to assure the acceptance of all traffic at all times without any delay whatever, even during the year's few extremely high-demand hours. The rated annual capacity of individual and of all trans-Hudson vehicular crossings thus reflects not only the pattern of hourly demand but also the tolerance of the public for a certain amount of delay during peak periods.

Taking these factors into account, in 1961 the aggregate annual trans-Hudson crossing capacity of the two-tube Holland Tunnel, the three-tube Lincoln Tunnel, the eight-lane George Washington Bridge, the six-lane Tappan Zee Bridge and the remaining Hudson River ferries was rated at about 122 million vehicles.

The Outlook for Increased Capacity

Six lanes were added to the George Washington Bridge in 1962, increasing its annual capacity by 30 million. The 2 million capacity of the Hudson River ferries, however, may not be available by 1965. Hence, it is estimated that the annual

capacity of trans-Hudson crossings, as of 1965, will be about 150 million vehicles.

The Verrazano-Narrows Bridge is expected to be opened sometime in that year. Its initial six lanes will add further annual capacity of about 30 million. Only about half of its traffic will be of an interstate character, however; the other half will consist of local Staten Island-Brooklyn traffic. Consequently, only 15 million is to be credited to interstate capacity. There will thus be available, late in 1965, an annual capacity for interstate traffic of 165 million vehicles.

The lower level of the Verrazano-Narrows Bridge, with another six lanes, when subsequently opened to traffic will add another 15 million capacity for interstate traffic. There will then be available a total of 36 lanes, with an aggregate capacity of about 180 million vehicles annually.

Demand Versus Capacity

With an annual capacity of 122 million vehicles, trans-Hudson crossings, including the Tappan Zee Bridge, handled a total of about 97 million in 1959, and about 99 million in 1960, and about 100 million in 1961. This left a margin of capacity of about 23 million in 1960, and 22 million in 1961.

Table 7 shows the estimated annual vehicular capacities of existing Hudson River crossings and the interstate capacity of the Verrazano-Narrows Bridge. Table 8 shows the recorded annual trans-Hudson traffic and that estimated for future years compared with the capacities of interstate crossings.

From origin-destination studies, it is known that a substantial proportion of trans-Hudson traffic is not tied to a particular crossing, but could use without material inconvenience the Holland Tunnel, the Lincoln Tunnel or the George

TABLE 7. ANNUAL CAPACITIES OF INTERSTATE CROSSINGS

| | Existing | | Additional Capacity Under Construction or Planned | |
	Lanes	Annual Capacity	Lanes	Annual Capacity
		(million vehicles)		(million vehicles)
George Washington Bridge	14	70	—	—
Lincoln Tunnel	6	33	—	—
Holland Tunnel	4	22	—	—
Hudson River Ferries	—	2	—	—
Tappan Zee Bridge	6	25	—	—
Verrazano-Narrows Bridge Available for interstate traffic				
(1965)	—	—	3	15
(1975–80)	—	—	3	15
Total (1980)	30	150[a]	6	30

[a]Interstate ferries are likely to be discontinued by 1965, reducing capacity by 2 million.

Washington Bridge. The effect of the expansion of the capacity of the George Washington Bridge, therefore, is likely to be a redistribution of trans-Hudson vehicular traffic. The bridge will absorb a greater load and will significantly relieve the tunnels. A certain amount of such redistribution, primarily affecting the George Washington Bridge, took place when the Tappan Zee Bridge was opened in 1956.

When the Verrazano-Narrows Bridge is opened to traffic in 1965, a substantial proportion of the Holland Tunnel traffic will be diverted to it. The relief thus afforded will provide a margin of capacity that will attract traffic to the Holland Tunnel from the Lincoln Tunnel, and the Holland and Lincoln tunnels together will attract traffic which theretofore traveled via the George Washington Bridge. Thus, the Verrazano - Narrows Bridge will tend to redistribute the fluid portion of the interstate (trans-Hudson–trans-Upper Bay) traffic among the three Hudson River crossings and the Verrazano-Narrows Bridge.

Trans-Hudson traffic is not so completely fluid as to routing, however, to warrant equating the aggregate capacities noted in Table 8 with the total projected traffic demand. The Verrazano-Narrows Bridge and the Tappan Zee Bridge, for example, will not be alternative routes except for a small share of the total traffic. Surplus capacity in the north may be no compensation for a serious shortage in the south, and vice versa. It is entirely possible, that by, say, 1975, in consequence of the origin-destination pattern which will have developed by then, there will be inadequate crossing capacity in the north, or south, or center, despite an over-all capacity margin for 19 million additional annual vehicles.

TRANS-HUDSON PASSENGERS IN 1980

In the foregoing sections the trans-Hudson *vehicular* traffic demand was projected to 1980, with the view of estimating when there would be a need for additional trans-Hudson vehicular crossing capac-

TABLE 8. ESTIMATED ANNUAL INTERSTATE TRAFFIC AND CROSSING CAPACITIES

(including Tappan Zee Bridge)

	No. of Lanes	Annual Traffic	Annual Capacity	Capacity Utilized	Margin of Annual Capacity
		(in millions)	(in millions)	(per cent)	(in millions)
1959	24	97	122	79.5	25
1960	24	99	122	81.0	23
1961	24	100	122	82.0	22
1962[a]	24	106	122	86.9	16
1963[b]	30	109	152	71.8	43
1965[c]	30	111	152	73.0	41
1965[d]	33[e]	111	165[f]	67.5	54
1970	33	128	165	77.5	37
1975	33	146	165	88.6	19
1975[g]	36[e]	146	180	81.0	34
1980	36	163	180	91.5	17

[a]Before George Washington Bridge lower deck was opened to traffic.
[b]After George Washington Bridge lower deck was opened to traffic.
[c]Before Verrazano-Narrows Bridge upper deck is opened to traffic.
[d]After Verrazano-Narrows Bridge upper deck is opened to traffic.
[e]Available for interstate traffic.
[f]Remaining Hudson River ferries assumed discontinued by 1965.
[g]Assuming Verrazano-Narrows Bridge lower deck is available.

ity. This section is directed to the examination of volumes and trends of trans-Hudson *passengers,* by all modes of transportation, and to an estimation of their probable future volumes.

A properly balanced concern for the various aspects of the metropolitan transportation problem demands consideration of the interrelationships between the different modes. The automobile, for instance, has clearly supplanted the common carrier for leisure-time travel. In some areas the buses and the railroads are in sharp competition. The suburbanization of homes and jobs and the increase of leisure time have different impacts on the different forms of transport. The deep-seated forces that have been influencing travel behavior in the region have been discussed at length in earlier chapters of this report, particularly Chapters 2 and 19.

Trans-Hudson Automobile Passengers

It will be remembered that the automobile traffic projections are based on projections of automobile registrations in the 18 counties of New York and New Jersey which are considered the trans-Hudson traffic-generating area, and which, in turn, are considered to be a function of the number of households and, therefore, to be dependent ultimately on regional population and household size characteristics.

The number of persons riding in an automobile crossing the Hudson River has been gradually declining over the years, from about 2.3 in 1930 to 2.1 in 1960. The tendency for average household size to shrink, discussed earlier, together with prospective wide dispersal of employment locations, leads to the view that the declining trend in persons per automobile will continue. It is estimated that the figure will approach 1.9 by 1980. Annual recorded trans-Hudson automobile passenger trips and projected interstate automobile passenger trip demand for selected years, 1930–1980, are shown in Table 9.

Trans-Hudson Bus Passengers

The trans-Hudson bus traffic data can be converted to bus passenger estimates by utilizing the sample data on passengers per bus compiled by the Public Service Coordinated Transportation Company of New Jersey and by the bus-carrier tenants of the Port Authority Bus Terminal.

Between 1950 and 1960 annual trans-Hudson bus passengers increased by about one-third, say somewhat more than 3 per cent a year. The rise was, at least in part, a response to increases in rail fares

and to the abandonment of certain rail services and the curtailment of others. Now that rail service and rail fares appear to have been stabilized, as a consequence of State assistance to the rail lines, it is likely that the rate of rise of bus patronage will be less in the future. During the most recent years of record the rate of rise has been less than 2 per cent annually. The projected volumes presented in Table 10 assume that the growth rate will moderate further, to little more than 1 per cent annually for the period 1960 to 1980.

Trans-Hudson Ferry Pedestrians

In 1921 some 50 million persons, one out of every four trans-Hudson passengers, crossed the river on ferries as foot passengers. They either walked to the ferries or

TABLE 9. ANNUAL TRANS-HUDSON PERSONS IN AUTOMOBILES, 1930 TO 1980[a]

	Automobiles	Persons Per Automobile	Persons in Automobiles
	(in thousands)		(in thousands)
Recorded			
1930	18,811	2.3	43,944
1940	30,231	2.4	74,161
1950	45,773	2.2	100,219
1955	65,326	2.1	139,348
1956	71,526	2.1	150,200
1957	74,705	2.0	149,400
1958	76,101	2.0	152,200
1959	80,898	2.05	165,850
1960	82,641	2.1	173,550
1961	83,310	2.1	174,950
Projected			
1965	92,300	2.1	194,000
1970	107,600	2.0	215,000
1975	123,600	1.95	240,000
1980	139,100	1.9	265,000

[a]Includes Tappan Zee Bridge and interstate traffic via Verrazano-Narrows Bridge.

TABLE 10. ANNUAL TRANS-HUDSON PASSENGERS IN BUSES, 1930 TO 1980

	Persons Per Bus Annual Average	Trans-Hudson Bus Traffic[a]	Bus Passengers[a]
		(in thousands)	(in thousands)
Recorded			
1930	11.9	730	8,658
1940	19.1	1,670	31,884
1950	25.9	2,397	62,078
1955	24.4	2,769	67,532
1959	25.8	3,177	81,882
1960	25.3	3,264	82,542
1961	24.8	3,426	84,881
Projected			
1965	25.0	3,640	91,000
1970	25.0	3,840	96,000
1975	25.0	4,040	101,000
1980	25.0	4,200	105,000

[a]Excluding railroad transfer buses.

traveled to them by trolley cars. On week ends, uptown ferries, such as the Dyckman Street and Fort Lee ferries, did a thriving business carrying hikers and picnickers from New York to parks in New Jersey.

The development of interstate bus service in the 1930's, however, was followed by declines in the volume of ferry pedestrians. In 1961 there were only 0.4 million persons who rode the ferries, other than the commuter railroad passengers. This is approaching a vanishing point. It is assumed that future volumes will be negligible.

Annual pedestrians via ferries for selected years, 1915–1961, are shown in Table 11.

Trans-Hudson Railroad Passengers

Records of trans-Hudson railroad passengers, classified as to commuters and other passengers, have been furnished the Port Authority by the railroads over the years, going back to 1911. Commuters are defined by the railroads as passengers riding on reduced or "commuted" fare tickets, regardless of time of day, purpose or frequency of trips. These statistics, however, do yield a reasonable approximation of the volume of local trans-Hudson (largely journey-to-work) rail travel, as distinct from interregional rail travel. In general, from 1911 to 1929 the trans-Hudson rail commuter volume increased steadily, to a high point of 113.1 million annual passengers; since 1929, with only minor fluctuations and with the exception of two war years, it has been shrinking steadily.

On closer examination it is seen that between 1912 and 1918, annual trans-Hudson rail commuters increased from 68.4 million to 77.4 million, about 1.5 million a year. In the first two years after the end

TABLE 11. ANNUAL TRANS-HUDSON
FERRY PEDESTRIANS
(in thousands)

1915	45,137
1920	50,891
1930	38,611
1940	22,045
1950	6,399
1955	2,288
1959	575
1960	435
1961	404

of World War I, volumes rose much more rapidly to a level, in 1920, of 95.8 million. Expansion continued thereafter, but at a moderate rate, until 1929 when the high point was reached.

During the depression years of the early thirties rail commuter volumes fell drastically from the 1929 level to 77.4 million in 1933, and then to 64.8 million in 1941. In the following two war years, the commuter volume jumped again to a level of 71.8 million in 1943, but since the end of the war it has been declining by about 2.4 million passengers a year, and in 1960 reached the level of 30.6 million. This postwar decline has been the consequence of many factors, which have been discussed in detail in Chapter 19. There have been the abandonment of the West Shore Railroad's passenger service, the development of bus service for the new low-density residential areas in the northern New Jersey counties, the uptown migration of Manhattan business establishments, the increase in New Jersey job opportunities, and others.

The volume of trans-Hudson noncommuter rail passengers has followed a generally similar pattern, but with several important variations. Between 1912 and 1918 it grew at the rate of 1.9 million a year. It rose much more rapidly, by 7 million, in the two post–World War I years (1918 and 1920), and then continued to grow steadily until 1929, when a high level of 64.8 million was achieved.

Like commuter passengers, noncommuter passengers dropped sharply in volume during the depression years, to a level of 44.1 million in 1933. Unlike commuter passengers, however, the volume then resumed its growth and reached a level of 51.8 million passengers in 1941. In the two war years, it bulged to 80.5 million, reflecting the high volume of wartime rail travel and the wartime restrictions on other forms of travel, but after the war it shrank again to 43.2 million in 1950, less than the 1933 depression level.

In the 1950–1960 decade, noncommuter passengers continued to decline at the rate of about 1.9 million persons a year to a level of 24.1 million passengers in 1960.

Prospects for Trans-Hudson Rail Travel

During the decade 1950 to 1960, the annual volume of trans-Hudson rail passengers declined from 98.0 million to 54.7 million, an average rate of more than 4 per cent a year. The rate of decline for commuters was about the same as that for noncommuters. The regional forces related to that decline have been discussed in earlier chapters. They include (1) population growth in New Jersey areas distant from the rail lines, (2) growth of employment opportunities in New Jersey, (3) decline in Hudson County's population, (4) approximate stability of employment levels in Manhattan's Central Business District, and (5) highway improvements and competition presented to the railroads by interstate bus service. Concomitant with the decline in rail patronage were fare rises and curtailment, and in some instances discontinuance, of service, which had further depressing effects on rail travel demand.

TABLE 12. RECORDED AND PROJECTED
ANNUAL TRANS-HUDSON RAIL PASSENGERS,
1915–1980

(in thousands)

	Commuters	Others	Total
Recorded			
1915	68,107	37,043	105,150
1920	95,778	54,741	150,519
1925	108,474	60,307	168,781
1930	109,874	60,787	170,661
1935	73,273	46,466	119,739
1940	66,140	48,785	114,925
1945	64,478	76,867	141,345
1950	54,759	43,269	98,028
1955	38,973	33,495	72,468
1960	30,589	24,069	54,658
1961	30,037	23,776	53,813
Projected			
1965			50,000
1970			48,000
1975			46,000
1980			46,000

The past few years of record, however, suggest that the pace of decline has slackened to little more than 2 per cent a year as service levels and fares have been stabilized through State assistance. Moreover, there are active plans in the making for the rehabilitation and improvement of trans-Hudson rail service and a prospect of Federal financial assistance for mass transportation. These newer forces should bring about a further slowing down of the decline in rail usage.

The volumes projected for the future, as presented in Table 12, assume a rate of decline of about 1 per cent annually and stability thereafter from 1961 to 1975.

Trans-Hudson Passengers, Via all Modes

Bringing together the projections of trans-Hudson passengers by all modes, on the basis of the assumptions stated, it ap-

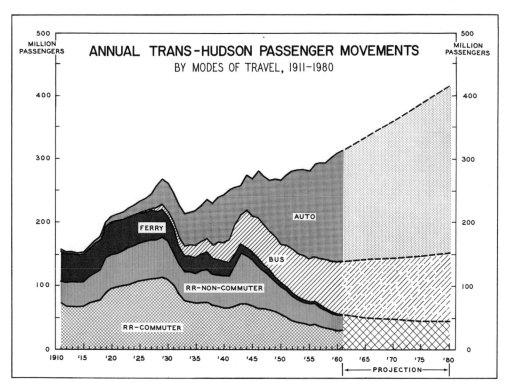

FIG. 2

pears that over-all trans-Hudson passengers will continue to expand for the next 20 years. However, most of the rise will be accounted for by more automobile passengers, an increase related closely to an increase in automobile registration in the region. Passengers using common-carrier transportation will rise moderately. This moderate rise seems likely in view of

the prospect, discussed in Chapter 2, that population growth in the New Jersey counties will outpace the rise in New Jersey job opportunities, particularly in the white collar categories which are expected to continue to increase in Manhattan. New Jersey residents traveling to jobs in Manhattan rely strongly on the common carriers.

TABLE 13. ANNUAL TRANS-HUDSON PASSENGERS BY MODE OF
TRANSPORTATION FOR SELECTED YEARS, 1915 TO 1980

(in millions)

	Common Carrier Passengers			Total Common Carrier	Passengers in Automobiles[a]	Total Passengers[a]
	Railroad	Ferry	Bus			
Recorded						
1915	105.2	45.1	—	150.3	2.6	152.9
1920	150.5	50.9	—	201.4	7.9	209.3
1925	168.8	45.3	0.9	215.0	18.1	233.1
1930	170.7	38.6	8.7	218.0	43.9	261.9
1940	114.9	22.0	31.9	168.8	74.2	243.0
1950	98.0	6.4	62.1	166.5	100.2	266.7
1959	57.3	0.6	81.9	139.8	165.9	305.7
1960	54.7	0.4	82.5	137.6	173.6	311.2
1961	53.8	0.4	84.9	139.1	175.0	314.1
Projected						
1965	50.0	—	91.0	141.0	194.0	335.0
1970	48.0	—	96.0	144.0	215.0	359.0
1975	46.0	—	101.0	147.0	240.0	387.0
1980	46.0	—	105.0	151.0	265.0	416.0

[a]An automobile driver is here considered a "passenger." Includes Tappan Zee Bridge and interstate travel via Verrazano-Narrows Bridge.

APPENDIX

APPENDIX

Population (Appendix Tables 1 and 2)

The projections of population and employment for the New York Metropolitan Region Study were prepared before the 1960 Census of Population and the 1958 economic censuses were available. As the recorded population gain in 1960 was significantly below what had been projected both for the Region and for the nation, the projections set forth in "Metropolis 1985" and in "Projection of a Metropolis" were revised by the same study group, under the sponsorship of the Regional Plan Association and supported, in part, by The Port of New York Authority.

The magnitudes involved in this revision are as follows:

REGIONAL POPULATION
(in thousands)

	Original Projection	Revised Projection
1965	18,033	17,180
1975	20,810	19,700
1985	23,712	22,170

The disparity between the 1960 census and the projected growth was manifest also in the constituent county figures. The revisions that were made had their greatest impact in reducing the prospective population of the inner-ring counties.

FORECASTS OF REGIONAL GROWTH
BY SECTORS: 1985
(population in thousands)

	Original Projection	Revision
Core counties	7,810	7,740
Inner ring	8,093	6,370
Outer ring	7,809	8,060

Employment

The estimate of employment was also scaled back in the revision, in view of the reduction in projected population.

The distribution of jobs by category as revised also differed substantially from the original projection. The differences are prominent in two categories: contract construction and government employment (Appendix Table 5).

RPA revised projections postulate a declining role for construction in the Region's employment. However, the estimate of future population growth in the Region, amounting to over 6 million persons, implies large-scale housing programs, the expansion of physical facilities for industry and the distributing trades, and accelerated urban renewal programs broader in scope than in the recent past. A review of historical trends, national and regional, in contract construction carries no suggestion that productivity will rise

EMPLOYMENT
(in thousands)

	Original Projection	Population to Job Ratio	Revised Projection	Population to Job Ratio
1965	7,202	2.50	6,860	2.50
1975	8,307	2.51	7,686	2.56
1985	9,462	2.45	8,846	2.51

enough in this industry to bring about a decline in employment. It is assumed here, therefore, that the percentage of total employment in contract construction which prevailed in the base year of the forecast (1956) — neither the highest nor lowest ratio in the postwar period — will prevail in the future.

Government employment in the revised forecast was scaled back drastically, dropping, as a percentage of total regional employment, from 9.9 per cent to 8.7 per cent. In absolute terms, the revised projection foresaw a rise from 633,000 in 1956 to 766,000 in 1985. Acceptance of this latter figure, however, poses a dilemma. If enough government employment for the performance of public services is allocated to the growth areas, a sharp reduction of government employment in New York City is implied. On the other hand, a reasonable allowance for the growth of such employment in New York City, in line with postwar trends, implies a reduction of government service employment outside the city to a point below existing levels. Moreover, the revised projection for the regional total would call for a reduction in the volume of government employment in relation to population, contrary to the broad historic trend, public service employment rising faster than population.

The original projection of government employment made for the New York Metropolitan Region Study is consistent with the national trend. This study, therefore, adopts the basic relationship embodied in the original forecast, with government employment rising as a percentage of total regional employment from 9.9 per cent in 1956 to 11.5 per cent in 1985.

The projected rise in government employment is 384,000 between 1956 and 1985, a gain of 61 per cent. Maintenance of government services at existing levels

for the increased regional population would, in itself, require an increase of 298,000 government jobs by 1985. The addition of 86,000 jobs, presumably for *new* or expanded government services, represents a modest increase.

With these considerations in mind, this study accepts the revised projection for total regional employment, but accepts, with one reservation, the proportioning of employment among the various categories in the original projection. The exception is in contract construction, where it is felt that the proportion recorded in 1956, 3.6 per cent, is likely to prevail in the future. In order to accommodate these modifications within the forecast parameters, employment in categories other than construction and government has been scaled back proportionately to their weight in the remainder of the distribution.

Geographic Distribution of Employment

Since the revision of the employment projections prepared by the New York Metropolitan Region Study was confined to estimates of the aggregate employment in each category of industry, it was necessary in this study to allocate employment among the counties.

In two categories of industry, manufacturing and wholesale trade, jobs have been allocated among the counties in the same proportions as in the original study. In the other industries it is believed that the distribution of population will affect the location of jobs. The distribution of total jobs is shown in Appendix Tables 3 and 4.

Estimate of Manhattan's Current and Future Employment

Despite the seeming wealth of statistical materials it has long been virtually impossible to arrive at a reliable estimate of employment in Manhattan. The economic censuses of the U. S. Bureau of the Census cover only those categories that in most areas constitute the bulk of employment: manufacturing, wholesale trade, retail trade and "selected" service industries. In Manhattan, the employment falling outside these fields assumes extraordinary importance, and cannot be approximated by the usual estimating procedures.

There are other sources of information, but all have definite limitations. Employment data provided in *County Business Patterns* of the Census Bureau are limited in coverage to firms in the Federal Old Age and Survivors Benefit Program. An additional limitation is the fact that these data as published show only aggregates for New York City, with no breakdown for the boroughs. The employment data reported by the labor departments of the states of New York, New Jersey and Connecticut are limited to the kinds and sizes of firms covered by unemployment insurance. Until recently, these data, too, have been available only for the New York City aggregate.

The New York City Planning Department, in a joint project with the New York State Department of Labor, has developed borough-by-borough employment information, an intricate task of sorting main office from branch employment, and dealing with jobs that are peripatetic in character.

The economic censuses of the federal government regularly measure employment as of the work week nearest November 15 in a census year. The New York Metropolitan Region Study used the month of June 1956 as its bench mark for employment, while the City Planning Department data used the September level of employment in its estimate for 1958. The available data, therefore, conceal important seasonal differences.

Yet the question of Manhattan's future level and pattern of employment is of such importance that it is well worth the effort to attempt to frame an estimate of it. The goal of this estimating process is to determine the degree to which the various industries will rise above or fall from current levels. In effect, the current bench mark as an absolute value is not so important as the differences the future might bring. A summary of the estimates is contained in Appendix Table 6. A few words of explanation are in order.

In manufacturing, the percentage of New York City employment found in Manhattan is based on the Census of Manufactures. The historical trend derived from the same source indicates a decline to about 40 per cent from the present proportion.

With respect to wholesale trade, Manhattan's current share of the city's employment is based on the proportions evident in the Census of Wholesale Trade. Manhattan's level of employment appears to be stable; it is likely, nevertheless, that Manhattan's share will decline slightly, owing to the expected growth in Queens.

In consumer trade and services, Manhattan's future share of employment, 54 per cent, is based on the historical trend, 1939–1958 in the U. S. Census.

In the finance, business and professional services group, the proportioning of financial employment follows the Robbins Terleckyj forecast in *Money Metropolis*, which estimates current and future employment in Manhattan south of 60th Street. This sum was increased moderately to allow for employment north of 60th Street.

In the business services group, the estimate of current employment in real estate has been computed by subtracting the financial employment, from the source indicated above, from the finance–insurance–real estate employment developed by the New York City Planning Department. Currently, Manhattan appears to account for about 87 per cent of the employment in real estate, and it is thought that this share will drop to 69 per cent by 1985.

With respect to central office employment, it is estimated that Manhattan contains about 90 per cent of the city's headquarters type of employment. In view of recent trends in the manufacturing industries, where administrative employment exhibits no marked tendency to decentralize, it is believed that Manhattan will continue to absorb roughly 90 per cent of the city's jobs in this category.

Census data also indicate that Manhattan accounts for 95 per cent of the advertising employment in the city. Film production for TV has an even higher concentration in Manhattan. It is believed, therefore, that there are no grounds for assuming a dispersal of advertising, radio and TV as a group out of Manhattan into the other boroughs.

The estimate of "other business services" is based on the Selected Business Services covered by the U. S. Census, which indicates a high concentration of the city's employment in Manhattan (90 per cent), although there has been some dispersal to other portions of the Region. With respect to "professional services," and "employment in nonprofit organizations," our closest approximation is that Manhattan's current share is in the neighborhood of 60 per cent. It is thought that it might decline to 50 per cent in 1985.

In the "utilities" group, Manhattan's current share is 68 per cent of the city's employment, and it is assumed that this same relationship will prevail in 1985. With respect to employment in "construction" and in "government," Manhattan's current shares are 41.1 per cent and 45.3 per cent, respectively, as revealed by the data developed by the New York City Planning Department. It is assumed that these fields will account for a constant share of the city's employment, resulting in a slight absolute rise.

TABLE 1. POPULATION IN THE NEW YORK METROPOLITAN REGION, 1920–1960, AND PROJECTIONS TO 1985
(in thousands)

	1920	1930	1940	1950	1960	1965	1970	1975	1980	1985
Metropolitan Region	9,139	11,643	12,518	13,951	16,141	17,180	18,440	19,700	20,935	22,170
New York sector	6,469	8,224	8,985	9,866	11,087	11,560	12,019	12,480	12,907	13,335
New York City	5,620	6,930	7,455	7,893	7,782	7,750	7,694	7,640	7,632	7,625
Bronx	732	1,265	1,395	1,451	1,425	1,400	1,375	1,350	1,350	1,350
Kings	2,018	2,561	2,698	2,739	2,627	2,600	2,549	2,500	2,475	2,450
New York	2,284	1,867	1,890	1,960	1,698	1,625	1,575	1,525	1,500	1,475
Queens	469	1,079	1,298	1,551	1,810	1,875	1,900	1,925	1,925	1,925
Richmond	117	158	174	192	222	250	295	340	382	425
Other New York	849	1,294	1,530	1,973	3,305	3,810	4,325	4,840	5,275	5,710
Dutchess	92	105	121	137	176	200	260	320	373	425
Nassau	126	303	407	673	1,300	1,400	1,499	1,500	1,525	1,550
Orange	120	130	140	152	184	205	278	350	445	540
Putnam	11	14	17	20	32	35	45	55	70	85
Rockland	46	60	74	89	137	170	195	320	335	350
Suffolk	110	161	197	276	667	910	1,103	1,295	1,477	1,660
Westchester	344	521	574	626	809	890	945	1,000	1,050	1,100
New Jersey sector	2,349	3,032	3,114	3,581	4,400	4,870	5,513	6,155	6,785	7,415
Bergen	211	365	410	539	780	920	1,009	1,100	1,150	1,200
Essex	652	835	837	907	924	940	950	960	955	950
Hudson	629	691	652	647	611	590	575	560	550	540
Middlesex	162	212	217	265	434	535	690	845	995	1,145
Monmouth	105	147	161	225	334	400	573	745	950	1,155
Morris	83	110	126	164	262	320	425	530	630	730
Passaic	259	302	309	337	407	435	448	460	472	485
Somerset	48	65	74	99	144	170	243	315	433	550
Union	200	305	328	398	504	560	600	640	650	660
Conn. (Fairfield) sector	321	387	418	504	654	750	908	1,065	1,243	1,420

Sources: U. S. Census and New York Metropolitan Region Study projections, revised.

TABLE 2. DISTRIBUTION OF POPULATION IN THE NEW YORK METROPOLITAN REGION, 1920–1960, AND PROJECTIONS TO 1985

(per cent of total)

	1920	1930	1940	1950	1960	1965	1970	1975	1980	1985
Metropolitan Region	100.0	100.0	100.0	100.0	100.0	100.0	100.0	100.0	100.0	100.0
New York sector	70.8	70.7	71.8	70.7	68.6	67.3	65.2	63.4	61.7	60.2
New York City	61.5	59.6	59.6	56.6	48.1	45.1	41.7	38.8	36.5	34.4
Bronx	8.0	10.9	11.1	10.4	8.8	8.1	7.5	6.9	6.5	6.1
Kings	22.1	22.0	21.6	19.7	16.2	15.1	13.8	12.7	11.8	11.0
New York	25.0	16.0	15.1	14.0	10.5	9.5	8.5	7.7	7.2	6.7
Queens	5.1	9.3	10.4	11.1	11.2	10.9	10.3	9.8	9.2	8.7
Richmond	1.3	1.4	1.4	1.4	1.4	1.5	1.6	1.7	1.8	1.9
Other New York	9.3	11.1	12.2	14.1	20.5	22.2	23.5	24.6	25.2	25.8
Dutchess	1.0	0.9	1.0	1.0	1.1	1.2	1.4	1.6	1.8	1.9
Nassau	1.4	2.6	3.2	4.8	8.2	8.1	8.2	7.6	7.3	7.0
Orange	1.3	1.1	1.1	1.1	1.1	1.2	1.5	1.8	2.1	2.4
Putnam	0.1	0.1	0.1	0.1	0.2	0.2	0.2	0.3	0.3	0.4
Rockland	0.5	0.5	0.6	0.6	0.8	1.0	1.1	1.6	1.6	1.6
Suffolk	1.2	1.4	1.6	2.0	4.1	5.3	6.0	6.6	7.0	7.5
Westchester	3.8	4.5	4.6	4.5	5.0	5.2	5.1	5.1	5.1	5.0
New Jersey sector	25.7	26.0	24.9	25.7	27.3	28.3	29.9	31.2	32.4	33.4
Bergen	2.3	3.1	3.3	3.9	4.8	5.3	5.5	5.6	5.5	5.3
Essex	7.2	7.2	6.7	6.6	5.8	5.5	5.2	4.9	4.6	4.3
Hudson	6.9	5.9	5.2	4.6	3.8	3.4	3.1	2.8	2.6	2.4
Middlesex	1.8	1.8	1.7	1.9	2.7	3.1	3.7	4.3	4.8	5.2
Monmouth	1.1	1.3	1.3	1.6	2.1	2.3	3.1	3.8	4.5	5.2
Morris	0.9	0.9	1.0	1.2	1.6	1.9	2.3	2.7	3.0	3.3
Passaic	2.8	2.6	2.5	2.4	2.5	2.5	2.4	2.3	2.3	2.2
Somerset	0.5	0.6	0.6	0.7	0.9	1.0	1.3	1.6	2.0	2.2
Union	2.2	2.6	2.6	2.8	3.1	3.3	3.3	3.2	3.1	3.0
Conn. (Fairfield) sector	3.5	3.3	3.3	3.6	4.1	4.4	4.9	5.4	5.9	6.4

Sources: U. S. Census and New York Metropolitan Region Study projections, revised.

TABLE 3. EMPLOYMENT IN THE NEW YORK METROPOLITAN REGION,
1956 AND PROJECTIONS TO 1985
(in thousands)

	1956	1965	1970	1975	1980	1985
Metropolitan Region	6,402.6	6,860.0	7,273.0	7,686.0	8,266.0	8,846.0
New York sector	4,629.9	4,811.3	4,944.9	5,078.5	5,449.5	5,820.6
New York City	3,894.8	3,830.5	3,853.7	3,877.0	4,058.5	4,240.2
Other New York	735.1	980.8	1,091.2	1,201.5	1,391.0	1,580.4
Dutchess	53.6	69.9	82.5	95.1	114.0	132.9
Nassau	274.2	337.5	355.8	374.4	416.1	457.8
Orange	49.6	58.8	72.4	85.9	109.4	132.9
Putnam	5.5	8.1	8.7	9.3	13.4	17.5
Rockland	29.7	40.4	55.3	70.1	78.3	86.5
Suffolk	105.6	195.2	230.9	266.5	320.9	375.2
Westchester	216.9	270.9	285.6	300.2	338.9	377.6
New Jersey sector	1,532.0	1,786.2	2,038.5	2,290.7	2,450.7	2,610.6
Bergen	208.1	278.3	322.0	365.7	388.7	411.6
Essex	402.1	393.8	409.4	425.2	426.5	428.3
Hudson	279.2	273.3	282.5	291.7	289.8	287.9
Middlesex	130.8	184.3	227.5	270.6	302.7	334.7
Monmouth	66.1	89.5	127.9	166.3	199.1	231.8
Morris	58.1	80.3	111.3	142.2	161.0	179.7
Passaic	161.4	200.3	221.6	242.9	260.4	277.8
Somerset	35.3	49.1	68.4	87.6	109.5	131.3
Union	190.9	237.3	267.9	298.5	313.0	327.5
Conn. (Fairfield) sector	240.7	262.5	289.6	316.8	365.8	414.8

Source: New York Metropolitan Region Study.

TABLE 4. DISTRIBUTION OF EMPLOYMENT IN THE NEW YORK METROPOLITAN REGION,
1956 AND PROJECTIONS TO 1985
(per cent of total)

	1956	1965	1970	1975	1980	1985
Metropolitan Region	100.0	100.0	100.0	100.0	100.0	100.0
New York sector	72.3	70.2	68.0	66.1	66.0	65.8
New York City	60.8	55.9	53.0	50.5	49.2	47.9
Other New York	11.5	14.3	15.0	15.6	16.8	17.9
Dutchess	0.8	1.0	1.1	1.2	1.4	1.5
Nassau	4.3	5.0	4.9	4.9	5.0	5.2
Orange	0.8	0.9	1.0	1.1	1.3	1.5
Putnam	0.1	0.1	0.1	0.1	0.2	0.2
Rockland	0.5	0.6	0.8	0.9	0.9	1.0
Suffolk	1.6	2.8	3.2	3.5	3.9	4.2
Westchester	3.4	3.9	3.9	3.9	4.1	4.3
New Jersey sector	23.9	26.0	28.0	29.8	29.6	29.5
Bergen	3.3	4.1	4.4	4.8	4.7	4.7
Essex	6.2	5.6	5.6	5.4	5.1	4.8
Hudson	4.4	4.0	3.9	3.8	3.5	3.3
Middlesex	2.0	2.7	3.1	3.5	3.7	3.8
Monmouth	1.0	1.3	1.8	2.2	2.4	2.6
Morris	0.9	1.2	1.5	1.9	1.9	2.0
Passaic	2.5	2.9	3.1	3.2	3.2	3.1
Somerset	0.6	0.7	0.9	1.1	1.3	1.5
Union	3.0	3.5	3.7	3.9	3.8	3.7
Conn. (Fairfield) sector	3.8	3.8	4.0	4.1	4.4	4.7

Source: New York Metropolitan Region Study, revised.

TABLE 5. DISTRIBUTION BY INDUSTRY OF EMPLOYMENT IN THE NEW YORK
METROPOLITAN REGION, 1956 AND PROJECTIONS TO 1985
(per cent of total)

	1956	1985		
		N.Y.M.R.S.[a]	N.Y.M.R.S. Revised	Adjusted Revision[b]
Total Employment (thousands)	6,402.6	9,462.0	8,846.0	8,846.0
Manufacturing	29.5	28.3	30.2	28.0
Wholesale trade	6.9	6.5	6.9	6.4
Consumer trade and services	21.5	20.0	22.1	19.8
Finance, business and prof. services	20.2	24.3	24.2	24.1
Public utilities	7.7	6.0	5.8	6.0
Construction	3.6	2.8	1.8	3.6
Miscellaneous	0.7	0.6	0.3	0.6
Government	9.9	11.5	8.7	11.5

[a]New York Metropolitan Region Study.
[b]By C. A. Franzmann and R. J. Watkins.

TABLE 6. ESTIMATE OF EMPLOYMENT IN MANHATTAN, 1956 AND 1985
(in thousands)

| | 1956 Employment | | | | 1985 Employment | | | |
| | New York City | Manhattan | | | New York City | Manhattan | | |
	N.Y.M.R.S.[a]	As Per Cent of N.Y.C.	Number	Per Cent Distribution	N.Y.M.R.S.[b]	As Per Cent of N.Y.C.	Number	Per Cent Distribution
All industries	3,894.9	61.8	2,405.8	100.0	4,240.2	58.3	2,473.7	100.0
Manufacturing	942.3	53.0	499.4	20.7	909.0	41.0	372.7	15.1
Wholesale trade	338.8	75.9	257.1	10.7	338.5	76.0	257.1	10.4
Consumer trade and services	808.8	54.0	436.8	18.2	847.8	54.0	458.0	18.5
Finance	250.6	84.2	211.0	8.8	347.5	83.6	290.5	11.7
Business and prof. serv.	726.9	77.0	559.6	23.2	950.8	69.3	659.2	26.7
Real estate	127.0	87.0	110.5	4.6	206.5	69.0	142.5	5.8
Central offices	143.3	90.0	129.0	5.4	176.1	90.0	158.4	6.4
Adv., TV, radio	41.7	95.0	39.6	1.6	59.0	95.0	56.1	2.3
Other business serv.	105.2	90.0	94.7	3.9	119.0	90.0	107.1	4.3
Prof. services and nonprofit organ.	309.7	60.0	185.8	7.7	390.2	50.0	195.1	7.9
Public utilities	323.3	67.7	218.9	9.1	270.7	67.7	183.0	7.4
Construction	110.8	41.1	45.5	1.9	158.3	41.0	65.0	2.6
Miscellaneous	5.2	33.0	1.7	0.1	6.6	30.0	2.0	0.1
Government	388.0	45.3	175.8	7.3	411.0	45.3	186.2	7.5

[a] New York Metropolitan Region Study.
[b] As revised.

TABLE 7. DISTRIBUTION OF MANUFACTURING EMPLOYMENT IN THE UNITED STATES, BY GEOGRAPHIC REGION, 1899–1955

Per Cent of U. S. Total

	Total Manufacturing Employment[a] (millions)	New England	Middle Atlantic	East North Central	West North Central	South Atlantic	East South Central	West South Central	Mountain	Pacific
1899	4.9	17.6	34.1	23.2	5.8	9.5	3.7	2.4	1.0	2.7
1909	7.0	16.0	33.8	23.3	5.9	9.7	3.9	3.0	1.1	3.3
1919	9.8	14.6	31.9	27.0	5.7	8.5	3.5	3.1	1.1	4.6
1929	9.7	12.3	29.8	29.1	5.6	10.1	4.1	3.3	1.1	4.6
1939	9.5	11.8	28.9	28.3	5.2	11.6	4.3	3.5	0.9	5.5
1947	14.3	10.3	27.6	30.2	5.5	10.7	4.4	3.9	1.0	6.4
1950	14.5	9.8	27.0	29.9	5.6	11.1	4.4	4.1	1.1	7.0
1951	15.3	9.6	26.5	29.9	5.8	10.9	4.4	4.2	1.1	7.7
1952	15.7	9.4	26.5	29.4	6.0	11.0	4.4	4.2	1.1	8.0
1953	16.7	9.4	26.2	30.0	5.8	10.7	4.4	4.3	1.1	8.1
1954	15.7	9.1	26.2	28.5	6.0	11.2	4.6	4.6	1.2	8.7
1955	16.3	8.9	25.6	29.0	5.8	11.3	4.7	4.6	1.3	8.9

[a]Includes employment of both production workers and nonproduction personnel at operating manufacturing plants only; excludes employees of manufacturing firms at separately reported central administrative offices, sales offices, auxiliary units, and other nonmanufacturing activities.

Data: 1954 Census of Manufactures Bulletin, Series MC-201; and 1955 Annual Survey of Manufactures, Series MAS-55-5.

U. S. Department of Commerce, Office of Area Development.

TABLE 8. REGIONAL INDEX OF INDUSTRIALIZATION,[a] 1899–1955

Ratio of Regional Manufacturing Employment per Thousand Population to U. S. Average

Year	Average U.S. Manufacturing Employment per Thousand Population	New England	Middle Atlantic	East North Central	West North Central	South Atlantic	East South Central	West South Central	Mountain	Pacific
1899	64	2.52	1.76	1.15	.45	.73	.39	.29	.45	.86
1909	78	2.37	1.69	1.24	.49	.77	.45	.34	.43	.78
1919	94	2.20	1.62	1.42	.52	.69	.44	.34	.40	.95
1929	79	1.93	1.46	1.48	.54	.80	.53	.36	.41	.87
1939	73	1.83	1.37	1.40	.50	.87	.53	.35	.30	.75
1947	100	1.64	1.38	1.49	.59	.76	.58	.40	.31	.68
1950	96	1.59	1.35	1.48	.60	.79	.58	.42	.32	.73
1951	100	1.61	1.34	1.49	.62	.77	.59	.42	.32	.77
1952	101	1.59	1.34	1.46	.67	.77	.57	.43	.32	.79
1953	106	1.56	1.32	1.47	.64	.75	.60	.44	.31	.79
1954	97	1.52	1.33	1.39	.66	.79	.64	.48	.34	.83
1955	100	1.50	1.31	1.41	.64	.79	.66	.48	.35	.84

[a] Index of Industrialization is the ratio of each region's average manufacturing employment per 1,000 population to the U. S. average.

Data: 1954 Census of Manufactures Bulletin, MC-201; 1955 Annual Survey of Manufactures, Current Population Reports, Series P-25, Nos. 139 and 165.

U. S. Department of Commerce, Office of Area Development.

TABLE 9. TRENDS IN WHOLESALE TRADE EMPLOYMENT IN THE NEW YORK METROPOLITAN AREA
(employment in thousands)

	1939 Number	1939 Per Cent	1948 Number	1948 Per Cent	1954 Number	1954 Per Cent	1958 Number	1958 Per Cent
Metropolitan Area	277.4	100.0	363.8	100.0	368.7	100.0	392.8	100.0
New York sector (S.M.S.A.)	248.2	89.5	317.8	87.3	306.7	83.2	322.8	82.2
New York City	241.4	87.0	305.9	84.1	287.4	78.0	295.9	75.3
Bronx	7.7	2.8	10.8	3.0	11.3	3.1	11.9	3.0
Kings	21.0	7.6	25.4	7.0	28.5	7.7	28.7	7.3
New York	203.5	73.2	253.2	69.5	224.2	60.9	224.7	57.2
Queens	8.7	3.2	15.8	4.4	22.6	6.1	29.9	7.6
Richmond	.5	0.2	.7	0.2	.8	0.2	.7	0.2
Other New York	6.8	2.5	11.9	3.2	19.3	5.2	26.9	6.9
Nassau	2.2	0.8	4.1	1.1	7.9	2.1	12.0	3.1
Rockland	.2	0.1	.3	0.1	.6	0.2	.7	0.2
Suffolk	.9	0.3	1.6	0.4	2.5	0.7	3.3	0.8
Westchester	3.5	1.3	5.9	1.6	8.3	2.2	10.9	2.8
New Jersey sector	29.2	10.5	46.0	12.7	62.0	16.8	70.0	17.8
Jersey City S.M.S.A. (Hudson)	7.0	2.5	9.4	2.6	12.6	3.3	13.7	3.5
Newark S.M.S.A.	15.9	5.7	26.5	7.3	30.2	8.2	34.1	8.7
Essex	14.1	5.1	21.7	5.9	21.5	5.8	22.3	5.7
Morris	0.3	0.1	.6	0.2	1.0	0.3	1.2	0.3
Union	1.5	0.5	4.2	1.2	7.7	2.1	10.6	2.7
Paterson–Clifton–Passaic S.M.S.A.	4.0	1.5	7.2	2.0	14.3	3.9	17.2	4.4
Bergen	1.2	0.4	3.1	0.8	7.7	2.1	10.6	2.7
Passaic	2.8	1.1	4.1	1.2	6.6	1.8	6.6	1.7
Middlesex	2.1	0.7	2.6	0.7	4.3	1.2	4.1	1.0
Somerset	0.2	0.1	.3	0.1	.6	0.2	.9	0.2

TABLE 10. TRENDS IN WHOLESALE SALES IN THE NEW YORK METROPOLITAN AREA
(sales in millions of dollars)

	1939 Sales Amount	Per Cent	1948 Sales Amount	Per Cent	1954 Sales Amount	Per Cent	1958 Sales Amount	Per Cent
Metropolitan Area	$14,056	100.0	$42,210	100.0	$48,459	100.0	$54,435	100.0
New York sector (S.M.S.A.)	13,155	93.6	38,828	92.7	43,594	90.0	47,505	87.3
New York City	12,954	92.2	38,171	91.1	42,209	87.1	45,076	82.8
Bronx	226	1.6	647	1.5	748	1.5	917	1.7
Kings	628	4.5	1,609	3.8	1,934	4.0	2,282	4.2
New York	11,884	84.6	34,773	83.1	37,427	77.3	38,805	71.2
Queens	200	1.4	1,100	2.6	2,056	4.2	3,022	5.6
Richmond	16	0.1	42	0.1	44	0.1	50	0.1
Other New York	201	1.4	657	1.6	1,385	2.9	2,429	4.5
Nassau	54	0.4	226	0.5	565	1.1	1,052	2.0
Rockland	5	(a)	11	(a)	33	0.1	91	0.2
Suffolk	25	0.2	91	0.2	177	0.4	241	0.4
Westchester	117	0.8	329	0.9	610	1.3	1,045	1.9
New Jersey sector	901	6.4	3,031	7.3	4,865	10.0	6,930	12.7
Jersey City S.M.S.A. (Hudson)	228	1.6	706	1.7	1,033	2.1	1,217	2.2
Newark S.M.S.A.	483	3.4	1,599	3.9	2,435	5.0	3,495	6.4
Essex	420	2.9	1,299	3.2	1,721	3.6	2,257	4.1
Morris	11	0.1	33	0.1	61	0.1	102	0.2
Union	52	0.4	267	0.6	653	1.3	1,136	2.1
Paterson–Clifton–Passaic S.M.S.A.	121	0.9	460	1.1	984	2.0	1,720	3.2
Bergen	47	0.3	197	0.5	513	1.0	1,127	2.1
Passaic	74	0.6	263	0.6	471	1.0	593	1.1
Middlesex	62	0.4	251	0.6	373	0.8	418	0.8
Somerset	7	0.1	15	(a)	40	0.1	80	0.1

a Less than 0.05 per cent.

TABLE 11. TRADE SHARES AND LEVELS OF WHOLESALE SALES PER EMPLOYEE
BY COMMODITY LINE IN THE NEW YORK METROPOLITAN AREA, 1958

	New York Area's Share of National Sales (per cent)	Index of Sales per Employee, Nation = 100		
		New York Area	Manhattan	Rest of Area
Total	19.2	137	170	92
Automotive goods	12.0	144	198	116
Drugs, chemicals	26.8	135	155	113
Dry goods, apparel	67.8	124[a]	128	62
Groceries, confectionery, meat	15.6	153	224	99
Electrical goods	15.1	108	130	90
Hardware, plumbing, heating goods	10.8	109	118	103
Machinery and equipment	13.9	119	140	91
Metals, metalwork	20.4	131	217	42
Scrap, waste materials	13.5	122	215	91
Tobacco	19.1	162	186	130
Beer, wine, spirits	18.3	142	245	99
Paper, paper products	27.4	147	177	98
Furniture, furnishings	28.2	124	132	100
Lumber, construction materials	10.3	115	186	89

[a]Transaction level in this line affected by New York's preponderant share of the nation's trade. The index value for the New York Area if computed in relationship to the rest of the nation rises to 192.

TABLE 12. WHOLESALE TRADE TRENDS IN THE NATION, THE MIDDLE ATLANTIC REGION,
AND THE NEW YORK METROPOLITAN AREA, 1929–1958

	Nation	Middle Atlantic Region		New York Area	
	Amount	Amount	Per Cent of Nation	Amount	Per Cent of Nation
	Sales in Billions of Dollars				
1929	67	23	33.9	17	24.9
1939	55	19	34.3	14	25.4
1948	191	58	30.6	42	22.2
1954	233	69	29.4	49	20.6
1958	284	79	28.0	54	19.2
	Employment in Thousands				
1929	1,510	411	27.2	(235)[a]	15.6
1939	1,562	429	27.5	277	17.7
1948	2,305	591	25.6	364	15.8
1954	2,590	629	24.3	369	14.2
1958	2,796	627	22.4	393	14.1

[a]Includes estimated employment in area outside of New York City.

TABLE 13. DISTRIBUTION OF SALES BY COMMODITY LINE OF EXPORT MERCHANTS
IN THE NATION AND IN THE NEW YORK METROPOLITAN AREA, 1954
(thousands of dollars)

| | Nation | New York Area | | |
	Amount	Amount	Per Cent Distribution	Per Cent of Nation
Total	$4,355,553	$2,679,480	100.0	61.5
Groceries, confectionery, meat	247,990	117,589	4.4	47.4
Farm products (edible)	27,797	11,661	0.4	42.0
Beer, wine, spirits	2,810	655	(a)	27.3
Tobacco	5,579	3,806	0.2	68.2
Drugs, chemicals	140,017	107,656	4.0	76.9
Dry goods, apparel	175,979	173,098	6.5	98.4
Furniture, furnishings	12,126	10,930	0.4	90.1
Paper, paper products	42,348	38,006	1.4	89.7
Farm products (raw materials)	2,178,694	1,005,107	37.5	46.1
Automotive goods	98,722	55,623	2.1	56.3
Electrical goods	142,439	130,990	4.9	92.0
Hardware, plumbing, heating goods	11,485	7,569	0.3	65.9
Lumber, construction materials	43,548	5,521	0.2	12.7
Machinery and equipment	237,688	140,562	5.2	59.1
Metals, metalwork	308,871	296,491	11.1	96.0
Scrap, waste materials	55,551	33,162	1.2	59.7
Other exports	623,909	541,054	20.2	86.7

a Less than .05 per cent.

TABLE 14. DISTRIBUTION OF SALES BY COMMODITY LINE OF IMPORT MERCHANTS
IN THE NATION AND IN THE NEW YORK METROPOLITAN AREA, 1954
(thousands of dollars)

| | Nation | New York Area | | |
	Amount	Amount	Per Cent Distribution	Per Cent of Nation
Total	$4,264,999	$3,471,277	100.0	81.4
Groceries, confectionery, meat	1,394,238	1,108,924	31.9	79.5
Farm products (edible)	62,415	4,383	0.1	7.0
Beer, wine, spirits	183,952	162,300	4.7	88.2
Tobacco	2,330	1,664	0.1	71.4
Drugs, chemicals	54,359	49,068	1.4	90.3
Dry goods, apparel	165,898	156,940	4.5	94.6
Furniture, furnishings	121,806	98,831	2.8	81.1
Paper, paper products	21,619	20,412	0.6	94.4
Farm products (raw materials)	395,275	257,714	7.4	65.2
Automotive goods	18,210	10,523	0.3	57.8
Electrical goods	26,737	23,687	0.7	88.6
Hardware, plumbing, heating goods	4,371	3,021	0.1	69.1
Lumber, construction materials	53,469	27,051	0.8	50.6
Machinery and equipment	134,483	95,380	2.7	70.9
Metals, metalwork	419,590	397,819	11.5	94.8
Scrap, waste materials	4,204	2,703	0.1	64.3
Other imports	1,202,043	1,050,857	30.3	87.4

TABLE 15. DISTRIBUTION OF MERCHANT WHOLESALERS' WAREHOUSE SPACE
BY KIND OF BUSINESS AND BY TYPE OF STRUCTURE
IN THE NEW YORK METROPOLITAN AREA, 1954
(floor space in thousands)

	Total Net Warehouse Space		Division by Type of Structure (per cent)	
	Square Feet	Share of Total (per cent)	Single Story	Multi-Story
Total	116,028	100.0	43.7	56.3
Groceries, confectionery, meat	10,426	9.0	52.6	47.4
Farm products (edible)	3,855	3.3	56.0	44.0
Beer, wine, spirits	2,528	2.2	55.3	44.7
Tobacco	892	0.8	56.8	43.2
Drugs, chemicals	4,367	3.7	43.8	56.2
Dry goods, apparel	12,607	10.8	21.5	78.5
Furniture, furnishings	7,149	6.2	27.8	72.2
Paper, paper products	8,111	7.0	26.3	73.7
Farm products (raw materials)	1,756	1.5	26.5	73.5
Automotive goods	6,125	5.3	69.6	30.4
Electrical goods	6,703	5.8	33.9	66.1
Hardware, plumbing, heating goods	8,851	7.6	44.3	55.7
Lumber, construction materials	6,761	5.8	56.9	43.1
Machinery and equipment	13,101	11.3	48.6	51.4
Metals, metalwork	6,031	5.2	74.9	25.1
Scrap, waste materials	6,124	5.3	54.6	45.4
Other	10,641	9.2	32.3	67.7

TABLE 16. DISTRIBUTION OF WAREHOUSE SPACE IN MANUFACTURERS' SALES BRANCHES
BY KIND OF BUSINESS AND BY TYPE OF STRUCTURE
IN THE NEW YORK METROPOLITAN AREA, 1954
(floor space in thousands)

	Total Net Warehouse Space		Division by Type of Structure (per cent)	
	Square Feet	Share of Total (per cent)	Single Story	Multi-Story
Total	10,974	100.0	41.8	58.2
Food and kindred products	1,759	16.0	38.2	61.8
Textile mill products	718	6.6	14.2	85.8
Apparel and related products	207	1.9	37.7	62.3
Furniture and fixtures	219	2.0	31.5	68.5
Paper and allied products	311	2.8	26.7	73.3
Chemicals and allied products	1,321	12.0	36.0	64.0
Rubber products	543	4.9	42.2	57.8
Leather and leather products	112	1.0	2.7	97.3
Stone, clay and glass	273	2.5	48.4	51.6
Primary metal products	173	1.6	53.2	46.8
Fabricated metal products	565	5.1	56.1	43.9
Machinery (except electrical)	873	8.0	40.3	59.7
Electrical machinery	1,316	12.0	33.6	66.4
Transportation equipment	1,378	12.6	82.5	17.5
Instruments and related products	260	2.4	28.8	71.2
Other products	946	8.6	34.9	65.1

TABLE 17. MERCHANT WHOLESALERS' INVENTORIES AS PER CENT OF SALES
IN THE NEW YORK METROPOLITAN AREA, 1954

	All Establishments	Establishments with more than 500 sq. ft. of Storage	Establishments with less than 500 sq. ft. of Storage
Total	8.1	10.8	6.1
Groceries, confectionery, meat	4.2	5.0	3.7
Farm products (edible)	1.5	1.4	1.6
Beer, wine, spirits	8.9	10.5	5.7
Tobacco	4.0	3.6	5.2
Drugs, chemicals	7.0	9.6	5.1
Dry goods, apparel	12.5	14.5	10.6
Furniture, furnishings	11.5	13.6	7.9
Paper, paper products	5.1	9.5	1.6
Farm products (raw materials)	8.0	11.8	7.4
Automotive goods	10.2	13.1	5.9
Electrical goods	9.8	11.1	5.8
Hardware, plumbing, heating goods	12.9	14.7	7.3
Lumber, construction materials	7.1	10.3	4.5
Machinery and equipment	11.7	15.1	7.2
Metals, metalwork	8.0	19.0	4.2
Scrap, waste materials	5.4	6.6	4.2
Other	7.5	11.1	6.2

TABLE 18. TRENDS IN THE DIVISION OF SALES BETWEEN MANUFACTURERS'
SALES OFFICES AND MANUFACTURERS' SALES BRANCHES

	1935	1954	1958
Sales (millions of dollars)			
Nation	$11,066	$69,533	$87,701
Branches	7,446	36,811	41,820
Offices	3,620	32,722	45,881
New York Metropolitan Area	2,651	14,781	a
Branches	1,645	7,729	a
Offices	1,007	7,052	a
Share of Sales (per cent)			
Nation	100	100	100
Branches	67	53	48
Offices	33	47	52
New York Metropolitan Area	100	100	a
Branches	62	52	a
Offices	38	48	a

aNot available.

INDEX

INDEX